Asia's Energy Trends and Developments

Innovations and Alternative Energy Supplies

volume 1

Asia's Energy Trends and Developments

Innovations and Alternative Energy Supplies

volume 1

Editors

Mark Hong
Asan Institute for Policy Studies, South Korea

Amy Lugg
Institute of Southeast Asian Studies, Singapore

World Scientific

NEW JERSEY • LONDON • SINGAPORE • BEIJING • SHANGHAI • HONG KONG • TAIPEI • CHENNAI

Published by

World Scientific Publishing Co. Pte. Ltd.

5 Toh Tuck Link, Singapore 596224

USA office: 27 Warren Street, Suite 401-402, Hackensack, NJ 07601

UK office: 57 Shelton Street, Covent Garden, London WC2H 9HE

Library of Congress Cataloging-in-Publication Data

Asia's energy trends and developments (in 2 volumes) / [edited by] Mark Hong, Asan Institute for Policy Studies, South Korea, Amy V.R. Lugg, Institute of Southeast Asian Studies, Singapore.

volumes cm

Includes index.

ISBN 978-9814425612 (Set)

ISBN 978-9814425575 (Vol. 1)

ISBN 978-9814425605 (Vol. 2)

1. Power resources--Asia. 2. Energy development--Asia. 3. Energy policy--Asia. I. Hong, Mark, editor of compilation. II. Lugg, Amy V. R., editor of compilation.

HD9502.A782A77 2013

333.79095--dc23

2013000742

British Library Cataloguing-in-Publication Data

A catalogue record for this book is available from the British Library.

In-house Editor: Lum Pui Yee

Typeset by Stallion Press
Email: enquiries@stallionpress.com

Printed in Singapore by B & Jo Enterprise Pte Ltd

FOREWORD

This book continues the sterling work published by the Institute of Southeast Asian Studies (ISEAS) of the ISEAS Energy Studies' Books series. They are based on lectures delivered at the ISEAS Energy Forum, which was launched in June 2004, and ended in September 2011, having organized 135 energy seminars and conferences. This volume also includes papers contributed by invited writers, who are experts on various energy issues. These books serve to capture in a permanent book format the knowledge and data which were delivered in the Forum lectures, and might serve to help educate and sensitize the public about energy issues, as well as the persons who for some reason or other, had missed the lectures.

Energy issues, such as energy security, energy efficiency and related subjects, such as climate change, global warming and global competition for resources, are still salient on the international agenda. The global financial crisis serves to underline the key roles that dependable, affordable and accessible energy resources play in the global economy. Global economic recovery would be difficult if oil and gas prices should reach the spike in energy prices seen in 2008. China's continuing high growth rates in the past few years, which have enabled China to play the role of global economic locomotive at a time when the G3 economies, namely, USA, EU and Japan were all simultaneously suffering from low growth, also depend on affordable energy prices.

What is remarkable about this book is the wide range of energy issues addressed therein. From climate change to clean energy; from energy innovation to Nano-energy, this volume ranges far and wide. It provides much useful data and expertise on energy issues. Readers all over the world might benefit by careful reading of this publication.

The book concludes with a special section on nuclear energy issues in Asia. It is important to note that at the time of submission of the nuclear papers, the Fukushima disaster had not yet happened and it is clear that since that tragic event, there has been a severe rethink about nuclear safety.

This section examines the potential role of nuclear power in Asia as a whole and in some individual Southeast Asian countries. It also describes the possibilities for cooperation in terms of the regulatory infrastructure and safeguards that need to be put in place, and soberly assesses all the various risks involved in building and operating nuclear power plants.

We are happy to contribute to the global debate on energy issues via this volume and this series. Finally, we would like to thank all contributors for their immense patience and understanding throughout the publications process.

Mark Hong & Amy Lugg
Editors

July 2012

CONTRIBUTORS

Tan Yong Soon was Permanent Secretary for National Climate Change in the Prime Minister's Office until his retirement on 1 October 2012, after 35 years in public service. He studied at Raffles Institution and National Junior College, Singapore, and graduated with a BA (Hons) and an MA from Cambridge University, an MBA from the National University of Singapore and an MPA from Harvard University. He also attended the Advanced Management Program at Harvard Business School. He began his career in the Singapore Armed Forces and rose to the rank of Brigadier General before joining the Administrative Service. He has served as Principal Private Secretary to the Prime Minister, Deputy Secretary in the Ministry of Defence and the Ministry of Finance, CEO of the Urban Redevelopment Authority and Permanent Secretary for the Ministry of the Environment and Water Resources. He was awarded the Public Administration Medal (Military) (Gold) and the Public Administration Medal (Gold). He is married and has two children.

Goh Chee Kiong has been Head of Environment and Clean Energy at the Singapore Economic Development Board (EDB) since 2003. In this capacity, he leads the development of strategies and promotion of the cleantech industry, including water technologies and solar energy, which has been identified as a key growth area for Singapore. He is concurrently Director of Cluster Development in the multi-agency Environment and Water Industry Development Council (EWI). Prior to this, Mr. Goh was Director of the EDB Chicago office from 2000 to 2003 where he managed the relationship with potential and existing American investors in the Midwest region.
E-mail: ckgoh@edb.gov.sg

Hiranmayee Vedam is a commercialisation expert specialising in technology-based companies in materials, wireless and energy. She combines her experience in technology, business, IP and finance to provide venture capital companies and SMEs with deal sourcing, due diligence and business development services. She provides strategic policy support to governments and maintains the Singapore Nanotechnology Ecosystem Map as part of the SingNano initiative. She also provides interim management and project management support to young startups in the nanotech space. She has authored multiple reports, journal articles and book chapters. She has organised seminars on the Singapore nanotechnology landscape and has been a speaker at nanotech conferences. Prior to her current role, Hiran was a senior manager at the National University of Singapore (NUS) Industry Liaison Office. There, she was involved in spinning off companies, licensing technologies to commercial companies and in business development activities to promote collaboration between NUS and the industry. She consolidated NUS's nanotechnology capabilities and championed the setting up of a proof-of-concept centre for nanotechnology, which in its modified form is part of the NanoCore group at NUS. Prior to joining NUS, Hiran founded and managed MAtrika Pte. Ltd., a wireless applications company. There, she developed a location tracking product by securing angel funding. She was a programme manager at Honeywell Singapore Technology Centre where she was employee number one and managed relationships with business units, academic institutions and government funding agencies. While there, she also established the Asia-Pacific abnormal situation management consortium with several petrochemical companies in the Asia-Pacific region. She has been working in Singapore for more than 10 years. She has an MBA from INSEAD, a PhD in Chemical Engineering from Purdue University and a BTech in Chemical Engineering from the Indian Institute of Technology, Madras.
E-mail: hiranvedam@nanoconsulting.com.sg

Geoffrey C. Nicholson was born in 1938 in Co. Durham, England and attended Grammar School in Houghton-le-Spring. He was awarded his PhD degree in Chemistry from Imperial College London in 1963. With employment very limited, and the space race being on, he became part of the brain drain and joined 3M in 1963 in Minnesota, USA. After several years in 3M's Central Research Laboratories, he was appointed

to positions in the company's Visual Products and Commercial Tape business units. In the latter, he was instrumental in the development of 3M's highly successful Post-it Notes and the subsequent line of Post-it products. The Chairman of the Board and CEO of 3M described him as the "Father of the Post-it Note Program" long before the program reached its potential of some several hundred thousand dollars in sales. He was then appointed to a succession of international assignments, including Vice President, 3M International Technical Operations, which included the establishment of extensive laboratories in more than 25 countries such as the UK, Germany, Japan, Singapore, China and India. Geoff was responsible for the activities of more than 2,500 technical people around the world. After retirement in February 2001, Geoff has been involved with some startup companies as well as various publications such as *In Search of Excellence*, *Built to Last* and *Breakthroughs*.
E-mail: GCNicholson@nicholsontech.com

Erik Knive is Executive Vice President (EVP), Asia, for Statkraft Norfund Power Invest AS (SN Power). SN Power is a significant international hydropower and renewable energy company and is a commercial investor, developer and operator of renewable energy and hydropower projects in emerging markets. As EVP, Asia, Knive is responsible for all operational entities and business development in Asia, as well as global support functions managed through the Singapore corporate entity. Knive has comprehensive executive experience from Norconsult Telematics and Teleplan, having been responsible for global business development and all European and Asian operations. He has a GMP from Harvard Business School and holds a BSc from the University of New Orleans.
E-mail: Erik.Knive@snpower.com

N. A. Orcullo, Jr. is an academic and researcher with long-experience on energy matters, particularly on the renewable energy sector in the Philippines and the ASEAN region having been previously connected with the Department of Energy. On various occasions, he has rendered services to various international organizations which include serving as Research Fellow with the Singapore-based Institute of Southeast Asian Studies (ISEAS), consultancy engagements with Bangkok-based United Nations Economic and Social Commission for Asia and the Pacific

(ESCAP) and also served as Resource Person on renewable energy events espoused by Asia Pacific Economic Cooperation (APEC) and the US Department of Commerce and several other private organizations. He is affiliated with the Philippines' De La Salle University-Dasmarinas (Cavite) and a senior Consultant of the Dr. Blackman Group, Inc. (DBGI), a management and engineering consultancy organization. He has travelled to various countries in pursuit of delivering his research outputs in various forums and is an author of four books and several other publications released locally and internationally.
E-mail: my_eclass_professor@yahoo.com.ph

Steve Puckett is Managing Director of Tri-Zen International Pte. Ltd. and founded and leads the business. He focuses on business development and creating strategic alliances for the company. Steve has more than 25 years of broad international business experience and a deep knowledge of the energy industry. Prior to founding Tri-Zen, he had regional accountabilities for Asia Pacific with Mobil Corporation in gas and power and additional country responsibilities for China. He has a track record of leading and managing various businesses in high-growth areas and has also managed Asia-wide supply and trading operations. Functionally he has held leadership roles in marketing and refining, upstream ventures and corporate planning. In Asia, he has held senior executive positions based in Tokyo, Hong Kong, China and Singapore. He has had business development experience across most of Asia, and particularly in China, while his reach and experience extends to the Middle East, Europe and the US. He serves on a number of industry representative bodies and on the boards of several emerging businesses. A business leader, a Chartered Engineer and a Fellow of the IChemE, he has extensive experience in the development, financing and structuring of both corporate and private businesses. In Singapore he serves on the National Engineering Council and is Chairman of the Institution of Chemical Engineers. He is a Board Member of the British Chamber of Commerce, where he chairs the Energy Business Group and Corporate Social Responsibility, and is a Board Member of the Centre for Asian Philanthropy. He has particular interest in the promotion of continuing professional development. Steve features regularly in regional

media, providing advice on the development of businesses in Asia. He is also a frequent speaker at business conferences. Tri-Zen has been profiled on CNBC's Managing Asia.
E-mail: steve@tri-zen.com

Tony Regan is Principal Consultant with Tri-Zen International Pte. Ltd., a Singapore-based energy consultancy providing technical, commercial and financial advisory services to the oil, gas, chemical and power sectors in Asia Pacific. Tony focuses on natural gas, LNG and CBM. Tony has extensive international oil and gas experience, much of it gained during his 25 years with Shell International and more recently with Nexant where he was a Principal responsible for their gas practice in Asia. With Shell he developed several new businesses and held senior management positions in Europe and Asia. He was first introduced to the world of LNG in the early 1990s when he held the position of Vice President, Energy, with Shell Korea and arranged the first spot cargoes of LNG into Korea from Australia and Brunei and facilitated discussions that led to KOGAS becoming a lead customer in Oman LNG. With Nexant he led the team providing LNG technical and commercial advisory services to PowerGas, the developers of the Singapore LNG receiving terminal. Tony has been an oil and gas consultant since 1998 and is a frequent speaker at conferences and on television.
E-mail: tony.regan@tri-zen.com

William I. Y. Byun is a specialist in renewable energy and climate change project development based in Singapore with Asia Renewables, a clean energy company focusing on investment in and end-to-end development of renewable energy, carbon abatement and sustainable development assets in emerging markets. He previously served as Managing Director of Renewables and Climate Change (Asia and Middle East) at AES Corporation, Senior Vice President at Sindicatum Carbon Capital, and Principal of an investment firm specialising in Asia-related infrastructure. William was also the first US Fulbright Scholar in residence at the Ministry of Finance in Korea, and has degrees from the University of Chicago, University of Michigan and the University of London, in Economics, Law and Sociology.
E-mail: william.byun@asiarenewables.org

Djoko Prasetijo is Head of the Division of System Planning at the Indonesia State Electricity Company, PLN, based in Jakarta.
E-mail: djoko_pras@pln.co.id; dprasetijo@yahoo.com

Hae Ryong Hwang is Senior Vice President, NSSS Business Division, KEPCO Engineering Construction Company Inc., or KEPCO etc, based in Yongin. He holds an MS and a PhD in Nuclear Engineering from Purdue University (thesis: "Optimal Space-Time Fuel Distribution for the LWR") and a BS in Nuclear Engineering from Seoul National University. His significant career achievements include the following: 1998–2003, Engineering Group Manager of the Radiation Safety Analysis Group in several Korean nuclear power plant construction projects; 1998–2000, Project Manager of KEPCO-supported project "Advanced Methodology Development for Radiation Physics and Criticality Safety Analysis"; 1997–1998, Group Manager of the Reactor Engineering Group for reactor physics and criticality safety analysis relating to several Korean nuclear power plant construction projects; 1993–1996, Principal Researcher and Manager at the Reactor Engineering Department, Korea Atomic Energy Research Institute, dealing with reactor physics and criticality analysis for constructing and operating PWRs and CANDU reactors; 1988–1993, Senior Researcher and Group Leader for the Radiation Physics and Criticality Analysis Group, Korea Atomic Energy Research Institute, dealing with reactor physics and criticality analysis for constructing and operating PWRs; and 1989–1990, Group Leader for Reactor Engineering, at Combustion Engineering, Windsor, Connecticut. He has over 30 publications in journals, conference proceedings and technical reports relating to computational methods and criticality safety applications, radiation shielding, and source term characterisation of nuclear facilities and reactor physics analysis.
E-mail: hae@kepco-enc.com

Shin Whan Kim is Vice President at KEPCO E&C where he is also Team Leader for the Business Team and Project Manager for the Development of Standard European APR1400 and Development of Core Technologies for EU-APR1400. Prior to joining KEPCO E&C in 1997, Dr Shin was Senior Researcher at the Korea Atomic Energy Research Institute (KAERI) from 1994 to 1996. Dr Shin has a PhD in Nuclear Engineering from the Rensselear Polytechnic Institute, Troy, N.Y., U.S.A. *E-mail:* sleepy@kepco-enc.com

Shahidan bin Radiman is Lecturer in Advanced Nuclear Physics at the School of Applied Physics, Faculty of Science and Technology, at Universiti Kebangsaan Malaysia. He is also currently editor for the *Journal of Nuclear and Related Technologies* and on the Editorial Board of *Malaysian Nuclear Bulletin*. He is also a reviewer for several local and international journals including *Material Letters*, *Journal of Crystal Growth*, *Journal of Solid State Chemistry*, and the *Journal of Nanoparticle Research*. Since 1990, he has published over 250 papers. Dr. Shahidan obtained his PhD from the University of Cambridge in Experimental Physics and his area of specialisation concerns small-angle X-ray and neutron scattering techniques, rheology of soft matter, nanoparticle synthesis and applications using colloidal and electrochemical methods, Sufism and Islamic sciences (especially from the Malay world and theosophy of Ibn Arabi, al Qunawi and A. Rahman Jami), and fundamental problems in quantum mechanics, especially quantum biology.
E-mail: shahidan@ukm.my

Anthony J. Jude is Director of the Energy and Water Division, Southeast Asia Department (SERD), of the Asian Development Bank based in the Philippines, covering Brunei, Cambodia, Indonesia, Lao PDR, Malaysia, Myanmar, the Philippines, Singapore, Thailand and Viet Nam. Prior to this he was Director of the Energy and Transport Division. He joined the Asian Development Bank in 1992 and worked on the energy sector (energy planning and policy, and power sector) in the PRC, Nepal and Central Asia. He was responsible for the publishing of the ADB's *Energy Data Book* and *Electric Utilities Data Book* for the Asia-Pacific region as well as other technical publications on demand side management and solar photovoltaics. From 2000 to 2004, he was ADB's Deputy Country Director in Cambodia, responsible for portfolio management, transport, energy and rural development.
E-mail: ajude@adb.org

Francisco G. Delfin Jr.'s nearly 30 years of professional experience spans private industry, government service, academia and non-profit sectors, and

focuses on the intersection of geological sciences, energy resource development and public policy. Since 2008, he has been Vice President of PetroEnergy Resources Corporation, where he oversees the company's petroleum and renewable energy projects. In 2007, he served as Assistant Secretary and later Undersecretary (Vice Minister) at the Philippine Department of Energy (DOE) where he was responsible for the upstream energy, planning, finance, legal and administrative bureaus. Dr. Delfin was also Assistant Professor at the University of the Philippines' National College of Public Administration and Governance (UP-NCPAG) in 2005–2007 and 2008–2009, where he taught undergraduate and graduate courses in public policy and conducted research on natural resources, disasters and energy issues. His research works have been published in refereed international journals such as *Nonprofit and Voluntary Sector Quarterly*, *Environment and Planning A* and *Public Administration and Development*. Prior to his stint in academia, he was Head of Geothermal Exploration and Deputy Manager (Superintendent) of Scientific Services at the PNOC Energy Development Corporation (PNOC-EDC). His work from 1981 to 2001 involved exploration, development and monitoring of various PNOC-EDC geothermal projects in the Philippines, Iran and Japan. He holds a PhD in Public Administration from the University of Southern California, a Master of Science in Geology from the University of South Florida and a Bachelor's degree in Geology from the University of the Philippines. He was the 2009 President of the Geological Society of the Philippines and since 2001 has served as associate editor of the *Journal of the Geological Society of the Philippines.*
E-mail: fgdelfin@petroenergy.com.ph

Lee Yoong Yoong is Research Fellow at the Institute of Policy Studies at the Lee Kuan Yew School of Public Policy in Singapore, and his research interests concern the ASEAN Economic Community (AEC) and its impact on the Singapore economy and its policy options. Yoong Yoong has over 14 years of accumulative working experience, in the areas of international relations, international business and economic development. Prior to his current IPS appointment, Yoong Yoong spent four years working in the ASEAN Secretariat based in Jakarta, Indonesia. He started off handling the investment portfolio, which included regional industrial

cooperation and small and medium-sized enterprise (SME) integration, as well as tabulating FDI statistics. He was also involved in the ASEAN's FTA negotiations with Korea and Australia/New Zealand. His last appointment in the ASEAN Secretariat was as Head of the Infrastructure Unit, where he was responsible for the regional cooperation and integration of the transport/logistics, energy and minerals sectors. Given the traits of the three sectors, he was also one focal point in the secretariat to handle issues relating to climate change. Further to that, Yoong Yoong spent seven years with the Singapore Economic Development Board, responsible for driving talent outreach initiatives and programmes to facilitate the inflow of global talent into specific Singapore-based industries, as well as for evaluating business/market opportunities for firms in Taiwan, Korea, South Africa, Australia, New Zealand and the Philippines to invest in Singapore. Yoong Yoong also has had stints with the Ministry of Home Affairs and Sembawang Parks Management, where he was responsible for the business development of Singapore industrial park investments in Batam and Bintan islands. Yoong Yoong has contributed to various ASEAN compendia and publications on investment, industrial cooperation, economics, logistics, transport and energy. In IPS, his major research area is to provide substantive analyses, assessments and inputs on the progress and implementation of the ASEAN Economic Community vis-à-vis Singapore's economic development and competitiveness. He is also responsible for facilitation in the organisation of the Singapore Economic Roundtable (SER) series, which is held twice a year. Yoong Yoong holds a BA in Business Administration from RMIT, Australia, and a Master in International Relations from the Institute of Defence and Strategic Studies (now the S. Rajaratnam School of International Studies) of the Nanyang Technological University, Singapore.
E-mail: lee.yoongyoong@nus.edu.sg

Thaung Tun is Visiting Senior Research Fellow at the Institute of Southeast Asian Studies, Singapore. He retired from the Myanmar Foreign Service in April 2010. His last posting was in Brussels as Myanmar Ambassador to Belgium, the Netherlands and the European Union. He previously served in Manila as Myanmar Ambassador to the Philippines. His other overseas assignments include Washington, DC, New York,

Geneva and Bern. He is a former Director-General of the Political Department of the Ministry of Foreign Affairs and ASEAN SOM leader of Myanmar. He was educated in Myanmar, India and the United States. He was a Fulbright scholar and has a Master in International Public Policy from the School of Advanced International Studies (SAIS), The Johns Hopkins University.
E-mail: thaungtun@iseas.edu.sg

Mark Hong was born in Singapore and educated at Raffles Institution, Singapore. After completing his secondary school education, Mr. Hong was awarded a President's Scholarship in 1965 and a Humanities Scholarship and Best Entrant scholarship at Singapore University. He obtained a BA in Economics from Cambridge University in 1969 and an MS in International Relations from Georgetown University in 1982 on a Fulbright Scholarship.

Mr. Hong joined the Ministry of Foreign Affairs in 1969. He served at the Singapore Embassy in Phnom Penh as Charge d'Affaires (1974–1975), at the Singapore Commission in Hong Kong as First Secretary (1975–1976), at the Singapore Embassy in Paris as Counsellor (1982–1986) and at the Singapore Permanent Mission to the United Nations in New York as Deputy Permanent Representative (1988–1994). At the Ministry of Foreign Affairs headquarters, he has served in various senior capacities as the director of several departments. His last foreign posting was as Singapore's Ambassador to Russia and Ukraine from November 1995 to March 2002. From May 2002 to January 2004, he was attached to the Institute of Defence and Strategic Studies, Nanyang Technological University, Singapore, as a Visiting Senior Fellow.

He is currently a Vice-Chairman of the International Committee of the Singapore Business Federation, and was a Visiting Research Fellow at ISEAS from February 2004 to October 2011. After his retirement in October 2011, he was appointed Visiting Senior Lecturer at James Cook University on its Australia and Singapore campuses, and also at Capilano University in Vancouver, and as Senior Visiting Fellow at Asan Institute in Seoul.

He has delivered over 300 papers and lectures to various international seminars and conferences, and attended many UN General Assemblies, ASEAN conferences and other regional meetings. He has edited 10 books

for ISEAS, four on energy issues, two forthcoming in 2012, three on ASEAN-Russia relations, and one each on Southeast Asia and Cambodia. He has also contributed many chapters to various books, given lectures to groups such as the Young PAP, schools, and visiting delegations.
E-mail: markhong@gmail.com

Amy V. R. Lugg is in charge of public information and communications for the ASEAN Studies, Centre at the Institute of Southeast Asian Studies (ISEAS). Before joining the Centre, she was Associate Editor with a leading provider of energy and metals information. Prior to that, she was Executive Search Director at a boutique executive search company in Singapore with extensive networks in the banking and finance, academia, hospitality, retail and energy sectors. Amy has also been a Visiting Associate at ISEAS since June 2009, with the ISEAS Energy Studies Programme. She is co-editor of the ISEAS Energy Series publications with Mark Hong. Amy holds a Master's degree in International Relations from Curtin University, Australia, and her research interests include energy security, human security and transnational crime.
E-mail: amy@iseas.edu.sg

CONTENTS

PART I

INNOVATIONS AND ALTERNATIVE ENERGY SUPPLIES

CHAPTER 1

CLIMATE CHANGE: A GLOBAL ISSUE

Tan Yong Soon

Former Permanent Secretary, National Climate Change, Prime Minister's Office
1 July 2010 -1 October 2012

ABSTRACT

As a small and low-lying island state, Singapore is vulnerable to the impact of climate change. Therefore, we work closely with other stakeholders to address this global challenge. Singapore plays a constructive role in international climate change negotiations under the United Nations Framework Convention on Climate Change (UNFCCC). We have pledged to reduce emissions by 16% below 2020 Business as Usual (BAU) levels, contingent on a legally binding global agreement. Ahead of this, measures are being implemented to reduce our emissions by 7% to 11% below 2020 BAU. Singapore is also building capabilities to adapt to the impact of climate change, harness green growth opportunities as well as forge partnerships on climate change action.

1.1 BACKGROUND

The National Climate Change Secretariat (NCCS) was set up on 1 July 2010 as a dedicated agency under the Prime Minister's Office to coordinate Singapore's domestic and international climate change strategies. NCCS has launched the National Climate Change Strategy 2012 (NCCS-2012) to explain Singapore's plans to address climate change. A multi-agency working group has also been formed under the Inter-Ministerial Committee on Climate Change to study how Singapore can stabilise its long term emissions.

Climate change is one of the most important and pressing challenges facing the international community. As is known, the UN Climate Change Conference in Copenhagen last December did not result in a global legally binding agreement to address climate change. However, it is not easy to reach an agreement to address climate change as the issues are complex and the politics inherently divisive. Many governments are reluctant to sacrifice current economic growth as the most severe consequences of climate change will only be evident over the long term, spanning many election cycles and changes of leadership, while the economic costs of preventive actions are huge and must be paid upfront.

For Singapore, climate change and its associated impacts are of concern. As a small and low-lying island state, we are vulnerable to the impacts of climate change. A rise in sea level and temperature can have significant consequences for us. Now, if Singapore were to stop emitting carbon tomorrow, it would do little to alleviate climate change. After all, our contribution to global emissions is minuscule, at less than 0.2 percent of the global total. So for us, we have a stake in seeing the issue effectively addressed. It is important to have an agreed global regime that commits everyone to take action.

We must not lose sight of the end goal of reaching a global legally binding agreement on climate change with comprehensive targets for all countries. Without such a global regime, every country would act for itself, promoting undesirable unilateral actions. Carbon tariffs would offer an inevitable backstop against those countries that fail to take adequate action to curb their emissions. This will provoke retaliations that will severely undermine global economic trade and growth. It is only with open trade and economic growth that countries muster the resources to deal with the challenge of climate change effectively.

Against this backdrop, the EU's efforts to address climate change, despite the effects of the economic crisis, are commendable. Europe is not letting up its efforts to contribute to climate change actions, and is contributing towards climate change action in Southeast Asia.

1.2 SINGAPORE'S ROLE

Singapore has been very active in the UN negotiations to arrive at a new global framework for long-term cooperation to address climate change, participating in both the ministerial and official tracks. As a member of the Group of 77 (G77/China) as well as the Alliance of Small Island States (AOSIS), and also given our unique position as a small but successful developing country, Singapore has tried to play a constructive and moderating role in the negotiations.

Even now, in the aftermath of Copenhagen, we have actively participated in the discussions of the UN Secretary-General's High-Level Advisory Group on climate change finance and different partnerships on reducing emissions from deforestation and forest degradation (REDD) and measurement, reporting and verification (MRV) to move the process forward. ASEAN countries are vulnerable to climate change. Singapore will do its part in promoting greater awareness of the issues involved, as well as to encourage closer cooperation and common understanding on the issue of climate change and its impact. In 2009, the ASEAN Working Group on Climate Change was launched during the ASEAN Ministerial Meeting on the Environment in Singapore. This Working Group will seek to build a common understanding of climate change issues, and enhance regional sharing of information on vulnerability risks and adaptation measures to climate change.

1.3 SINGAPORE IS SERIOUS ABOUT CLIMATE CHANGE

The Singapore government is serious about our domestic efforts to address climate change. Before Copenhagen, Singapore had announced that we would undertake actions to reduce our emissions by 16 percent below business-as-usual (BAU) levels in 2020, contingent on a legally binding global agreement and all countries implementing their commitments in good faith. This is a significant contribution, given our constraints in switching to non-fossil alternatives to reduce emissions from the power sector. Our early actions in the past, such as our policy to limit car population growth and our switch from oil to natural gas for electricity generation, have also limited our ability to further reduce emissions.

To ensure that Singapore is prepared and ready for climate change threats and opportunities, we have set up a dedicated National Climate Change Secretariat (NCCS), which I head, under the Prime Minister's Office with effect from 1 July 2010. The NCCS will coordinate climate change policies across government agencies and ensure that plans are prepared and progress tracked and monitored. The NCCS is set up not only to support the international negotiations but also to coordinate our domestic mitigation and adaptation responses to climate change.

1.4 DOMESTIC MITIGATION AND ADAPTATION MEASURES

While Singapore is working on the international front to secure a global agreement, we have also started to look at what can be done now, especially on the mitigation and adaptation fronts. As the conference organisers have identified, the responses post-Copenhagen will need to focus on what actions we can take now, even as intense and difficult negotiations are ongoing to achieve a global legally binding agreement.

1.4.1 Mitigation

On mitigation, we have already started to undertake various initiatives domestically. With limited access to alternative energies, we have fewer options to reduce emissions compared to better-endowed countries. Our approach to reducing emissions is primarily to improve energy efficiency in all sectors. At the same time, we have put in resources to testbed alternative energy sources so that Singapore will be better positioned to adopt these technologies when they improve and their costs come down.

The Sustainable Singapore Blueprint (SSB) launched in April 2009 represents a major national effort to reduce our energy intensity. It lays out measures to reduce emissions up to 2030 and sets targets of reducing our energy intensity and emissions in four key sectors of our economy — industry, transport, households and buildings. The National Environment Agency (NEA) also recently set up the Energy Efficiency National Partnership (EENP) in April 2010. The intent is to help engage the industry and allow for specific industry groups to interact with energy efficiency experts and learn about best practices to reduce emissions. The government has announced plans for an Energy Conservation Act to come into effect in 2013 to facilitate a coordinated approach to standards for energy efficiency and energy management for companies that consume significant amounts of energy. Effective processes for energy management in turn will enable companies to better manage costs and profits. The measures under the SSB will contribute to a 7% to 11% reduction in emissions growth below 2020 Business as Usual (BAU) levels.

Singapore businesses have already started taking steps to run energy-efficient operations and facilities. That is not to say that it is all smooth sailing. For energy efficiency, there are low-hanging fruits, but there are also barriers to higher efficiency which could be due to a multitude of factors. For example, lack of cost analysis on a life-cycle basis where the upfront cost may be high but the pay-off over the operation of the equipment may only be apparent over a longer period, lack of management attention and focus on energy efficiency practices, split incentives where developers may not be incentivised to put in more efficient equipment due to costs or lack of expertise, leaving tenants to bear the higher energy cost.

We have also been actively investing in the R&D and testbedding of alternative sources of clean energy. With limited scope for wind, geothermal and tidal energies, solar energy is the alternative energy source that presents more opportunities. The Clean Energy Programme Office under the Economic Development Board (EDB) has launched a Clean Energy Research and Testbedding Programme to support the testbedding of clean energy applications in government buildings. As part of its solar capability building programme, the Housing and Development Board (HDB) recently announced an initiative to install solar panels in six public housing precincts across Singapore. By far the single largest solar panel procurement in Singapore to date, this green initiative will power common service areas such as lifts and will benefit 3,000 households.

1.4.2 Adaptation

Apart from mitigation, we must also start thinking about adaptation. We have undertaken vulnerability studies to better understand our long-term physical impacts such as sea-level rise, temperature profile and wind. Preliminary results indicate that our existing infrastructure is sufficient to address the risks in the short to medium term. Studies on secondary impacts such as biodiversity, energy demand and public health implications are also ongoing.

However, uncertainties remain about the extent of climate change and the timing with which it will unfold. Making sense of these uncertainties will require risk assessments and regular reviews and updates of our design parameters as global models and the understanding of climate science improves.

1.5 NEW OPPORTUNITIES

We should also seize new opportunities arising from addressing climate change. While Singapore is a small player, we have sought continually to stay relevant. We have been successful in turning challenges and potential adversities into opportunities. For instance, with the development of NEWater, we have stayed at the forefront of water technology.

Singapore is also a living laboratory for testing new technologies and new business models to accelerate the deployment of exportable low-emission technologies. The Electric Vehicle (EV) Taskforce co-chaired by the Energy Market Authority (EMA) and the Land Transport Authority (LTA), and the Intelligent Energy Systems Taskforce chaired by the EMA are looking into possible urban solutions for the deployment of electric vehicles and smart grids respectively.

With advances in technology, Singapore will be well placed to turn our disadvantage in alternative energy into a competitive advantage in the long run. We can be a reference site for emerging ideas to be tested before larger cities adapt and adopt similar practices. Although alternative energies are unlikely to form a significant part of our fuel mix in the near term, testbeds are ongoing in HDB estates and key installations so that we can better understand the technologies and be better prepared to adopt them on a larger scale when technology improves. I am happy to note that this conference will be covering both energy efficiency and alternative energies.

1.6 CONCLUSION: WORKING TOGETHER

Singapore's Prime Minister Lee Hsien Loong has articulated Singapore's commitment to climate change through his active involvement since the negotiations in Bali in 2007. Singapore has declared an emissions target, which can only be met with concerted and sustained efforts from all sectors and stakeholders, and which will be meaningful when other countries who have pledged targets join in to implement their targets and actions under a global legally binding agreement.

Climate change affects us all. Government actions alone will not be sufficient. The government working in collaboration with our partners in the public, private and people sectors can together come up with efficient solutions and share best practices as part of the global effort to address climate change. For example, businesses can ensure they run energy-efficient operations and facilities. Academia can highlight solutions to barriers. NGOs and grassroots organisations can drive action by spreading the message on energy efficiency at the local level. For the general public, simple energy-saving gestures help to save costs and reduce the environmental impact.

Prime Minister Lee Hsien Loong has placed the National Climate Change Secretariat under his Office and appointed Singapore's Senior Minister S. Jayakumar to advise on climate change policies. Senior Minister Jayakumar chairs the Inter-Ministerial Committee on Climate Change, whose members are the Minsters for Finance, Trade and Industry, Foreign Affairs, Transport, National Development, and the Environment and Water Resources. I am privileged to be part of this Secretariat, and at the same time humbled as climate change is one of the most difficult challenges facing Singapore and, indeed, the global community.

We will need ideas, innovation and to make some trade-offs. I believe we can, and must, succeed in balancing our fight against climate change and in ensuring a high standard of living with good jobs for all. Singapore has always taken a balanced approach to growth and sustainability and we have been reaping the fruits of our ongoing efforts as a reference site for other countries and cities. Only by us working together, can we have a chance of success. The NCCS and agencies will engage the general public, companies, NGOs and academia to drive actions in Singapore.

CHAPTER 2

GROOMING CLEAN ENERGY AS A KEY GROWTH AREA FOR SINGAPORE

Goh Chee Kiong

ABSTRACT

In 2007, the Singapore government endorsed the clean energy industry as a key economic growth area and allocated S$350 million funding to build R&D and manpower capabilities. In 2011, the National Research Foundation (NRF) further injected S$195 million of R&D funding for industry development as well as S$300 million under the National Innovation Challenge for "Energy Resilience for Sustainable Growth".

Singapore has a comprehensive industry development plan focused on four key ingredients: technology, market access, capital and talent. Today, we are home to a vibrant ecosystem comprising multinational companies, start-ups, international organisations, financing firms, test-bed platforms and R&D centres. Industry, government agencies and research institutes can easily collaborate and co-create new ideas across the entire research, innovation and commercialisation continuum. Companies can also use Singapore as a "Living Lab" to develop, test and commercialise innovative solutions before scaling them globally.

The multi-agency Energy Innovation Programme Office (EIPO) was established to plan and execute strategies to position Singapore as a global clean energy hub where products and services are developed here for global markets. EIPO had also set up key industry-oriented research centres, namely Solar Energy Research Institute of Singapore (SERIS) and Energy Research Institute at Nanyang Technological University (ERI@N).

By 2015, the Clean Technology industry, comprising clean energy, environment and water, is expected to contribute S$3.4 billion to Singapore's gross domestic product and employ some 18,000 people. Given the initial private sector investments and strong governmental commitment, Singapore is well positioned to ride the growth of the clean energy sector and serve as a hub to reach global markets.

2.1 INTRODUCTION

In the face of continued global challenges arising from climate change and environmental degradation, coupled with robust growth in energy demand, the quest for cleaner energy solutions remains unabated. This need is amplified by rapid urbanisation across the world, particularly in Asia. Today, more than half of the world's population lives in cities. The world's urban population is expected to double from 3.3 billion people in 2007 to 6.4 billion by 2050, with more than half of this increase coming from Asia. Given the higher standards of living and therefore increased energy usage per capita, cities and governments are naturally turning to innovative clean technologies and solutions to maximise the use of resources and improve the quality of life for their residents.

Recognising these trends, the Research, Innovation and Enterprise Council (RIEC) chaired by our Prime Minister, Mr. Lee Hsien Loong, endorsed the clean energy industry as a key growth area for Singapore's economy in 2007. The National Research Foundation (NRF) consequently allocated a funding of S$170 million to build R&D and manpower capabilities in clean energy. Combined with the funding from other agencies, the whole-of-government funding came up to S$350 million. In 2011, the NRF also approved S$300 million under the National Innovation Challenge for "Energy Resilience for Sustainable Growth" which aims to develop cost-competitive energy solutions for deployment within 20 years to help Singapore improve energy efficiency, reduce carbon emissions and increase energy options.

Singapore has developed a comprehensive industry development plan focused on developing four key ingredients: technology development, markets access, ease of raising capital and talent development.

Today, we are home to a vibrant clean energy ecosystem comprising multinational companies, start-ups, international organisations, financing firms, test-bed platforms and R&D centres. We believe that this clustering is a unique differentiator for Singapore, in that the industry, government agencies and research institutes can easily come together to collaborate and jointly create new ideas. Companies here are also supported by conducive business environment which includes Singapore's top-ranked position in the protection of intellectual property. These factors help companies to co-create new solutions and push the boundaries of innovation in a vibrant business integrated environment, build a track record and use Singapore as a reference site to launch into growth markets in Asia and beyond.

2.2 ENERGY INNOVATION PROGRAMME OFFICE

The multi-agency Energy Innovation Programme Office (EIPO), formerly known as Clean Energy Programme Office (CEPO), was established in 2007 to synergise the whole-of-government's efforts to develop the clean energy industry. Co-led by the Singapore Economic Development Board (EDB) and the Energy Market Authority (EMA), EIPO also comprises key government agencies such as the Agency for Science, Technology and Research (A*STAR), Building and Construction Authority (BCA), International Enterprise (IE) Singapore, National Environment Agency (NEA) and Ministry of Trade and Industry (MTI). EIPO is responsible for planning and executing strategies to develop Singapore into a global clean energy hub where clean energy products and services are developed here for global markets. By 2015, the entire Clean Technology (or Cleantech in short) industry, which comprises clean energy, environment and water, is expected to contribute S$3.4 billion to Singapore's gross domestic product and employ some 10,000 people.

The clean energy industry encompasses a wide range of areas spanning solar energy, wind energy, biomass and biofuels, fuel cells, energy efficiency green building and carbon services. EIPO has identified solar energy as one key focus area for industry development, for two main reasons. First, the manufacturing of solar wafers, cells and modules builds on our existing capabilities in the semiconductor and other high-end electronics sectors in Singapore. Singapore also has all-round capabilities in precision engineering and chemicals which are highly applicable to the solar industry. Second, Singapore is located in the tropical sun-belt region which receives about 50 percent more solar radiation than the temperate regions where the major markets are today. The Asian sun-belt region has been identified as one of the first solar markets to experience strong growth without subsidies, when grid parity is reached. Our excellent supply chain capabilities and extensive linkages in the region make us an efficient base for companies to serve the Asian sun-belt. In addition, there are about one billion people in the region without access to grid electricity. Singapore-based companies can develop off-grid clean energy solutions tailored to this large under-served market.

2.3 HOME FOR INNOVATION

Singapore has identified R&D as a growth driver for our economy. Building on this, Singapore aims to be a home for innovation where companies can conduct activities along the entire research, innovation and commercialisation continuum. Today, clean energy companies in Singapore enjoy a wide array of options to forge research collaborations with our local research and educational institutions. (Figure 1).

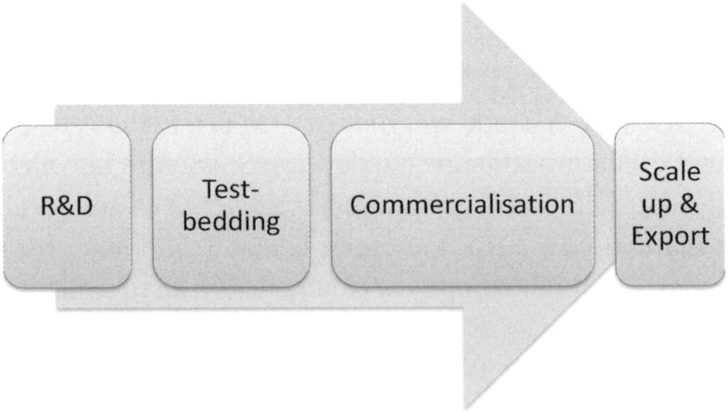

Figure 1 Research, Innovation and Commercialisation Continuum

Source: Economic Development Board (EDB), Singapore.

Our solar energy research activities received a major boost with the establishment of the Solar Energy Research Institute of Singapore (SERIS) in 2008. Located at the National University of Singapore (NUS), SERIS will spearhead solar energy research in Singapore in a few areas, namely silicon-based solar cells, solar modules, system integration, new solar concepts and integration of solar technologies into green buildings. With an investment of S$130 million over five years, SERIS conducts world-class industry-oriented R&D and train specialist manpower for the solar energy sector. The first CEO cum founder was Professor Joachim Luther, former Director of the Fraunhofer Institute for Solar Energy Systems, and a renowned technology leader in this field. Following in the footsteps of Professor Luther, SERIS has attracted other leading scientific talent, including Professor Armin Aberle, who has taken over as the new CEO in 2012. To date, SERIS has entered into research collaborations with many leading solar companies such as Renewable Energy Corporation and Trina Solar.

SERIS is well complemented by the Energy Research Institute at Nanyang Technological University (ERI@N), which has a comprehensive focus on sustainable energy, energy efficiency and infrastructure, and socio-economic aspects of energy research. With a five-year budget of S$200 million, ERI@N will develop and strengthen its expertise in wind energy, marine energy, energy storage, electric mobility, smart grids and fuel cells. They have already established research collaborations with leading companies such as Vestas, Bosch IBM and Rolls Royce.

The Energy Innovation Research Programme (EIRP) is another major initiative to develop our clean energy R&D capabilities. Structured as a competitive funding programme, EIRP is open to educational and research institutes, private sector companies and not-for-profit research laboratories. The programme has successfully funded 29 projects in areas ranging from building-integrated photovoltaics and novel thin-film solar cells to storage systems for renewable energy during the 2007–2011 period.

Startup companies in the clean energy space are also contributing to new innovations in this rapidly changing industry. As part of our goal to increase the commercialisation avenues in Singapore, EIPO is also

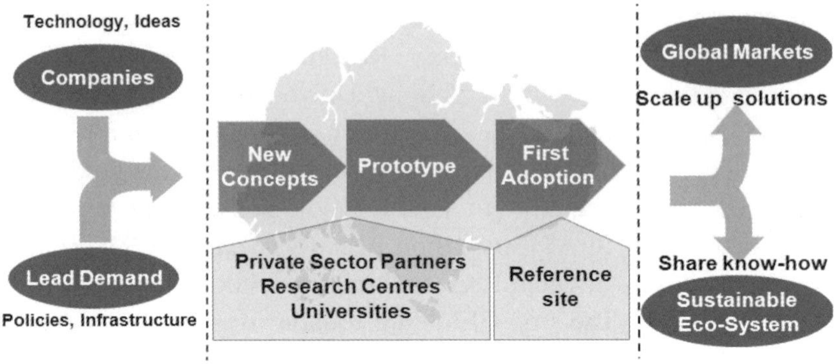

Figure 2 Singapore as a Living Lab

Source: Economic Development Board (EDB), Singapore.

actively nurturing early-stage companies in parallel with the establishment of a network of cleantech incubators in Singapore to support the growth of these companies. In addition, EIPO administers the Quick-Start programme which offers repayable grants of up to S$500,000 to help Singapore-based early-stage companies to develop innovative clean energy technologies and solutions to serve global markets.

Cleantech companies can also use Singapore as a "Living Lab" to develop, test and commercialise innovative green solutions before scaling them up for Asia and beyond (Figure 2). Examples of such platforms in Singapore include Punggol Eco-Town, CleanTech Park, Jurong Lake District, electric vehicles testbed and the Intelligent Energy System (IES) testbed. In particular, CleanTech Park will serve as a large-scale integrated "Living Lab" for the experimentation of system-level clean technology solutions. As Singapore's first eco-business park, it is an ideal business location for companies in the Cleantech business or companies which have embraced sustainability as a means to differentiate their businesses. The CleanTech Park will house a core nucleus of clean energy activities which will serve as an epicentre for research, innovation and commercialisation. When fully built in 2030, the Park will have a working population of 20,000. (Figure 2).

Due to the rapid growth rate of the clean energy industry, there is a global shortage of specialised manpower. The development of skilled manpower for the clean energy industry would therefore provide

Singapore with a differentiating advantage and support the innovation aspirations of the industry. Recognising this, EIPO ran the Clean Energy Graduate Scholarship programme to develop future research leaders for the industry. The scholarship supported post-graduate degree courses in clean energy related areas in leading universities such as Stanford, MIT, Cambridge, NUS and NTU. Along with other initiatives like the Workforce Development Agency's (WDA) Continuing Education and Training programmes, the government expects to train over 2,000 clean energy specialists over five years.

2.4 HOME FOR BUSINESS

Singapore is emerging as a global clean energy hub that is home to a vibrant ecosystem of international companies and serves as a springboard to key markets in Asia. The range of business activities includes R&D and engineering, regional headquarters and high-value manufacturing. Examples of key companies are as follows:

Atlantis Resources Corporation, one of the world's leading tidal energy companies, has its Global Headquarters and innovation centre in Singapore to take advantage of Singapore's pro-business environment, excellent logistics connectivity, respect for intellectual property and innovation capability.

China Guangdong Nuclear Power Holding Corporation (CGNPC) recently established its integrated biomass–solar power generation plant, fuelled by wood and horticultural waste, with a sizeable solar installation on the rooftop. CGNPC also set up its Regional Headquarters for its renewable energy operations in Singapore.

DNV, a leading testing and professional services company from Norway, operates the Clean Technology Centre (CTC) in Singapore. The CTC covers diverse sectors such as renewable energy, shipping, oil and gas, and sustainable cities.

GreenWave Reality, a building and grid-level energy management systems company, has established its Global Headquarters and R&D Centre in Singapore. The R&D centre will further develop the energy management software and hardware for smart grid applications and LED lighting.

Panasonic set up an energy solutions R&D centre in Singapore. This is a key part of Panasonic's global strategy to grow revenues from eco-friendly products and solutions. In partnership with government agencies in Singapore, Panasonic will also conduct a first-of-its kind test-bed of these total energy systems and solutions, before commercialising these solutions globally.

Phoenix Solar, a leading photovoltaic solutions provider from Germany, established its Asia Pacific hub in Singapore. Phoenix Solar has been using Singapore as the springboard to become the market leader in PV system integration in Singapore and the region.

Renewable Energy Corporation (REC) established one of the world's largest integrated solar manufacturing complexes in Singapore. The company has invested some S$2.5 billion in its first phase expansion, which would provide 800MW of wafers, cells and modules. The Singapore facility currently employs about 1,500 employees.

Trina Solar, a leading integrated manufacturer of solar photovoltaic (PV) products, has established its Asia-Pacific, Middle-East and Africa regional headquarters in Singapore to strengthen its growing customer base in the region. This comes on top of Trina Solar's existing collaboration with SERIS to develop high-efficiency back-contact solar cells.

Vestas, the world's largest supplier of wind power systems, has chosen Singapore as the base for a global wind R&D centre with expertise including grid management.

2.5 CONCLUSION

Given the initial wave of entrants in the clean energy ecosystem and strong governmental commitment, Singapore is well positioned to ride the growth of the clean energy sector and serve as a hub to reach global markets.

CHAPTER 3

NANOENERGY IN SINGAPORE

Hiranmayee Vedam

ABSTRACT

Climate change and energy in terms of resources and therefore supply present one of the greatest global challenges. One possible solution could be nanotechnology and energy or "nanoenergy". At the time of writing in 2009, nanoenergy was still in its infancy. However nanotechnology itself had already proved its commercial viability in other sectors such as electronics, healthcare and information storage to name a few. In Singapore, the energy industry has been dominated by oil and gas companies, however in 2007, the Government established programmes to expand the range of energy sources to include solar, biofuels and other energy solutions. The nanotechnology industry in Singapore has been increasing with two dedicated research departments, one at Nanyang Technological University, the other at the National University of Singapore, and other research institutes and government linked organisations, as well as private sector participation. Examples of how nanotechnology contributes to electricity generation, distribution and storage are provided and how nanotechnology is acknowledged as a key factor in the sustainable development of the Singapore economy.

3.1 INTRODUCTION

Of all the current challenging issues in the world, there are few as difficult to rectify as the climate change–energy link. Much has been stated about the grave need to create a less carbon-intensive global economy. Of course there is no single, silver bullet solution. The nearest remedy could be the marriage between nanotechnology and energy.

Imagine the synergy that could arise when micro-mini machines, products and processes are made possible by the application of nanotechnology to manufacturing and other processes. How much less energy could be used to power such microscopic production, how much less pollution and less consumption of resources and fewer emissions of greenhouse gases (GHGs) could occur? Nanotechnology has already seen commercial success in multi-billion-dollar industries such as the electronics and information storage industries, petroleum, chemical and healthcare industries, amongst others. It is still at an embryonic stage but development is fast moving.

In the 4 July 2009 issue of *The Economist*, in the Science and Technology section, an article "The Power of Being Made Very Small" described how nanotechnology will assist in the production of new materials, which in turn will help produce big improvements in energy production. Scientists will build these new materials on a nanoscale, where things are measured in billionths of a metre. On this nanoscale, materials can have unique properties.

A US team at the Massachusetts Institute of Technology (MIT), led by Dr. M. Demkowicz, working with the Los Alamos National Laboratory, is seeking to quicken research into energy technologies. This team is researching material which will resist damage from radiation, which will extend the working life of the reactor and allow it to operate more efficiently by burning a larger percentage of nuclear fuel. The team is looking for a new type of nanocomposite material.

A second example is the search for nanoengineered materials which will play an important role in the more efficient generation of solar cells. This is done by the manufacture of multi-junction solar cells, in which each layer captures energy from a specific colour in the light spectrum. This is more efficient than a conventional solar cell which converts energy from only part of the spectrum. Such a cell will have an efficiency of over 40 percent, much higher than the 20 percent of conventional cells.

A third example is the possibility of incorporating solar cells into the structure of buildings, including windows. These three examples illustrate how nanotechnology can boost energy efficiency and help combat climate change.

3.2 SINGAPORE ENERGY POLICIES

The energy industry encompasses all organisations involved in generating, storing and distributing energy. As in the rest of the world, this industry in Singapore is currently dominated by the oil and gas companies, which account for nearly 5 percent of its gross domestic product (GDP). However, in 2007, the Singapore government recognised energy as a strategic sector and embarked on new programmes to broaden the base of this industry by exploring growth opportunities in solar power, fuel cells, biofuels and energy management solutions.

The Singapore energy policy report[1] that was released in 2007 set a goal of increasing the value added by the energy sector from S$20 billion to around S$34 billion by 2015, and tripling the employment generated by this sector from 5,700 in 2007 to 15,300 by 2015.

The policy also outlined strategies to intensify energy R&D efforts in areas where Singapore has expertise or a competitive advantage. As part of this strategy, the Singapore Initiative in New Energy Technologies (SINERGY) Centre[2] was set up. It will provide technical infrastructure such as a micro-grid and a command and control facility to facilitate research on clean and sustainable energy solutions. The Centre also has in-house expertise in systems integration, testing and evaluation of energy technologies. In addition, the Agency for Science, Technology and Research (A*STAR), an umbrella agency within the Ministry of Trade and Industry (MTI), which encompasses 11 different research institutes in Singapore, has established an Energy Technology R&D programme[3] to

[1] Ministry of Trade and Industry Singapore. "Energy for Growth: National Energy Policy Report", November 2007.

[2] Agency for Science, Technology and Research (A*STAR). *SINERGY Centre*. http://energy.astar.edu.sg/cos/o.x?c=/wbn/pagetree&func=view&rid=10123 [Accessed July 2009].

[3] Agency for Science, Technology and Research (A*STAR). *Energy Technology Research and Development Centre*. http://energy.a-star.edu.sg/ [Accessed July 2009].

integrate and expand existing knowledge and work in areas such as fuel cells, alternative fuels and next-generation solar technologies.

3.3 BUILDING THE NANOTECHNOLOGY SECTOR IN SINGAPORE

Since the late 1990s, in response to the increasing interest in nanotechnology worldwide, Singapore government agencies, including the Ministry of Education (MOE) and A*STAR, have increased their emphasis on nanoscience and nanotechnology research. In the recent report by the MTI, titled the Science and Technology Plan 2010, nanotechnology was repeatedly emphasised. The main practitioners in nanotechnology research are the two main Singapore universities, Nanyang Technological University (NTU) and the National University of Singapore (NUS), which have set up the Nanoscience and Nanotechnology Cluster (NanoCluster) and Nanoscience and Nanotechnology Initiative (NNI) respectively, in response to the emphasis on nanotechnology.

Apart from the private sector, there are many research institutes, schools and government bodies conducting cutting-edge R&D in this field. From A*STAR's Institute of Materials Research and Engineering (IMRE) to the National University of Singapore, there is a considerable amount of research activity in this field; excluding corporate research labs, there are currently 15–20 other research centres engaged in nanotechnology projects. It is estimated that the number of researchers and engineers working in nanotechnology-related fields in the Republic, in both the public and private sectors, totals about 1,000.

There are also commercial companies which help researchers make the transition into the market with their business support and incubation services. These include the Nanyang Technological University–owned R&D and business incubation company called NanoFrontier. More foreign venture capitalists have also been entering the scene in recent years, such as the American company, Innosight and the 50 per cent German funded Nanostart Asia Pacific Pte Ltd, joining Singapore's emerging Nanotech industry. Dr. Lerwen Liu, Director of NanoGlobe, says:

> In the past five years, we are seeing an increasing growth of nanotech start-ups in Singapore and in the Asia-Pacific region. Also, due to the rising

number of foreign venture capitalists entering the market, increased government incentives and more networking platforms such as NanoEquity Asia, we expect to see further growth in the number of start-up projects in the near future.

3.4 NANOTECHNOLOGY IN ENERGY

Nanotechnology is the technology of creating and applying materials and structures with at least one critical dimension below 100 nanometres, which leads to new functionalities and properties.[4] Nanoscale materials and structures exhibit many novel properties, such as electric conductivity, magnetism, fluorescence, hardness and strength changes, which are significantly different from their macroscale counterparts. Due to these new functionalities, nanotechnology has a profound impact on the generation, storage, distribution and utilisation of energy. The following section describes the numerous ways that nanotechnology contributes to electricity generation, distribution and storage.

3.5 ENERGY GENERATION

3.5.1 Photovoltaic Cells

Photovoltaic (PV) cells that convert sunlight into electricity face two key challenges, namely low efficiency and high cost of production. Inefficiency in conventional PV cells arises since the incoming photons must have energy equivalent to the band gap energy of silicon. This accounts for a loss of 70 percent of radiant energy incident on the cell. Nanotechnology can help increase the efficiency of solar cells via multiple techniques. For example, creating nanostructures such as quantum dots can help optimally adjust the semiconductor band gaps and improve conversion efficiency. Anti-reflective coatings using photonic crystals or non-metallic nanolayer systems can also improve efficiency. The use of plasma-aided procedures is another approach to optimise the cell structures of all solar cell types and thus increase efficiency.

---

[4]Luther, Wolfgang. "Application of nanotechnologies in the energy sector", Volume 9, *Aktionslinie Hessen-Nanotech*, August 2008.

With the use of nanotechnology, it is also possible to manufacture inexpensive solar cells with the same efficiency as current technology. For example, semiconductor nanorods or organic semiconductors can be embedded within a polymer matrix to create flexible and low-cost solar cells. Thin-layer solar cells also have the potential to reduce costs due to material savings, low-temperature processes and integrated cell insulation. Dye-sensitised solar cells made using titanium dioxide nanoparticles doped with dye molecules can be screen-printed, thus reducing manufacturing costs, and they can generate energy even from diffused light.

3.5.2 Fuel Cells

A fuel cell is an electrochemical conversion device that produces electricity from fuel on the anode side and an oxidant on the cathode side, which react in the presence of an electrolyte. Key challenges in a fuel cell system are the high costs of producing and storing hydrogen. Apart from that, the fuel cells use precious metal catalysts that are expensive and can be spoilt easily. Second, the membranes used in the fuel cells cannot operate at temperatures that are optimal for maximising energy generation. Third, it is also critical to measure the temperature profile inside a fuel cell in a robust and cost-effective manner.

Hence, apart from PV cells, nanotechnology has the most impact on this energy sector. For example, nanoporous materials such as complex hydrides, for instance $LiBH_4$, and nanoporous metal-organic compounds are being developed to store hydrogen in solid-state fuel tanks. Ceramic nanopowder based on yttria-stabilised zirconia (YSZ) is used to increase ion conductivity in solid oxide fuel cells (SOFCs).

Nanotechnology enables the use of low-cost metal oxides to produce photo-electrodes that can increase the efficiency of water decomposition. Nanotechnology can also enhance the activity of electrode materials and noble metal catalysts for electrochemical conversion of hydrogen. The temperature stability of membranes in the fuel cells can be enhanced through the application of inorganic-organic nanocomposites such as functionalised polymers with inorganic nanoparticles. Nanotechnology can also help overcome the key challenge of the need for hydrogen as a feed, as nanocatalysts can be mobilised to directly activate hydrocarbons in the fuel cells. Microfuel cells with higher energy density than current batteries are also possible because of nanotechnology.

3.5.3 Wind Energy

Wind energy provides less than 1 percent of worldwide energy needs, but it is growing more rapidly than other energy sources. Key challenges faced by this energy source are low efficiency and reliability of the turbines and difficulty in generating high-quality energy at low cost. Nanotechnology can improve the efficiency of turbines through nanocomposite materials, based on carbon nanotubes that can be used to make lightweight and high-strength rotor blades. Nanoscale coatings for bearings can also improve the efficiency of wind turbines.

3.5.4 Fossil Fuels

Fossil fuels currently provide more than 80 percent of the energy needs in the world. As oil reserves become depleted, methods to extract more oil from existing reserves and new sources of oil such as shale oil are being explored. Nanotechnology is being increasingly utilised by this industry to increase production and efficiency. For example, nanosilicate particle suspensions are used for viscosity control in oil production. Nanoporous materials are also used for the separation of contaminations in oil deposits and to increase yield. Another application of nanotechnology in fossil fuel production is the use of nanolubricants to reduce mechanical wear of drill probes used in exploration.

3.5.5 Others

Nanotechnology also has a strong impact on energy generation, using other sources such as geothermal and coal-fired power plants. For example, nanostructured membranes can be used for separating carbon dioxide in carbon-neutral coal-fired power plants. Another example is the use of plasma coating processes which can be used for thermal barrier layers in gas turbines. Nanoparticulate coating materials can also be used as ceramic anti-adhesive layers to reduce caking in heat exchangers in coal-fired power plants.

3.6 ENERGY STORAGE

3.6.1 Lithium-Ion (Li-Ion) Batteries

The Li-ion batteries that are ubiquitous in the market today have relatively high energy densities, but high/low temperatures affect their capacity permanently. Also, the shelf life of the battery irrespective of use causes its capacity to deteriorate. None of the existing electrode materials and electrolytes can deliver optimal performance in conditions of high capacity, high operating voltage and a long cycle life. Nanocomposite structures such as lithium titanate are being explored for use as anode material in these batteries. Similarly, electrolytes containing nanoparticles are being developed to enhance the capacity of these batteries. These nanostructured materials also enhance the safety of Li-ion batteries, which can potentially explode at high temperatures or when exposed to stress.

3.6.2 Supercapacitors

A supercapacitor is a device which consists of two electrodes surrounded by an electrolyte, separated by a membrane, and which stores energy by charge transfer at the boundary between the electrode and electrolyte. The amount of energy stored is a direct function of the available electrode surface. Hence, using nanostructured materials like carbon aerogels, activated carbon or carbon nanotubes can significantly enhance the performance of a supercapacitor.

3.7 ENERGY DISTRIBUTION

As energy costs continue to escalate, the power industry is looking for ways to reduce transmission costs while ensuring availability and flexibility. Nanocomposite materials like aluminium conductor composite reinforced wire or carbon nanotube composites have 5–10 times more capacity than wire such as aluminium conductor steel reinforced wire which is currently used in the market. This will lead to a smaller footprint and lower construction/maintenance costs. Nanotechnology can also potentially help reduce the cost of high-temperature superconductor (HTS) wires that carry more power than the current-generation HTS cables and have lower maintenance costs. Fluids containing nanoparticles can cool HTS transformers more efficiently without the need for flammable liquids, increasing the flexibility in locating the transformers. Magneto-resistive nanosensors based on magnetic nanolayers and power electronic components are potentially self-calibrating and self-diagnosing, enabling remote monitoring of infrastructure on a real-time basis. This would help decrease losses and increase availability and flexibility.

3.8 ENERGY UTILISATION

Apart from enabling energy generation, storage and transmission, nanotechnology has a marked impact on increasing the efficiency of energy utilisation in different industry sectors.

3.8.1 Transportation

Nanotechnology affects energy utilisation in the transportation industry via nanocatalysts in fuels, nanolubricants to reduce friction, more efficient batteries and lightweight nanocomposite materials that do not compromise on strength. Nanoparticles made of cerium oxide which catalyse the combustion between diesel fuel and air have been shown to increase fuel efficiency by up to 10 percent in field trials by Oxonica in 2006. Nanolubricants based on boric acid have the ability to reduce frictional losses by as much as 80 percent while increasing component durability and reliability. Nanostructured metal matrix composites and polymer composites can reduce the overall weight of vehicles. In addition, miniaturisation of components through use of nanosensors can further reduce the overall weight of the vehicles.

3.8.2 Building

The most significant contribution of nanotechnology to the building industry is enabling the development and use of energy-efficient light-emitting diodes or LEDs, based on inorganic and organic semiconducting materials. A quantum dot is a semiconductor whose excitons are confined in all three spatial dimensions. As a result, they have properties that are between those of bulk semiconductors and those of discrete molecules. They are also known as nanocrystals, a non-traditional type of semiconductor with limitless applications as an enabling material across many industries.

Quantum dots can help improve the energy efficiency and light yield of existing LEDs by minimising scattering effects. Nanotechnology can have a significant impact on organic LEDs by optimising the field carrier materials, succession and thickness of layers, application of dopants and the purity of materials used. Nanocomposites made of polymers reinforced with carbon nanotubes can lead to ultra-light high-stability construction materials. Heating and cooling of buildings account for a significant share of energy consumption worldwide. Nanoporous materials, such as porous aerogels based on silicon dioxide and nanoporous polymer foams that have smaller pore size than the average free path length of a gas molecule, can help reduce these costs.

3.8.3 Manufacturing

Nanotechnology can increase the energy efficiency of industrial processes through better insulation materials, as discussed earlier. Nanostructured catalysts with larger surface areas per unit volume can increase yield and give us the ability to synthesise materials in new, energetically favourable ways. Nanoscale powders can reduce sintering temperatures in high-temperature manufacturing processes like ceramics, due to their large surface area and natural tendency to coalesce. Another way to increase the energy efficiency of manufacturing is to use micro-reactors where heat and mass can be controlled more optimally.

3.9 NANOENERGY IN SINGAPORE

Nanotechnology is recognised as a key enabler to sustain the future development of the Singapore economy. Singapore agencies have put more and more emphasis on it since the late 1990s in response to the growing awareness of nanotechnology worldwide. The Singapore government spent about US$300 million between 2003 and 2007 on nanotechnology-related R&D and manpower development. It is estimated that the number of researchers and engineers working in nanotechnology-related fields in the Republic, in both the public and private sectors, totals almost 1,000. Singapore is an active member of the Asia Nano Forum (ANF) as well as a participating member of the International Organization for Standardization (ISO) and International Electrotechnical Commission (IEC) technical committees on nanotechnology. Singapore also chairs the standardisation working group in the ANF. The remainder of the paper will discuss some key developments in Singapore in this area.

3.10 PHOTOVOLTAIC (PV) CELLS

PV cells are a strategic area of growth for Singapore. With its strong experience in the semiconductor industry, it has the engineering knowledge, infrastructure and experienced people required for the silicon-based PVs. It is also well positioned to integrate PVs into urban buildings. To capitalise on these advantages, in August 2007, the Singapore Economic Development Board (EDB) launched the Clean Energy Research and Testbedding (CERT) programme which will provide S$17 million in funding to testbed PV technologies. The National Research Foundation (NRF) of Singapore has also set aside S$170 million to boost Singapore's clean energy R&D efforts, starting with a focus on solar technologies and fuel cells. In February 2008, the National University of Singapore set up a new national solar research institute called SERIS, to develop critical technological capabilities to drive the solar energy sector in Singapore. As part of its sustainable development programme, Singapore has earmarked S$31 million to install rooftop solar panels in 30 public housing precincts.

3.11 FIRST-GENERATION PV CELLS

Norway's Renewable Energy Corporation (REC) has set up the world's largest solar manufacturing complex in Singapore. NorSun has set up a major mono-crystalline wafer manufacturing facility in Singapore. Eco-Solar and Solar Power (acquired by Solar-Fabrik) have set up solar panel manufacturing in Singapore. Also, clean energy companies such as SolarWorld and Conergy have set up their Asia-Pacific headquarters in Singapore.

3.12 NEXT-GENERATION PV CELLS

3.12.1 Dye-Sensitised PV Cells

Researchers at NUS are investigating the use of diameter-controlled anatase TiO_2 nanofibres in dye-sensitised solar cells. They are also researching the impact of electrospinning and hot pressing one-dimensional metal oxide nanorods onto substrates as guides for electron transport. Initial results indicate that they can produce dye-sensitised solar cells with conversion efficiencies of ~6 percent. Another group at NUS is investigating mesoscopic metal oxide electrodes (TiO_2, Al_2O_3, etc.) and their assemblies with functional molecules to produce high-efficiency, low-cost dye-sensitised and three-dimensional solar cells. Other groups are investigating the use of conjugate polymers and nanocrystalline inorganic materials for solid-state dye-sensitised solar cells. At NTU, researchers have developed dye-sensitised solar cells based on ZnO nanoflowers with a conversion efficiency of 1.9 percent.

3.12.2 Organic PV Cells

A*STAR's IMRE has developed translucent organic solar cells that can be easily printed on flexible substrates. These solar cells can not only be produced cheaply but also have a wider variety of applications, from window panes to portable electronics. At NTU, researchers are incorporating silver nanoprisms as median layers between the electron and hole to increase the amount of light absorbed and enhance charge transport. Bosch has set up a S$30 million R&D facility in Singapore and will collaborate with NTU to reduce the cost of their organic PVs while raising their efficiency and service life. At NUS, platform technologies such as advanced nanometal inks, deep ultraviolet (DUV) and i-line cross-linkable formulations for producing organic transistors and novel columnar heterostructures for highly efficient PVs are being developed. Researchers at NUS are also investigating production of low-cost, high-quality graphene by chemical exfoliation and its use in transistors and solar cells.

Commercial activity in this area is just getting started in Singapore. Oerlikon has set up manufacturing and R&D facilities related to its thin-film silicon solar panels. NanoBright Technologies Pte. Ltd., a spin-off from NUS, is increasing the efficiency of silicon-based solar cells, using their up- and down-conversion materials. Mentarix, another startup from Singapore, also uses quantum dots and photonic technologies to enhance the efficiency of all types of solar cells.

3.12.3 Fuel Cells

Singapore is one of the leading countries in fuel cell research.[5] The technology scan done by A*STAR in 2005 as part of developing the Singapore Science and Technology Plan 2010[6] included hydrogen production and storage and fuel cell–based energy conversion technologies as two of the high-priority research areas in the energy sector for Singapore.

NTU has had an ongoing strategic programme on fuel cells[7] for more than 10 years to develop next-generation fuel cells, more specifically high-performance solid oxide fuel cells (SOFCs) that can operate at lower temperatures of around 600 °C and membrane electrode assembly for low-temperature proton-exchange membrane fuel cells (PEMFCs).[8] Key achievements of this work include the synthesis of ultra-dense high ionic conductivity YSZ electrolyte of 0.17 S/cm, design of an anode-supported fuel cell, development of a PEMFC model that is validated experimentally, modelling of an autothermal fuel reformer and hybrid gas turbine SOFC for high-efficiency power generation.

NTU is also developing power electronics for power conversion and power conditioning in fuel cell systems. Among the A*STAR institutions, IMRE is developing new proton-exchange membrane electrolytes and small PEM fuel cell stacks.

The Institute of High Performance Computing (IHPC) has research in computational modelling and analysis of PEM and solid oxide fuel cells, fuel cell materials and associated electrochemical and chemical processes.

---

[5] Naumanen, Mika. "NanoRoadMap Project", VTT Technology Studies, October 2004.

[6] Ministry of Trade and Industry Singapore. *Other Publications.* http://app.mti.gov.sg/default.asp?id=885 [Accessed July 2009].

[7] Ho, Hiang-Kwee, Siew-Hwa Chan, and San-Ping Jiang. "Fuel cell research, development and demonstration activities in Singapore", *Fuel Cells Bulletin*, June 2004.

[8] Nanyang Technological University. *School of MAE – Fuel Cell SRP.* http://www3.ntu.edu.sg/mae/Research/Programmes/Fuelcell/intro.htm [Accessed July 2009].

The Singapore Institute of Manufacturing Technology (SIMTech) is developing microfuel cells and new manufacturing technologies for fuel cells. The Institute of Chemical and Engineering Sciences (ICES) has research in fuel processing, fuel cell catalysts and hydrogen storage.

NUS is developing nanostructured catalysts and methanol-blocking proton-conducting polymer electrolyte membranes to overcome the challenges of catalyst deactivation and methanol cross-over from fuel electrode to air electrode in direct methanol fuel cells.

In the commercial world, DaimlerChrysler along with BP and Michelin has announced a fuel cell demonstration project along with installation of hydrogen refuelling stations by BP. Rolls-Royce has set up an advanced technology centre to collaborate with A*STAR institutions and Advanced Materials Technologies to develop automated fuel cell manufacturing technology. Rolls-Royce also formed a partnership with a Singapore consortium led by Enertek Pte. Ltd. to form Rolls-Royce Fuel Cell Systems Pte. Ltd., in order to develop a 1-megawatt (MW) hybrid SOFC that meets electrical power system requirements. The EDB has set up a Singapore Fuel Cell Community, led by Temasek Polytechnic, to support the commercialisation of fuel cell technologies.

3.12.4 Li-Ion Batteries

Research in Li-ion batteries in Singapore, although world renowned, is a very niche area, with only one major group at NUS working on it. NUS has an advanced battery research group[9] which focuses on the preparation and characterisation of nanomaterials for Li-ion and lithium polymer batteries. They are formulating new transition metal oxide composites and modifying known oxide components ($LiNi_{1-x}Co_xO_2$ and $LiNi_xMn_xCo_{1-2x}O_2$ doped with Al and Mg) as cathode materials. These new materials can potentially result in batteries that are robust to cycling and elevated temperatures. The group is also investigating composite alloys such as nanocrystalline $CaSnO_3$, carbon-coated $CaMoO_4$, tin oxides with hollandite crystal structure, metal oxyfluorides TiO_2 and NbO_2F and thin films

[9] NUS Advanced Batteries Laboratory. *Advanced Batteries Laboratory*. http://www.physics.nus.edu.sg/solidstateionics/ [Accessed July 2009].

made of Fe_2O_3 and NiO nanoflakes and nanowalls as anodes. They have found that nanophase $ZnCo_2O_4$ material is the best oxide material to use as anode material for Li-ion batteries. The group is also investigating polyethylene oxide (PEO)-Li-salt complexes as solid electrolytes in crystalline, glassy and polymeric form. In terms of commercial activity in this area, Sony announced the opening of a new Li-ion battery plant in Singapore in August 2008.[10]

3.12.5 OLEDs

OLEDs are light-emitting diodes that generate light in a film of organic compounds. A significant benefit of OLED displays over traditional liquid crystal displays (LCDs) is that OLEDs do not require a backlight to function.

IMRE and NUS researchers have developed a technology to fabricate all-in-one white light LEDs by growing multiple quantum wells using InGaN/GaN on sapphire substrate. This is an important milestone in obtaining white light LEDs that are cheaper, more stable and less complex without using phosphors. Another research group at IMRE is developing top-emitting OLEDs on flexible substrates and has developed robust plastic substrates with effective barriers against oxygen and moisture to increase their lifetime. They have also achieved significant improvement in electro-luminescent efficiency in top-emitting OLEDs by overlaying an optical coupling layer on a semitransparent cathode.

Researchers at IMRE have also developed blue emitters with increased lifetime and efficiency that is solution-processible, making them cheap to produce. In 2008, there was an increasing emphasis on utilising the knowledge from this research in PV development, due to the strategic emphasis placed on PVs in Singapore. Singapore also has a lot of commercial activity in this area. BASF set up an organic electronics R&D laboratory in Singapore and will include collaborative projects on organic PVs with A*STAR's IMRE. Ness Display has set up organic LED manufacturing operations and conducts research in

---

[10]MIS-Asia. *Sony opens lithium-ion battery plant in Singapore*. http://www.mis-asia.com/news/articles/sony-opens-lithium-ion-battery-plant-in-singapore [Accessed July 2009].

large-scale display technologies in Singapore. Hyundai LCD Inc. has a collaboration with A*STAR's SIMTech to develop and commercialise display manufacturing technologies for PM/AM OLEDs and flexible OLEDs for mobile and automotive applications. AMR International Corp. has an ongoing collaboration with NTU to develop indium tin oxide (ITO) transparent electrodes for OLED applications.

3.13 CONCLUSIONS

Nanotechnology has a profound influence on all aspects of energy generation, storage, distribution and utilisation. Singapore has world-renowned research programmes in the areas of fuel cells and Li-ion batteries and is fast becoming a hub for research activity in PVs. Although this growth has attracted multinationals to conduct research and manufacturing in Singapore, the local industry's ability to capitalise on this expertise is just beginning to emerge. Perhaps the establishment of a dedicated Nanotechnology Institute in Singapore might provide the catalyst and organisational synergy needed to raise the level of research and application in this vital and high-potential sector. There is of course the Singapore Institute of Bioengineering and Nanotechnology (IBN), whose director is Professor Jackie Ying, ex-MIT. Established in 2003, IBN became the first A*STAR research institute with the most primary patents filed per budget dollar, attesting to its innovativeness. To date, the Institute has filed over 692 patent applications, including 188 primary patents, on its technologies.

As always, the key to success is funding. Jonathan Kua, Director of the New Businesses Group, EDB, says:

> Nanotechnology has enormous commercial potential because it impacts almost every industry. Yet in order to have useful applications, there must be adequate funding to commercialise the technology coming out of research labs, and close the gap to market.

CHAPTER 4

INNOVATION WITH ENERGY AND ENERGY WITH INNOVATION

Geoffrey C. Nicholson

ABSTRACT

The interdependence of energy and innovation is explored in this chapter and is based on the author's 40-year experience at 3M Company, a leader in innovation. Subjects tackled include imbuing an "innovation culture" and how to go about doing this, using 3M as the case study, the importance of innovation to a company and not forgetting the importance of the consumer or end-user of the product as the centre of all innovation. The significance of innovation to energy is also discussed particularly in the context of rising demand and finite supply, and how to increase effciency while decreasing ecologically detrimental effects.

4.1 INTRODUCTION

Innovation and energy are two key subjects at the centre of strategic thinking and planning in countries, companies and enterprises. This article will deal with these subjects. They may appear to be separate subjects and yet they are interdependent. Anyone who has been involved with innovative products and business models knows well the challenges one has to overcome to make them successful. One needs passion, commitment and personal energy to succeed.

Similarly, energy is faced with challenges, with the need for responsible and ecologically acceptable development of energy sources, as well as more productive uses of existing energy sources. There is a need for innovative business models as well as products. And so I ask the following questions:

- How do you define innovation?
- Is it part of your business plan?
- Is it the responsibility of all disciplines in your organization?
- Do you provide the resources to do it?
- Do you measure it?
- Are long-term research groups in touch with the customer?
- What volunteer employee activities foster innovation?
- How do you encourage volunteers?
- Does your organization have a history of stories that helps employees learn about innovation?
- Does the organization recognize innovative achievements?

This article will attempt to answer these questions, based on my experience during an almost 40-year career at the innovative 3M Company. I am not suggesting that all of the aspects and characteristics of 3M can be adapted or adopted into your company, but I am suggesting that some of them may have benefit for your company. There are sections on the innovative culture, the Chief Executive's role, hiring innovative people, benefits of a global technical community, examples of 3M innovation and some conclusions.

4.2 THE INNOVATIVE CULTURE

I would like to bring your attention to a paper titled "Innovation Nations" written by Ambassador Mark Hong and published in September 2008. He quotes Curtis Carlson: "A developed country's competitiveness now comes primarily from its innovation capability. It is the only path to growth, prosperity, environmental sustainability and national security."

Ambassador Hong also brings to our attention that Singapore has pursued four strategies to build knowledge; that is, investment in education, encouragement of free flow of information, awareness of global technology advances and maximizing the cross-fertilization of technologies.

It is also interesting that IBM's global innovation study in 2006 indicated that the creation of new and significantly differentiated products is an activity which requires a great deal of cross-fertilization between individuals. Thus it is not an individual activity but a group activity which involves the interaction of many technologies. I agree with these observations.

In order to put innovation in context at 3M, it is necessary for us to look at the company overview and our business sectors.

3M company overview:

- Sales: $24.5 billion
- Net income: $4.1 billion
- International sales: $15.5 billion (63 percent of company total)
- Companies in more than 60 countries
- Sales in nearly 200 countries
- Over 76,000 employees
- Over 55,000 products
- 45 established technology platforms
- 571 US patents issued in 2007
- 45,000 issued and pending patents worldwide

Six market-leading businesses:

- Consumer and office
- Display and graphics
- Electro and communications
- Safety, security and protection services
- Health care
- Industrial
- Transportation

The importance of the technology platforms and how they are linked to different markets and products is clearly shown in Figure 1.

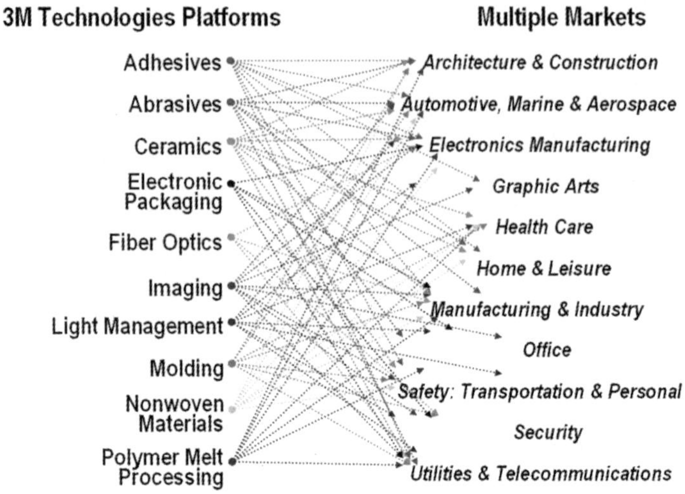

Figure 1 Linkages of 3M Technology Platforms and Markets

Source: 3M.

The culture of innovation at 3M is the responsibility of all 3M employees.

3M culture of innovation:

- Over 7,000 technical employees around the world
- R&D at ~6 percent of sales
- Technical depth and breadth
- Bringing multiple technologies to each customer
- Entrepreneurial culture
- Individual initiative: 15 percent of their time to work on new product ideas
- Legacy of boundary-less culture

The sharing of technologies, and the fact that the technology belongs to the company and not to a specific business unit, is a vitally important part of the culture of 3M. This will be discussed later in this article. And so to the definition of innovation in a corporation like 3M: "Research is the transformation of money into knowledge. Innovation is the transformation of knowledge into money." The customer must be at the center of this and it is indeed the circle of life of a company.

Why is innovation important to a company? Innovation brings growth. Innovation is a survival issue, for without it ultimately the company will die. Innovation also brings competitiveness to the company, and on a personal level, innovation brings satisfaction to the people who participate. Technical plans are driven by business plans, but the question is, "Is innovation part of your business plan?" It should be. As we have defined innovation, we must measure its success. This measure can take various forms in companies. One measure is the sale of new products and the profitability of those products. Thus we ask, "Do you support and encourage innovation in your company or enterprise?"

We must be driven to solve customer problems in order to be a successful enterprise. These problems are either perceived by the customer or unperceived by the customer. Perceived problems are those which the customer identifies to you, while the unperceived problems are the result of observing the activities of the customer and bringing new thoughts to the customer from your technology base.

The customer is at the center of all innovation. The customer determines whether your product is successful and has value, whether it is a physical product or a new business model. The customer, as you see in Figure 2, has perceived needs and unperceived needs. The customer asks the supplier for a product, and if 3M succeeds in producing it, 3M has satisfied the customer.

Of course, the customer, rightly so, asks for this product from several suppliers, and there is immediate competition. Such products tend to be

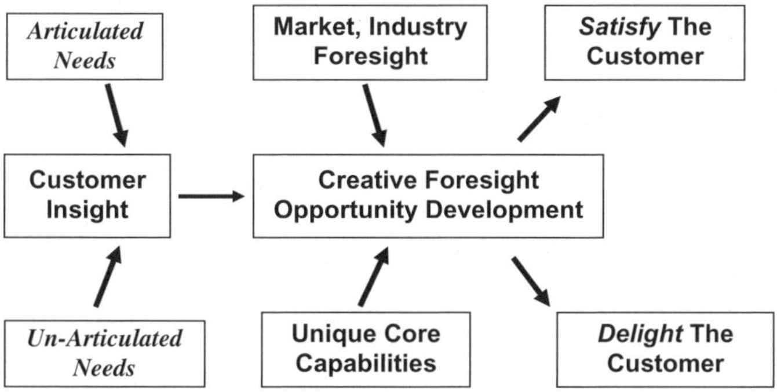

Figure 2 Customer-Inspired Innovation

Source: 3M.

evolutionary and are needed by any business. However, there are also the unperceived needs, or unarticulated needs, of the customer. These are most likely to be found when your company's technical people spend time with the customer. Your technical people should have a good breadth of knowledge of your company's technologies. The customer has a limited capability because he tends to base his needs on incremental changes in existing technology. Thus, if 3M introduces a very unique product, which is revolutionary to the customer, then 3M has the opportunity to delight the customer. The customer then can make a dramatic impact on his own business opportunities with this significant advance. 3M truly delights the customer and the employees of 3M. Remember the customer pays your salary, not your employer.

Now, I would like to discuss how one brings an environment to a laboratory that encourages creativity. Locating the laboratories close to each other does the following:

- Facilitates technology sharing
- Simplifies employee transfers
- Stimulates innovation
- Exposes customers to the breadth of 3M technology and encourages their inputs through the development of Customer Innovation Centers
- Build Customer Innovation Centers

In the United States the primary 3M laboratories, which consist of technology centers and business laboratories, are on our campus in St. Paul, Minnesota.

What is the environment in which one can encourage innovation in the laboratories? The location of laboratories close to each other has an important benefit. Such proximity of laboratories facilitates technology sharing which brings unique solutions to customer problems. It also simplifies the transfer of employees from one business laboratory to another business laboratory. Whereas we may think that written reports or technical meetings transfer technology, the transfer of employees is one of the most effective ways of transferring technology around the company. The opportunity for promotion of employees is available and easily accomplished. It stimulates innovation and provides customers with an incredible breadth of technology.

Another way to put the customer at the center of the innovation process is through our Customer Innovation Centers. Perhaps you have read about such centers in recent publications, with one being established in Dubai. In fact, it was our laboratories outside the United States which championed and developed this idea. When I was the head of our Japanese laboratory in 1978 to 1980, I asked that we have a room within our laboratory into which we would be proud to bring our customers. I did *not* want it to be a product display area. Yes, products would be displayed, but I wanted it to be a working laboratory where customers could use our products and be exposed to the variety of technologies that were used in the products. We would stir their imagination and their interest. It worked so well that when I was responsible for all of our laboratories outside the United States, we established such Customer Innovation Centers around the world. They are in Singapore, China, India, Korea, Germany, the UK, Mexico and Brazil, to name a few. 3M Indonesia has taken the same principles in a limited space with a small technical team to set up interactive displays of 3M technology and products throughout. And now we have a Customer Innovation Center in the US.

One of the challenges is that laboratories around the world are physically separated from each other. Fortunately there is a revolution in communication. There is the availability of video-conferencing, e-mail and reporting of activities to each other via other electronic means. I would note, however, that these are no substitute for the personal interaction that you have by visiting and spending time in each other's laboratories. The temporary transfer of employees between laboratories in different countries is considered training, but I believe that technology transfer is the key benefit. Moving employees from one laboratory to another, particularly those coming from our laboratories outside the United States, allows them to experience firsthand the informality of management with employees, and the multiple technologies that are available for them to use. They have the opportunity to meet product champions, champions who are usually self-appointed, and to experience the stories of failures that are told by employees and management, but failures which were learning experiences.

There are several requirements for new product success. The keys to success are as follows:

- Innovation culture
- New product expectation
- Permissive attitude of management
- Needs that are technology driven

- Product champions
- Multiple technologies
- Technical assessment
- 15 percent rule or bootleg slack, boundary crossing
- Recognition and rewards

There is a culture of sharing technology, which we have just described. There is a new product expectation in terms of sales and profits. The permissive attitude of management is the tolerance for failure and the learning experience of failure, which does not take away from the expectation of new product results. In any new product success, there is always a product champion. This champion is not necessarily appointed by management. Indeed the better champions are self-appointed because they take ownership and have a passion for the success of the project. Many of these products are combinations of several different technologies which are available to our technical employees.

Products may belong to operating business units, but technology belongs to the whole corporation. There is no cost of transferring technology from one business unit to another. And, of course, there is that rule we have, called the 15 percent rule, also known as bootleg slack or boundary crossing. We never measure the 15 percent. It is a strong message. The employee is encouraged to explore, encouraged to network and collaborate, and encouraged to experiment. We say to our technical employees that they have 15 percent of their time in which they can work on any project of their own choosing without supervisor or management approval. When you look at major successes at 3M Company, you see that, while they were within the general businesses of the company, they were not forecast or predicted in the business plan. They became a business plan. One of the most difficult parts of our culture to explain to visitors is this 15 percent rule, particularly when we say we never measure it. It is a clear message to employees that they have the freedom to explore new business opportunities and products for 3M Company.

As we look at the process of innovation as illustrated in Figure 3, at the beginning of the innovative process, there is high risk. It is individual risk with potential high failure with very little management involvement. There is no schedule; there is no discipline. Indeed you might describe it as chaos.

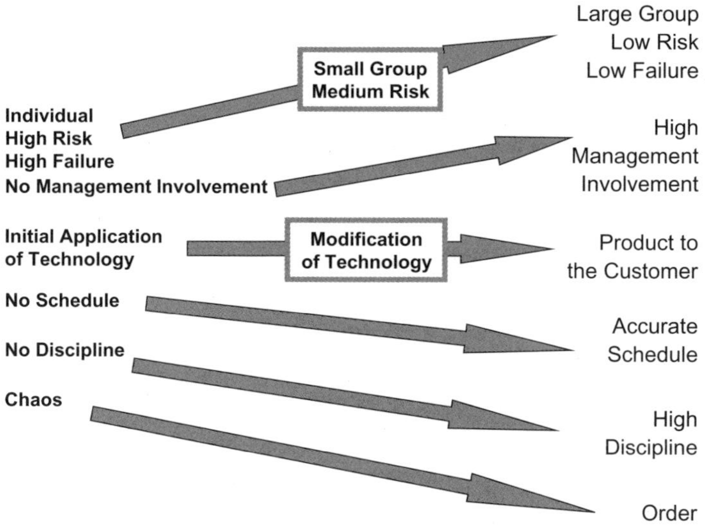

Figure 3 The Innovation Process and Risk Level

Source: 3M.

However, that environment allows the birth of new ideas without fear of failure and the opportunity to grow into significant new businesses.

As we proceed to the end of the process, with the product being delivered to the customer, large groups of people are involved, the risk is low, and the failure rate is low. There is high management involvement as they provide significant resources, accurate scheduling, and good discipline. During the process we must constantly look at the customer needs, both perceived and unperceived, to determine whether or not our solution fits the needs of the customer and brings value to the customer. I will also add that we tell our employees, "If you are going to fail, please fail quickly."

There are rules for avoiding innovation. The working environment can inhibit, or even kill, innovation. If management is always suspicious of every idea which originates below them, people will not bring their fresh ideas to management's attention. This is also true if we insist that people go through all levels of management with any new idea. If we express criticism and withhold praise, it kills initiative. If the attitude of management is that people at the top know everything, this will inhibit the expression of ideas, because of fear of failure.

Rules for avoiding innovation:

- Be suspicious of every idea that originates below you
- Insist that people go through all levels with a new idea
- Express criticism and withhold praise
- Make a decision to reorganize in secret and maximize surprise
- Be control conscious
- Never forget that people at the top know everything

Statements made by management can inhibit the expression of new ideas and the process of bringing them successfully to the market.

Wrong management signals:

- "It'll never work."
- "We explored that thoroughly 10 years ago."
- "OK, if we can get somebody else to pay for it."
- "We're too shorthanded to work on blue sky ideas."
- "It's not in the business plan."
- "It's not your job to talk to customers."

I have heard some of these in many companies — and at 3M. Notice the statement by management that "It is not in the business plan." It is true! New ideas are not in specific business plans. They are ideas which are being developed and become business plans in the future. We believe that it is always better to ask for forgiveness than to ask for permission. If management insists that you always ask for permission, you will finally find someone in a higher management position than yourself who will say that it is a bad idea and therefore you will have someone to blame for stopping the program. Discoveries and inventions are made in the laboratory by experimentation, not on computer screens. Computers give us the knowledge so that we can make discoveries.

4.3 CHIEF EXECUTIVE'S ROLE

In the process of innovation, you cannot manage creativity. You must be a leader that provides the environment and the encouragement for the process of idea generation, as well as for the innovative process to bring the idea to a successful conclusion. The role of the CEO is vital. They must provide that leadership and that environment which increases the probability of success. A former 3M CEO, Mr. Lew Lehr, stated, "The ordinary manager has a craving for order. The leader understands that innovation is almost always an untidy process. The ordinary manager wants proof of an idea before taking action. The leader understands the value of the power of faith."

That was a statement from the CEO in 1980, and today our CEO, Dr. George Buckley, originally from the UK, recently shared his views on innovation in a company publication. He stated:

> Creativity and imagination have to be managed differently than other aspects of the business. No matter who invests in the technology, it is communal property. We have many processes for sharing ideas in technology among the technical community. You cannot make creativity a process; it is more a process of controlling chaos. Process may constrain the people and kill the very thing that you want to achieve.

And so you see the importance of the role of the leader, the CEO, in encouragement and understanding. Understanding the need for creative ideas and providing the opportunity for the process of innovation to succeed, as well as the necessary resources, is essential. If our leaders and management are to activate innovation within their organization, they must embrace these traits:

VISION FORESIGHT STRETCH GOALS EMPOWERMENT
COMMUNICATION NETWORKING RECOGNITION

We must clearly define the vision that we have for our company. We need to know where we need to go. If you do not know where you are going, it does not matter which road you take. To be successful, we must know where the rest of the world is going, get there before they do, and provide products to help them be successful. Also, we must have ambition, that is, stretch goals, necessary and clearly defined results that are expected from the organization. If we are to empower people, we must insist upon freedom in the workplace to pursue innovative ideas. Such empowerment is achieved by having something like the 15 percent rule, recognizing that it is always better to ask for forgiveness rather than permission, and learning to live with failure and yet never to accept it.

Networking is an essential part of an organization's strength. We are able to draw from the experience and knowledge of others as well as use their equipment. Networking is not a waste of time; it is an effort to improve the operations of our business area and learn new techniques, technologies and processes. And, finally, we must be rewarded for our efforts. There is nothing more rewarding than recognition from our peers and management.

3M has a variety of Rewards and Recognition Programs:

- Carlton Society
- Circle of Technical Excellence and Innovation
- Innovator Award
- Dual-ladder structure

These are not monetary rewards but recognition rewards. The Carlton Society is the highest technical recognition in the company. In the history of 3M, there have been just over 100 people who have been awarded this honor. Every year the worldwide technical community nominates their peers. They have to provide specific data on the contribution of the individuals. It is expected that the nominees will have spent time mentoring other employees and will have been strong advocates in successfully sharing technology around the company. There is a voting process which identifies the winners, and once per year in front of a global 3M audience, the Chairman of the Board makes a presentation to those who have been chosen. The winners are not aware that they have been chosen until that moment.

All of our laboratories around the world participate in the Circle of Technical Excellence and Innovation program. Nominations for these awards are also prepared by their peers, not by management.

The company has a dual-ladder system where people are promoted on the basis of technical excellence and not necessarily to management. Promotion to management may require a separate skill set. Salary and benefits on either side of the ladder are the same. Therefore, if we promote a technical person to management purely on their technical record, we have the possibility of losing an excellent technical person and gaining a very poor manager.

4.4 HIRING INNOVATIVE PEOPLE

During the 1990s, the Chairman of the Board asked me to put together a small team so that we could study the characteristics of successful innovators at 3M, and hence have a better probability of success in hiring good innovators for the company. We interviewed some successful innovators at 3M so that they could tell us their background and careers *prior* to them joining the company. It was apparent that these people were very practical people. Typically they were from an agricultural background, as Minnesota has an agricultural economy. They were used to tackling problems and doing things themselves. In other words, if the tractor stopped during their work period, they would jump off the tractor and try to make the repair themselves. They did not have cell phones in those days to call the repair man. They were the repair people.

We found the primary characteristics of successful innovators, which they showed *before* they joined the company. It was then up to the current management to provide the environment for them to be creative and innovative. Our human resources and technical interviewers would look for these characteristics in potential new employees, as well as looking for technical capability.

Traits and characteristics of 3M innovators:

- Creative
- Broad interests
- Problem solvers
- Self-motivated, energized
- Strong work ethic
- Resourceful

Innovators are creative, they are inquisitive, they ask questions, they look for solutions, they are intuitive thinkers, ideas flow easily and they are visionary. When we interview these technical people we would give them a small problem and watch how they tackle it.

Innovators have broad interests, they are eager to learn, they explore ideas openly with others. They have a variety of hobbies, and they are often multi-disciplinary. Innovators are problem solvers. They have an experimental style — they try it first and explain it later. They tinker with things, they are hands-on, they are not afraid to make mistakes, they are willing to do the unobvious, they are very practical. They take multiple approaches to a problem, but at the same time they are very technically competent.

Innovators are self-motivated and energized. They are driven, they are results-oriented because they are doers, they are passionate about what they do, they have an urge to succeed and accomplish the objective. They are emotional and enthusiastic. They have a sense of humor. They also have a sense of social responsibility. They want to contribute and they look for the contribution to have value and purpose.

Also, very importantly, they are courageous and self-confident. They take the initiative. If they are given the freedom to be creative and innovative, they must have the courage to accomplish the program as they will run into many challenges and difficulties. These difficulties may be technological, but many times they involve resistance from management and colleagues. Another characteristic of an innovator is that they have a strong work ethic. They are committed and hardworking. They work in cycles and have flexible work habits. They drive towards work completion, they are dedicated to results. They are tenacious.

Finally, innovators are resourceful, they network with others because they can get things done through others. They are looking for both the expertise of their colleagues as well as the time their colleagues may use to help them. They are also looking for the free use of equipment. Again, that time can be available because their colleagues have 15 percent of their time in which they can work on any project they want, without management approval. It is good to get a group of these people together to work on problems which can have a major impact on both the business and the environment.

With this in mind, it is obvious that we can access technologies across 3M, and when we access technologies, we access the available equipment. We get back to the point that technologies belong to the company, products belong to business units. Integrating 3M technologies helps us to create new innovative products that change the basis of competition.

4.5 BENEFITS OF A GLOBAL TECHNICAL COMMUNITY

I referred to culture. One of the primary benefits of having laboratories around the world is the different backgrounds and cultures they bring to the company. I am sure that all of us, at some time, have said, "Why didn't I think of that? Why didn't I think of the Post-it Note?" The technology had been around for about 10 years.

I would suggest that you just had not looked at the technology with the right perspective. I strongly believe that as we provide our technologies to different countries with different experiences and cultures, they will see 3M's technologies from different perspectives. The laboratory in Germany will look at the technology differently compared to the laboratory in the UK, or in China or Brazil. I remember when we provided the resources for a few people to go to China to demonstrate their technology. In a few days they produced several records of inventions, and their patents provided sales in China that would not have occurred without this technology sharing — yet another example that networking is *not* a waste of time. When we see things differently, then we put ourselves in a position to create something new and something of value.

These ideas are summarized as follows:

- Leveraging across technologies: Integrating 3M technologies to create new innovative products that change the basis of competition
- Leveraging across countries: Applying 3M technological breakthroughs in as many geographic areas as possible

The benefits of having laboratories outside the United States are as follows:

- Serving our customers
- Growing our business
- Knowing the competition
- Access to global technology
- The innovation factor

The final point is the innovation factor which we have seen dramatically demonstrated in our laboratories outside the United States. The evolution over time of laboratories outside the United States can be outlined as follows:

Evolution of 3M laboratories outside the United States:

- Technical service
  - Product training
  - Product performance auditing
  - Comparative product analysis
  - Recommending product change for market fit and new market
- Product engineering
  - Technical support for manufacturing
  - Raw material standards
  - Cost reduction by raw material substitution
- Product modification
  - Modifying existing products to meet local market needs
- Product development
  - Innovating and developing new products using technology from 3M and other sources
  - Searching out new business opportunities consistent with company objectives and resources
- Technology development
  - Developing new technology to meet local customer needs
  - Developing technology based on availability of technology in country

Laboratories outside the US should be part of the company in that country. As you look at the evolution of a laboratory, you can see that the first activity of the laboratory is to conduct technical service for the products that are sold in that country. This provides product training and performance auditing for that country. It is customer focused. The second activity of that laboratory is the support of manufacturing, such as raw material substitutions, and drive towards reduced costs of manufacturing.

The third activity of the laboratory would be product modification to meet the needs of the local market.

That knowledge will come only from good technical service that has been provided by the laboratory. They will know what aspects of performance need to be improved. The fourth activity of the laboratory is product development, in which they are expected to innovate and develop new products using technology from 3M or from other sources such as universities and research institutes. They have a responsibility to search out new business opportunities which are consistent with the company's objectives and resources. Finally, after a laboratory has developed this kind of expertise, they are in the position and mature enough to start developing new technology to meet the future corporate needs. That technology will be based on the country's technology capability and availability. You will notice immediately we do not advocate putting research laboratories into countries, but we do advocate putting laboratories that will evolve into a research capability once they know the connection with the customers, local raw materials and technologies that are in that country.

4.6 ENERGY WITH INNOVATION

In this section we will deal with examples of innovation in the energy sector. There is a critical need for innovations in the energy sector in order to meet the challenges of ecology, the demand for increased energy, and the need for more productive products which do not require as much energy. I would like to refer you to a presentation that was given by Jon Brodd, CEO of Cima NanoTech, at the June 2009 meeting of the Institute of Southeast Asian Studies (ISEAS). In particular, I refer you to Figure 4, which shows the various resources that are being used to increase the capacity for energy.

You will see that a major part of that potential resource is in the solar area. Cima NanoTech Company[1] has discovered a technology in the production of high-volume, low-cost silver nanoparticles. These particles can be coated to form a self-assembling, transparent conductive coating. They can also be ink-jet printed for front electrodes on silicon cells.[2]

---

[1] For more information on the products and technologies of Cima NanoTech, see http://www.cimananotech.com/.

[2] http://www.cimananotech.com/silvernanoparticles.aspx.

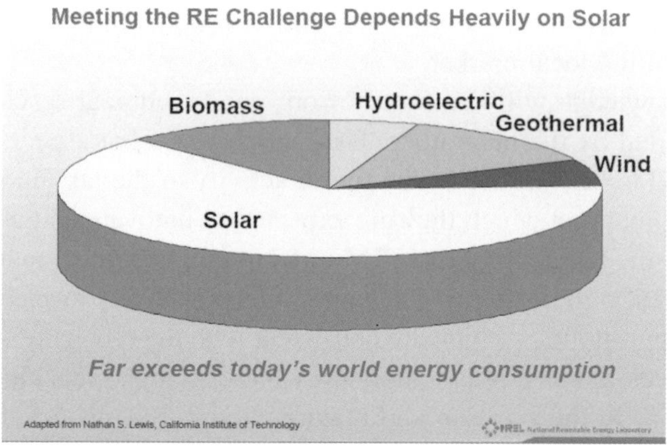

Figure 4 Worldwide Renewable Resources Potential

Source: 3M.

This unique technology truly changes the basis of competition. Cima NanoTech, Toda Kogyo and Toray Industries launched the production of this technology in the first quarter of 2009. The product has better properties with a 50 percent lower production cost than current film technologies. Nanomaterial production has been established in Japan and Cima NanoTech's film sales have already commenced. With regard to ink-jet printing on solar cells, the current screen printing method has a larger than 1 percent breakage of the solar cells. Ink-jet printing is a non-contact technique, and hence a non-breaking technique. It can also allow for thinner silicon wafers to be used, which can result in a 50 percent reduction of the direct cost of a silicon wafer.

Current line widths are 120 microns, whereas ink-jet printing will provide line widths of 40 microns, thus with improved and demonstrated productivity. We are looking at a two times faster throughput using this process. Again, I suggest you look at the paper that was given by Jon Brodd to ISEAS in June 2009 to learn more about this exciting technology. It changes the basis of competition and industry has recognized Cima NanoTech.

Industry recognition for Cima NanoTech:

- 2008 World Economic Forum Technology Pioneer
- Top 10 percent of Technology Pioneers, Davos, 2008

- Top 10 Greentech/Cleantech Award
- Participant in 2009 Asian Summit
- Invited speaker on nanotechnology
- World Economic Forum New Champions, Tianjin, China, 2008
- Japan Nanotechnology Conference, 2007 and 2008
- SEMICON West, "Self Assembling Electronics", 2009

4.7 EXAMPLES OF 3M INNOVATIONS

3M is also involved in many products in the energy area. For example, 3M, over a period of years, has launched many films which have been used as brightness enhancement materials in televisions, laptop computers and cellular phone systems. Although one of the primary benefits of using these films has been in brightness enhancement of the images, a significant benefit has been the reduction in the amount of energy required to drive these products. There is a continuing demand for low-power TVs without sacrificing performance. Recently 3M received the Alliance to Save Energy's Star of Energy Efficiency Award for its potential to save billions of kilowatt hours (kWh) in liquid crystal display TVs and monitors. This was awarded at a ceremony in Washington, DC.

In order to focus on the opportunities of renewable energy, 3M, with its strategic vision, has established a new business unit, the Renewable Energy Division.[3] When one sets up a business unit with that name, it focuses the attention of the business on those opportunities in that area. It focuses the technical community on products which may benefit the renewable energy business. The 3M Renewable Energy Division is looking at solar, biofuel and wind energy. The focus of the business activities is on products that reduce the cost per watt of renewable energy — as both components (films, tapes, adhesives, coatings) and consumables (filtration, abrasives, safety, etc).

In the solar energy area, I will focus on just a few products which benefit that energy source. For more than a decade 3M has been a trusted supplier of advanced materials to the solar industry. Today 3M offers a

[3] For more information on the products and technologies of the 3M Renewable Energy Division, see http://solutions.3m.com/wps/portal/3M/en_US/Renewable/Energy/.

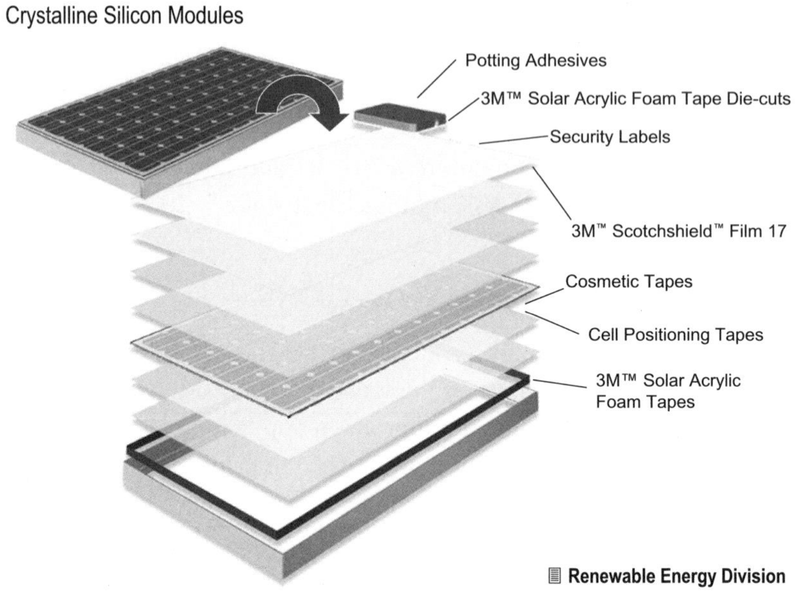

Figure 5 Crystalline Silicon Modules Design Used in Solar Energy

Source: 3M.

broad range of products and technologies designed to enhance product performance, improve reliability, and drive down the cost per watt. In Figure 5 you will see the general design of crystalline silicon modules that are used in solar energy.

As part of that structure, I would particularly draw your attention to the 3M Scotchshield Film 17. The technical community has experience in materials that provide barriers to oxygen and moisture in precision-coated, multi-layer films that are tuned to transmit or reflect specific wave lengths. The barrier film technology offers outstanding resistance to moisture and oxygen permeation. It is used to encapsulate sensitive components from the elements. It can provide a cost-effective solution for extended system life and reliability. The properties are outlined in Table 1.

As one looks at the materials that are used in this film, you see the use of fluoropolymers; fluorochemistry has been an important technology at 3M for decades. Fluoropolymers have excellent resistance to degradation from sources such as UV, heat and moisture. Their weather resistance

Table 1 Properties of Dyneon™ Scotchshield™ Film 17 Durable, a Fluoropolymer Backsheet with Tri-laminate Construction THV/PET/EVA

Requirement	Status	Test standard
Cut-through	Pass	UL 1703/IEC 61730
Hot spot	Pass	IEC 61215, ed 2
Damp heat	Pass	IEC 61215, ed 2
Thermal cycling	Pass	IEC 61215, (w/constant I,V)
Humidity freeze	Pass	IEC 61215, ed 2
Mechanical load	Pass	IEC 61215, ed 2
Robustness of termination	Pass	IEC 61215, ed 2
TÜV partial discharge	Pass	(1100 V) IEC 60664-1

Source: 3M.

exceeds that of non-fluorinated materials. The high-durability, UL- and IEC-certified 3M Scotchshield 17 Backsheets represent 3M's solar investments in Singapore and are now manufactured at the Tuas facility in Singapore.

In the area of wind energy, there are a number of opportunities for improvement of products in wind turbines. For example, when a turbine blade is moving at up to 300 km/h at the tip, it is affected by sand, rain and hail. This debris can cause significant erosion and pitting at the leading edge of the blade. This not only reduces the aero-dynamic efficiency, but can also lead to blade failure due to water penetration. Wind tapes based on the same technology used for over 40 years to protect helicopter blades and aircraft radomes can be applied to the leading edges of these blades to minimize the damage. These high-performance polyurethane tapes have proved their ability to maintain turbine efficiency, reduce downtime and maintenance, and extend the useful life of turbine blades, even in the harshest of environments. These tapes can be applied either at the manufacturing facility or in the field.

Finally, I would like to introduce you to a product that you would probably least expect to come from a company like 3M. I am referring to a high-voltage electrical transmission cable that is used in the electrical grid and utilizes new technology. This product illustrates many of the principles I have discussed in this paper on innovation, and the environment which encourages it to occur. How did this innovation occur?

This was not a product that management or marketing asked the technical people to develop. The idea for this product occurred during a fishing trip in Canada. This group of technical people was working on composites for aerospace applications. They were unable to overcome some of the technical challenges in that particular development. They began to explore the use of aluminum composites in other markets. On the fishing trip, they noticed a large transmission grid over water in Canada. What if they could reduce the number of towers that were required to carry such small cables?

The result was that they developed a composite material suitable for high-voltage transmission electrical cables. A key technical challenge was to have a very strong bond between the aluminum oxide fiber and the aluminum metal. Failure of that bond would cause catastrophic failure of the cable. Remember that these cables run at high temperatures. Again, through networking of the technical people, we became aware of a technology in the former Soviet Union, and were able to incorporate this into the cables.

Figure 6 shows the structure of these cables and Figure 7 illustrates the technology — wetting the fibers — that lead to significantly increased capacity without increasing the sag. Refer to Table 2 for related data.

Thermal upgrades are the primary applications for the use of this new cable. You get two to three times the gain in capacity with the restringing on existing structures. It is a quick and simple solution and there is no visual change or environmental impact.

Now, over 600 miles of these cables are installed in various parts of the world. It was recently announced that Indian power company Tata will install 3M's cable to boost electricity transmission near Mumbai. A 3M conductor will be installed in place of existing conductors. The right-of-way available was inadequate and the 3M conductor can be installed without the need to construct new transmission towers. The innovative lightweight sag-resistant overhead conductor can carry two to three times the amount of electricity compared to the conventional original steel conductors of the same diameter.

This product development illustrates many of the principles that were discussed at the beginning of this paper on the subject of innovation.

Figure 6 3M Aluminum Conductor Composite Reinforced, An Innovative Lightweight Conductor

Source: 3M.

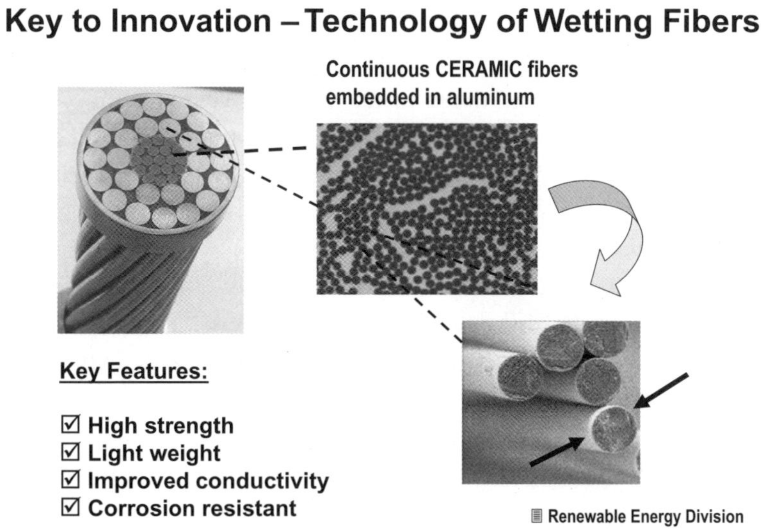

Figure 7 Aluminum Conductor Composite Reinforced: Technology of Wetting Fibers

Source: 3M.

Table 2 3M ACCR Significantly Increases Ampacity Without Increasing Sag

Temperature	795 ACSS	Height above ground (ft)	3M 795 ACCR	Height above ground (ft)
240 °C	2,274 amp	33	2,274 amp	36
125 °C	1,585 amp	27	1,585 amp	33
75 °C	1,096 amp	22	1,096 amp	31
50 °C	670 amp	15	670 amp	27
	Reached sag limit at 75 °C		Reached sag limit at 240 °C	

Source: 3M.

4.8 CONCLUSIONS

At the beginning of this paper, I asked a number of questions with regard to innovation. We define innovation as the process of taking a good idea and turning it into something of value to the customer. We asked if it was part of your business plan. Unless the need for innovation is part of the business plan, there will be little focus on it. Is it the responsibility of all disciplines in your organization? Yes, it certainly is. Without the input and participation of all disciplines, you risk failure because of lack of commitment.

Do you provide the resources to do the job? Yes, you must do this in order to have the organization believe that you are committed to innovative products. That is one of the reasons 3M allows 15 percent of time, particularly of the technical community, to investigate high-risk ideas. One never knows who will be the inventor.

Do you measure innovation? It must be measured in terms of new product sales, profitability and growth of your business. You have to provide the opportunity for your research groups to be in touch with and spend time with the customer.

What volunteer employee activities do you have that foster innovation? Do you have the freedom to allow your people to network and not consider it a waste of time? How do you encourage volunteers?

Do you have organizational activities which allow the employees to participate in networking?

Do you encourage the telling of stories that help employees learn about innovation? Does your management tell of their failures, as well as their successes?

Does the organization recognize innovative achievements? Do you have awards that are given to teams as well as individuals? Are they nominated by their peers?

Understand your customer and his needs. The technical community must know that it is not the company that pays their salary, but the customer who pays their salary.

Bring your technologies to bear on customer needs, both articulated needs and unarticulated needs. Network across the whole organization, and share technology that can be used by other business units.

And most importantly, have the courage of your convictions. If you are given the freedom to innovate, I assure you that it will take courage in order for you to succeed. There are many hills to climb and challenges of technology and management to overcome, but success is for those who are persistent with knowledge and courage. And so, innovate with energy, and innovate in the energy business.

I leave you with this message: No matter where you are…

Innovate for the customer! Network across the globe! Have courage!

CHAPTER 5

HYDROPOWER IN SOUTHEAST ASIA

Erik Knive

ABSTRACT

Energy demand in Asia is growing exponentially and with it the inevitable increase in carbon dioxide emissions. Renewable forms of energy have the potential to reduce these emissions and promote energy security throughout the region. Norwegian-owned SN Power with its expertise in hydropower as an energy source and investment capabilities has an important role to play in the power deregulated markets that have the potential to benefit the region and by extension the globe, through the development of clean sustainable energy.

5.1 INTRODUCTION

In 2008, Southeast Asian countries were riding high on unprecedented global commodity prices as economic growth for the region was even adjusted upwards to 5.6 percent at the peak of oil prices. Countries blessed with natural resources switched focus from plans for new gas-fired power

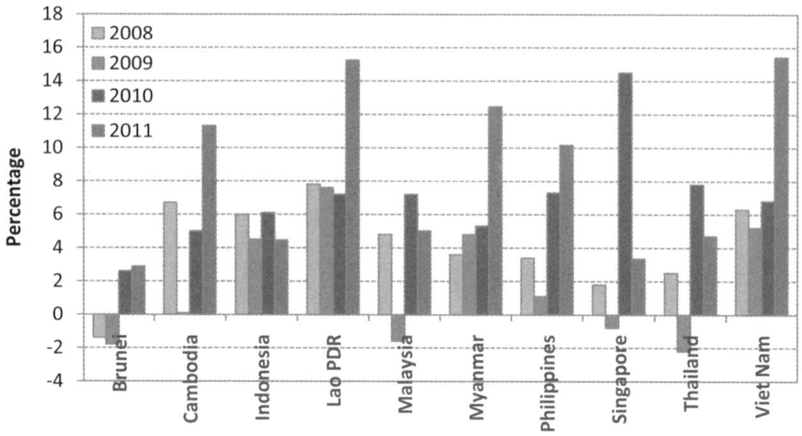

Figure 1 Association of Southeast Asian Nations (ASEAN) Gross Domestic Product Growth 2008 to 2011

Source: ASEAN key economic indicators and 2011 from Global Insight.

plants to coal-fired plants, anticipating better profits in selling gas as a commodity, and revived their renewable energy plans. When the global financial crisis hit in the later part of the year, the export-orientated group of nations fell into a recession. Affluent governments followed the lead of Europe and America in rolling out stimulus packages. Despite its initial euphoria, Southeast Asia grew at an average rate of 4.4 percent in 2008 (Figure 1).

The slowdown in economic activities in 2009 provided opportunities for a few to revisit their power development policies. Indonesia passed a new electricity act, Singapore invested heavily in renewable energy R&D, Malaysia commenced construction on hydropower projects in its northern states, Thailand adjusted its demand projections to more sobering rates instead of an exponential growth path, as Asia's rising star, Vietnam went full steam ahead with its power development plans.

The past two years saw economic growth rebounding strongly as did energy commodities prices such as oil and coal. While oil prices in 2011 and 2012 did not reach the highs of 2008, the annual average price was above $100 per barrel compared to the volatile 2008 which averaged $97 per barrel. The supercool Liquefied Natural Gas (LNG) price similarly crept up, and leaped to over $16 per mmbtu in the aftermath of the Fukushima nuclear crisis, as the future of nuclear power in the generation mix hangs in uncertainty.

5.2 ELECTRICITY MARKETS OVERVIEW

On the world stage, the International Energy Agency (IEA) in its World Energy Outlook 2011 estimates in its New Policy Scenario, that the demand for electricity will grow from 17,200 TWh to over 31,700 TWh, at an annual growth rate of 2.4 percent, between 2009 and 2035. On the supply side, coal remains the largest source for electricity generation with coal-fired power growing from 8,118 TWh in 2009 to 12,035 TWh in 2035. A significant increase in electricity generation from non-hydro renewable sources coming from wind, biomass, geothermal and solar power is expected, eight times the 2009 generation to 5,212 TWh in 2035.

However, the share of coal-fired power plants in the global generation capacity mix is expected to fall in the long run, from 32 percent to 26 percent in 2035, as renewable sources gaining a higher share, driven mainly by government policies. Gas-fired and hydropower are broadly expected to maintain their shares in the generation mix. Natural gas has the advantage of being widely available in many of these economies, and environmentally preferable to coal, since its greenhouse gas emissions are generally lower. Despite policy changes in some countries over the safety of nuclear power, nuclear is also likely to retain its share of global electricity generation mix from expansion in power hungry China and India.

Coal is by far the dominant source of fuel for electricity generation in Asia and is expected to be even more so. Coal similarly, has the advantage of being widely available and relatively inexpensive in many economies, some even subsidizing coal supply. China was the world's largest market for wind power in 2010, adding a staggering 16.5 GW of new capacity, and slipped past the U.S. to become the world's leading wind power country. At the end of 2011, the country has installed about 1,056 GW in generation capacity, however only less than 5 percent of which are wind power, while 72 percent of which are coal-fired capacity.

The other member of the billionaire club in terms of population, India is also highly coal dependent. With almost 200 GW in total installed generation capacity, 56 percent of which are coal-fired capacity. The country's plan to meet its burgeoning power deficits is through 12 Ultra Mega Power Projects (UMPP), all of which are coal-fired with a capacity of 4,000 MW per project. The first UMPP was successfully synchronized to the grid in early 2012.

The share of coal-fired capacity in China and India is expected to fall from present levels to 49 percent and 42 percent respectively in 2035. Nevertheless, their share of coal-fired generation is estimated to make up over 60 percent of the world's coal-fired generation. Globally, the trend towards greater diversity in the generation mix favoring renewable generation sources (Figure 2).

The global energy-related carbon-dioxide (CO_2) emissions reached 30 Gt in 2010, some 5.3 percent increase from 2009, representing almost unprecedented annual growth. In 2011, a record 31Gt was emitted globally. It seems that patterns in the global energy-related CO_2 emissions, mirrors that of the global economic conditions. In the IEA's New Policies Scenario, CO_2 emissions continue to increase, reaching 36 billion tones (Gt) in 2035, and leading to an emissions trajectory consistent with a long-term global temperature increase of more than 3.5°C. This expected warming of more than 3.5° would have severe consequences: a sea level rise of up to 2 meters, causing dislocation of human settlements and changes to rainfall patterns, drought, flood, and heat-wave incidence that would severely affect food production, human disease and mortality.

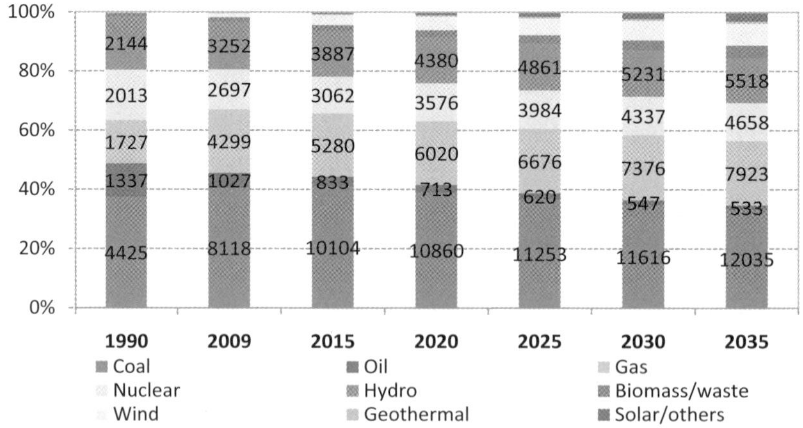

Figure 2 World Generation Mix (in TWh) in the New Policy Scenario
Source: IEA, World Energy Outlook 2011.

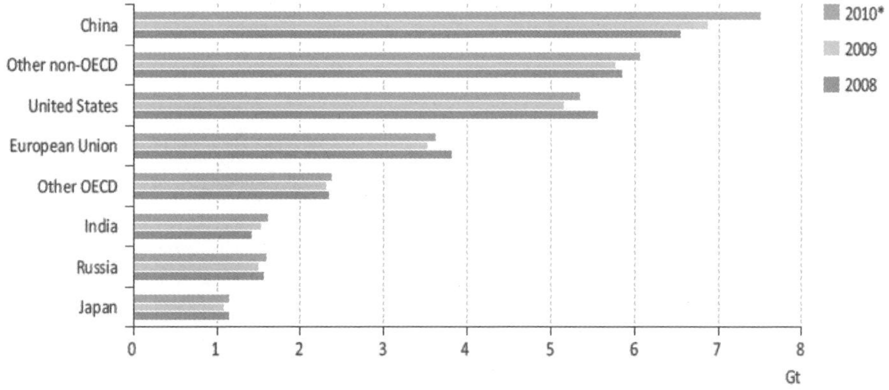

Figure 3 Energy-Related CO_2 Emissions by Country, 2008–2010
Source: IEA, World Energy Outlook 2011.

To bring CO_2 emissions back to historical levels, the world needs to reduce electricity generation from coal-fired plants, while renewable energy generation should double. The problem however, with most renewable generation sources such as wind and solar power, is that they are intermittent in nature and that electricity cannot be stored, a load balancing technology is required to react quickly to changing grid conditions.

The Asian economies account for almost half of the world CO_2 emissions from the combustion of fossil fuels. It is therefore, no exaggeration that what happens in Asia will largely determine what happens in the world. CO_2 emissions from the Asian economies are projected to increase to 35 Gt in 2035 from their present levels (Figure 3). Coal accounted for over 70 percent of CO_2 emission in the power generation sector, and is likely to retain this share in the longer term.

5.3 ELECTRICITY IN SOUTHEAST ASIA

A similar picture is painted for Southeast Asia. The region's CO_2 emissions are expected to double by 2030 to about 2 Gt, with power generation expected to be the major source of growth accounting for over half the increase, according to the IEA (Figure 4).

In Vietnam's Power Development Plan VII, over 30,000 MW of coal-fired capacity are planned to meet its projected demand by 2020. This

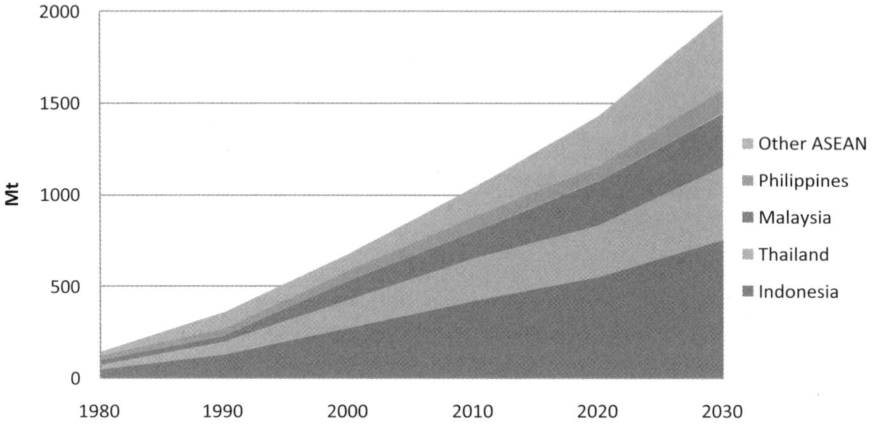

Figure 4 ASEAN Energy-Related CO_2 Emissions by Country

Source: IEA, World Energy Outlook 2009.

means an additional 100 million tons of coal will be required to fire up these power plants. As the second largest net exporter of coal, Indonesia is and will likely be the dominant supplier of coal for power generation to the region. It plans for some 4,000 MW of new coal-fired capacity in the country under the second phase of the 10,000 MW Fast Track Program, according to the latest 2011–2020 Electricity Power Supply Business Plan.

These projected scenarios will potentially lead to disastrous climate change consequences. Research shows that despite the global recession in 2009, total CO_2 emission crept up by 2% adding to the dire Global Carbon Project's data which shows that between 2000 and 2008, emissions rose by 29%. Clearly, this scenario is not sustainable and incompatible with APEC (Asia Pacific Economic Cooperation)'s commitment to "... prevent dangerous human interference with the climate system." With this linear pattern of growth, and increase of 5 to 6 degrees Celsius warming may be a likely plausibility, unsustainable even by conservative standards (Figure 5).

The Southeast Asian region encompasses a diverse set of economies in terms of energy demand and supply patterns, demand growth potential, and natural resource endowment. The Philippine is operating near full capacity, Thailand is dependent on imports from its neighbor's, Cambodia's power system is still rather backward, Singapore runs almost exclusively

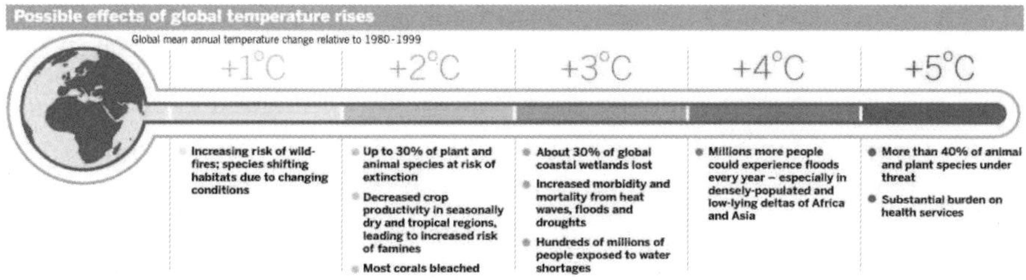

Figure 5 Possible Effects of Global Temperature Rises

Sources: Financial Times.

on gas-fired power plants with surplus capacity, Malaysia is predominantly based on subsidized natural gas with some excess capacity, and Lao PDR is contracted to export its generation, exclusively from its hydropower capacity to Thailand and more recently to Vietnam for the much needed revenue.

Electricity costs in Cambodia are among the highest in the world. The high cost is due to the country's almost total reliance on fuel imports firing-up more than 95% of the country's electric power generation from fuel oil or diesel power plants. The geography of energy supply options however, should not correspond to national boundaries. Opportunities exist to reduce the overall energy costs by exploring supply beyond borders since individual markets may be too small to justify large–scale investments to achieve scale efficiency.

On the demand side, GDP growth in the region is expected to grow on average of over 5 percent annually over the next five years. Vietnam and Indonesia are expected to grow at a faster rate, compared to more developed countries like Singapore and Malaysia. The Electricity-GDP elasticity measures the relation between the growth of the GDP and the growth of the electricity demand. The relationship can be explained by the increase electricity consumption in the production sectors and also on the demand side (households) as GDP increases. The elasticity of GDP electricity intensity decreases as economies industrialize due to demographic shifts from rural to urban areas, structural economic changes towards lighter industry, growth of the services, and the increased use of energy efficient devices and equipments.

The differences in economic growth rates and the uneven distribution of natural resources in the region provide an opportunity for greater electricity trade and cross-border exchanges. Power exchange is good economics, as it can result in benefits such as reduced costs of electricity supply and improved electricity availability. Countries such as Lao PDR which generates exclusively from hydropower can as well import electrical energy from neighboring Thailand's existing thermal power plants to supply its baseload demand in dryer months instead of investing in expensive coal-fired power plants for the same purpose. Cross-border energy supply additionally, provides diversification of sources and this is vital for energy security.

Two-way bilateral exchanges are the simplest form of trading arrangement currently in place among some countries in the region, Small–scale volumes cross the borders between Singapore–Malaysia, Thailand–Malaysia, Thailand–Lao PDR, Thailand–Myanmar, Lao PDR–Vietnam. With the commissioning of two large hydropower projects, the 1,070 MW Nam Theun 2 in 2010 and the Theun-Hinboun Expansion project (bringing the project to a new total of 500 MW) in Lao PDR towards the end of 2012, power flow from Laos to Thailand is expected to increase by over 6.5 TWh per annum. The relative simplicity of these arrangements and the benefits that can accrue to participating parties has encouraged increased cross-border electricity exchange in the region. The possibility of a Malaysia–Indonesia power exchange through a 275 kV undersea interconnection line may also be in the works as both countries signed a memorandum of understanding in June 2012.

System harmonization between economies is a more advanced trading arrangement. It involves the establishment of a common operating environment through the synchronization of member electricity systems and harmonization of financial, legal, political, social and environmental frameworks. This creates a huge single market with common procedures and standards for arranging electricity sales, day-to-day operations, dispute settlement, maintenance, system expansion, and governance. A feature of this arrangement is that the independent systems are managed by a single market operator and governed by a common body. This trading arrangement can bring greater benefits than cross-border exchange, but requires a coordinated approach by participating economies, which is challenging to achieve in a group of countries as economically, culturally and socially diverse in Southeast Asia.

There are plans to harmonize the electricity grid by ASEAN members (Brunei Darussalam, Singapore, Malaysia, Philippines, Indonesia, Thailand and Vietnam). The ASEAN Power Grid energy plan 2010–2015 aims to encourage "interconnections of 15 identified projects, first on cross-border bilateral terms, then gradually expand to sub-regional basis and, finally to a totally integrated Southeast Asian power grid system". As beneficial as these plans may seem, most will likely remain on the backburners for some time due to political challenges and energy security concerns. Feasibility may be another issue, take the 670 km undersea cable plan under the South China Sea to transport 2,400 MW hydro generated power from East Malaysia to Peninsular Malaysia at an estimated cost of about US$ 4.5 million per km. This costly and demanding endeavor was shelved in 2010 as the eastern state is expected to absorb all the power generated due to rapid industrial development. Nevertheless, the option is still open for the future as the state has the potential to generate upto 20,000 MW of hydropower.

Similarly, the Asian Development Bank (ADB) has been actively promoting the Greater Mekong Sub-region (GMS) Program focusing on energy as one of its priority sector. The sub-region comprises of five countries and two provinces in the People's Republic of China sharing the Mekong River: Cambodia, Lao PDR, Myanmar, Thailand, Vietnam, Yunnan Province and Guangxi Zhuang Autonomous Region in China. The challenges facing the GMS in the energy sector are not unique: high economic growth of the region is driving the demand for energy whereas almost 50 million people in the GMS lack access to electricity at present. The GMS Regional Trading and Environmentally Sustainable Development of Electricity Infrastructures aim to cope with the strong demand through improving electricity infrastructure and promoting trade whilst limiting the environmental impacts and promoting energy efficiency. A study by the ADB's Regional Technical Assistance Project simulated cross-border energy flows among countries in the GMS region, concluding that cross-border trading will reduce CO_2 emission, investment costs needed and operation costs (Figure 6). These improvements in efficiencies will further reduce tariffs to end customers in an environmentally sustainable manner.

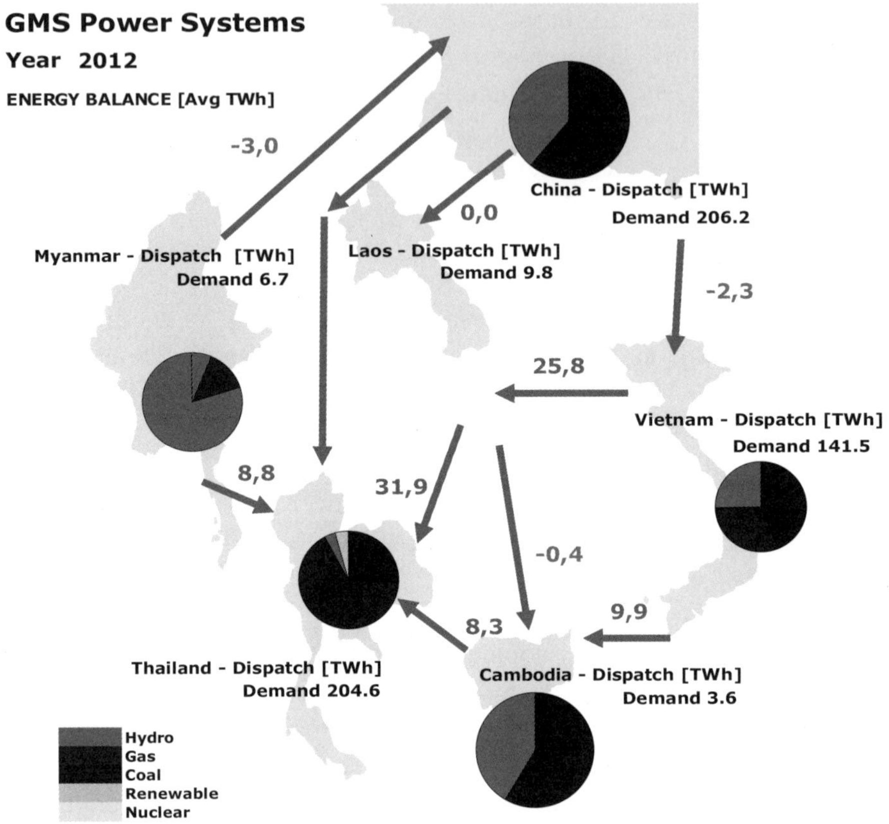

Figure 6 Simulated Average Net Cross-Border Energy Flows

Source: "Regional Power Trade Coordination and Development", Mercados EMI and Indra Sistemas S.A., 2008.

5.4 ENERGY SECURITY

Energy security is an important policy concern in the Southeast Asian region given the high and volatile fuel prices, and its heavy dependence on fossil fuels. Furthermore, all these non-renewable resources are finite and will ultimately be depleted. There are also environmental and social costs associated with meeting the region's rapidly rising energy demand. The exchange of power alone is not going to make a difference in global greenhouse emissions should countries continue to install new generating capacities according to the traditional rate of generation mix, largely of thermal or fossil fuels. The need therefore exists to integrate environmental sustainability issues in the design of the Southeast Asian energy strategy so as to reduce overall costs of energy.

5.5 RENEWABLE ENERGY: HYDROPOWER

Renewable energy has the potential to produce clean energy. Renewable energy systems help reduce greenhouse gas emissions and are being recognized as a major source of energy for the 21st century and beyond. Classified as a clean, renewable energy source, hydropower reduces the net production of greenhouse gases by displacing other forms of power generation. In contrast to most other renewable sources of electricity, hydropower can supply a significant portion of Southeast Asia's electricity needs.

The Southeast Asia region has a cumulative installed capacity of over 150 GW, of which hydropower makes up some 17% of the generating capacity. The region has potentially over 150 GW of hydropower capacity (Table 1).

Southeast Asia has immense growth potential in the hydroelectric sector, in particular within the GMS and Indonesia. Given that the region at present is highly dependent on fossil fuels to meet the majority of its power needs, a shift towards renewable power sources is inevitable. Fiscal and financial incentives provided and supported by the World Bank and

Table 1 Hydropower Potential in Southeast Asia

Country	Hydropower potential
Cambodia	7,000 MW
Lao PDR	18,000 MW
Myanmar	46,000 MW
Indonesia	37,000 MW
Malaysia (East)	28,000 MW
Vietnam	20,000 MW

Source: SN power team analysis.

ADB has led to many initiatives and action plans in the energy sector, including the development of several hydropower projects in the sub-region in recent years.

5.6 COMPETITIVE POWER MARKETS

While the Philippine began commercial operation of its Wholesale Electricity Spot Market in June 2006 and Singapore's National Electricity Market being Asia's first liberalized electricity market commenced trading in January 2003, Vietnam commercially operated its Competitive Generation Market on July 1, 2012, the first of its three phase process towards a fully competitive power market, and part of its major effort to deregulate its power market (Table 2).

The full benefits of comparative advantage can be observed as economies with an advantage generating from hydro, trades with economies generating from fossil fuels. The liberalization of power markets furthermore, brings down barriers of entry, surreptitiously attracting private investors to fill in supply gaps in the system, and consumers paying real prices based on the marginal costs of production.

The energy sector has environmental implications beyond national boundaries which need to be integrated in energy planning to achieve sustainable development. Developing economies in the region could

Table 2 Power Exchanges in Asia

Country	Korea	Singapore	Japan	Philippines	India	Vietnam
Electricity exchange	KPX	NEMS	JEPX	WESM	IEX	VCGM
Established (year)	2001	2003	2005	2006	2008	2012
Population (million)	49	5	128	92	1,155	87
Consumption 2011 (TWh)	481	42	1,070	50	755	90
Market – origin	Generation	Wholesale	Wholesale	Wholesale	Wholesale	Generation
Market – present	Generation	Wholesale	Wholesale	Wholesale	Wholesale	Generation
Market – objective	Retail (Restructuring Act expired in 2009)	Retail / Financial	Wholesale	Retail	Financial	Retail

leap-frog from hard and costly lessons learnt from industrialized nations, through developing clean hydropower, cross-border exchanges, and establishing a competitive power market. While huge challenges exist from the diverse stages of economic and political development in the Southeast Asian region, the necessity and benefits should provide development towards a cleaner environment, more energy efficient, secure and sustainable development in the future.

5.7 THE ROLE OF SN POWER

SN Power is at the crossroads of two mega-trends, namely, the demand for renewable energy and the growth in emerging markets (Figure 7). Its business model is based on active ownership, the transfer of Norwegian hydropower expertise, and responsible, sustainable development of renewable energy. SN Power has expertise in hydropower plant design and development as well as working in deregulated/emerging markets. It followed solid business principles, adopting the following investment criteria: industry returns, project finance, active ownership, solid partnership, balanced portfolios, and environmentally and socially manageable projects. SN Power will continue to combine profitability with responsible operations, be a pioneer in deregulated markets, engage the government and private sector and be innovative.

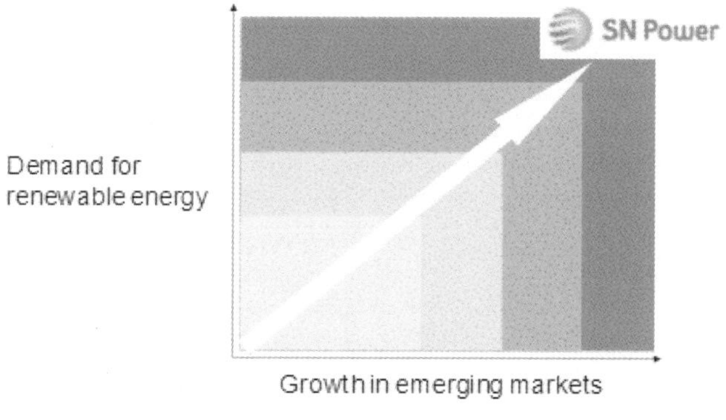

Figure 7 SN Power, Demand for Renewable Energy and Growth in Emerging Markets
Source: SN Power.

5.8 CONCLUSION

The consensus among climate scientists is that the world must cut emissions now. Rich countries cannot do it alone, and targets will fail unless developing countries contribute their share in reducing CO_2 emission. SN Power's presence in a region with huge hydropower potential coupled with a dire need for it puts it in a very interesting position. Its expertise in hydropower and deregulated markets allows it to help the region to build, manage and operate hydropower projects in an environmentally friendly and optimizing manner, reducing CO_2 emission by reducing energy costs overall through power exchange in a deregulated market.

CHAPTER 6

PHILIPPINE EXPERIENCES WITH GRID-CONNECTED RENEWABLE ENERGY POWER SYSTEMS

N. A. Orcullo, Jr.

ABSTRACT

The efforts of the Philippine government in developing the potential of renewable energy-based energy systems is discussed given the variety of legal mandates and programs/projects designed to address the long-term energy development agenda of the country. Focus is made on renewable energy POWER system of private investors producing relatively high capacity output and supplied or directly connected to the grid and distribution system serving a particular area. The particular projects cited include the 1 MW photovoltaic power plant of Cagayan Electric Power and Light Company (CEPALCO) which is tied up to its distribution system, the wind power systems of NorthWind Power Development Corporation (NPDC) with an aggregate capacity of 35 MW from which is supplied to a provincial electric cooperative (Ilocos Norte Electric Cooperative) and the garbage-based methane power plant installed in a landfill complex operated by the Montalban Methane Power Corporation (MMPC), whose output is directly connected to the Manila Electric Railroad and Light Company

(MERALCO), the biggest electric power distributor in the country, operating in Metro Manila region and the nearby provinces.

All three projects cited are just part of the many renewable-energy projects in the country and are owned and/or operated by private investors. These private companies are motivated by the Philippine government's energy plan and incentives to power producers to use renewable energy sources and supply power in their respective areas by way of supply agreements signed with clients. The exception being CEPALCO's photovoltaic power plant which sells the electric power output in its franchised area as it is an authorized electric power distributor. The particular projects cited appear to be operating profitably and plans are underway to expand the capacity of their respective power plants, hopefully giving impetus to the grand agenda of the Philippine government in the renewable energy sector which listed a number of projects including those meant to produce biofuels as mandated by law.

6.1 BACKGROUND

The energy crisis of the early 1970s made the world realise that the development of nations and volatile market prices of petroleum-based products are intertwined. Leaders of both developed and developing countries realised that something had to be done to address this concern and reality. The volatility of market prices of petroleum-based fuels in the global markets and its use as a political as well as economic tool among the major oil producers made it clear to world leaders that strategic decisions had to be made to cushion the implications of erratic prices of crude products and their derivatives.

The Philippine government accepted the reality and in the mid-1970s, then President Marcos reacted by putting in place a government corporation (Philippine National Oil Company) and established Petrophil Corporation (the successor of Esso Philippines). Realising the importance of energy as a dominant commodity with a pivotal role in the Philippines' economy, a Presidential Decree (PD) was issued creating the Energy Development Board (EDB) and PD 1206 creating the Department of Energy (DOE), thus having a cabinet-level post for energy matters. During the administration of President Marcos, an ambitious energy plan and policy was put in place and this included developing alternative sources of energy such as solar power, wind power, hydropower and geothermal power, if only to cushion the impact of high costs of imported oil, particularly on the country's foreign exchange reserves. Eventually, the National Energy Plan was crafted under the auspices of the DOE and its attached agencies. The development of the Philippine Energy Plan was institutionalised and it required a series of parallel programmes/projects to address energy supply amidst threats of a global energy crisis. Non-petroleum energy sources like geothermal power and hydropower were developed to the fullest extent and petroleum exploration in the domestic scene became a vibrant industry.[1]

6.2 LEGAL MANDATES ESTABLISHED

Over the last three decades commencing in the early 1970s when the Philippine government reacted to the global energy crisis brought by the unilateral moves of oil-exporting countries and the OPEC oil embargo, a number of decrees and laws were put in place. The relevant decrees and laws that resulted in a number of power development projects, including efforts related to renewable energy development, are shown in Table 1.

In the renewable energy sector, PD 1068 was issued in 1977, mandating wider and organised efforts in the development, promotion and commercial utilisation of non-conventional energy sources. The Non-conventional Energy Resources Development Program (NERDP) of the DOE was in the forefront of the efforts to develop the potential of renewable energy technologies, triggering research and development projects dealing with solar, wind and biomass energy sources. A number of academic institutions as well as research organisations were involved in various research and development efforts funded under the NERDP. A variety of undertakings were pursued, from research to technology promotions, all aimed at developing the potential of biomass-based resources and technologies, eventually popularising the use of biogas, gasifiers, solar water heaters, wind-powered pumps, wind power conversion systems, bioethanol, coco-diesel and most recently biodiesel in the form of crude methyl ester.

---

[1]A personal account of the author, who was one of the pioneering technical staff of the Non-conventional Energy Resources Division of the DOE and a part of the DOE circa 1979–1990.

Table 1 Legal Mandates and Motivating Laws and Policies

1. Presidential Decree 910 (Energy Development Board)–1976
2. Presidential Decree 1206 (DOE Charter)–1976
3. Presidential Decree 1068 (NERDP Program)–1977
4. Foreign Investment Act (RA 7042/RA 8719)–1991
5. Executive Order 215 (BOT projects)–1995
6. Executive Order 462/AEO 232–1997
7. DOE New Charter (RA 7638)–1992
8. BOT Law (RA 6967/RA 7718)–1994
9. Clean Air Act (RA 1234)–1999
10. Ecological Solid Waste Management Act (RA 9003)–2000
11. EPIRA Law (RA 9136)–2001
12. Biofuels Law (RA 9367)–2006
13. Renewable Energy Law (RA 9513)–2008

Source: Karunungan, E. "Renewable Energy Fuels: Key to Energy Independence and Security", Department of Energy, Makati City, Philippines, 2008.

This series of efforts led to administrative and legal frameworks being put in place. Major policy decisions were made by the government leadership and landmark laws were put in place via a decree during a period of martial law as well as Executive Orders and by acts of Congress. The Foreign Investment Act (Republic Act 7042 as amended by RA 8719) served as encouragement for many local and foreign investors due to the incentives it promised, and the investors in the power generation sectors took advantage of it. The issuance of Executive Order 215 that eventually resulted in the enactment of the Build-Operate-Transfer Law (RA 6957 as amended by RA 7718) resulted in a large number of private sector–financed power generation plants, once a major responsibility and monopoly of the government which later became a budgetary burden. Moreover, the enactment of the Clean Air Act (RA 8749) and Ecological Solid Waste Management Act (RA 9003) also gave a push and served as the motivator for investors to consider green, renewable and clean energy technologies. Furthermore, the enactment of the Electric Power Industry Reform Act (RA 9136), the Biofuels Act of 2006 (RA 9367) and most recently the Renewable Energy Act of 2008 (RA 9513) are developments that further triggered private sector investments in power generation as well as transmission and many looked at this particular law as a great booster for inviting more local and foreign investments in renewable energy projects.

Prior to the enactment of the aforementioned laws, investments in energy projects/ventures were included in the investment priorities programme of the Board of Investments, thus entitling investors to a number of incentives such as tariff/duty privileges as well as tax holidays. As a result of the political will of the government leadership as well as management initiatives of concerned government agencies, the renewable energy sector is now a vibrant sector of the economy. Several renewable energy companies are now serving the market and more conspicuous are the megawatt-level business projects in wind and solar photovoltaics that are now part of the electrical grid system.

6.3 RENEWABLE ENERGY RESOURCES AND POLICIES[2]

The country is endowed with natural resources which have allowed it to develop its potential and in many ways contributed a lot to the power supply of the country. In a study released by the National Renewable Energy Laboratory (NREL) of the United States, the following potentials of renewable energy were identified:

a) Wind resources — over 10,000 km^2 with 76,000 MW of potential installed capacity.
b) Micro-hydro applications — potential capacity of at least 500 kW in Luzon and Mindanao islands.
c) Solar radiation nationwide — an annual potential average of 5.0–5.1 $kWh/m^2/day$.
d) Mini-hydro applications — potential capacity of 1,784 MW for 888 sites.
e) Ocean energy resources — potential capacity of about 170,000 MW.
f) Biomass (Bagasse) — total potential of 235 MMBFOE.

[2]Karunungan, E. "Renewable Energy Fuels: Key to Energy Independence and Security", Department of Energy, Makati City, Philippines, 2008.

To enable the development of the potential of its renewable energy resources, the Philippine Energy Plan enshrined a commitment to a renewable energy policy development as follows:

a) Renewable energy policy framework launched in 2003.
b) Policy bias towards the development and utilisation of renewable energy:
    i) Promote more private sector participation in RE development.
    ii) Encourage the use of renewable energy in rural and off-grid electrification.
    iii) Renewable energy projects given "priority" for special incentives.
c) Having a renewable energy law to promote the development and utilisation of clean energy (enacted in 2008 as RA 9513)

Giving it substance and concrete meaning, the renewable energy development policy framework was translated into long-term objectives as follows:

a) Increase renewable energy-based capacity by 100% — "100–10".
b) Be the number one geothermal energy producer in the world.
c) Be the number one wind energy producer in Southeast Asia.
d) Double hydro-electric capacity.
e) Be the solar cell manufacturing hub in ASEAN.
f) New contribution of biomass, solar and ocean energy of more than 100 MW.
g) Increase non-power contribution of RE to energy mix by 10 MMBFOE within the next 10 years.

The concrete results of the long-term objectives, set forth as various completed and ongoing undertakings, are summarised in Table 2.

6.4 MARKET SYSTEM FOR ELECTRIC POWER

The monopoly of power generation by the National Power Corporation (NPC) under Presidential Decree was dismantled through a privatisation policy. This policy statement tempered with the enactment of the Electric Power Industry Reform Act or EPIRA (RA 9136) resulted in a new market system for the electric energy sector. The electric power sector in

Table 2 Renewable Energy Development Status

Resource	Existing capacity (MW)	Number of plants in operation	On-going projects
Geothermal	2,027.07	14 geothermal plants	10 projects offered to private investor (300–500 MW) thru Contracting Round
Hydro	3,367.07	21 large hydro, 52 mini-hydro, 61 micro hydro	4 mini-hydros, 14 large hydro under evaluation
Wind	33.2	33 MW In Ilocos Norte, 5 KW Camarines in 180 KW in Batanes, 6 KW in Boracay	NPDC wind farm, 7 sites on resource assessment
Solar	5.161	960 KW — CEPALCO, Cagayan e Oro 729 KW Camarines Sur	Sunpower Phil Solar Plant/rural electrification projects
Biomass	20.93		1 MW Isabela
Ocean			R & D activities — Demo projects in Leyte/Mindanao

Source: E. Karunugan (Department of Energy)/Philippine Daily Inquirer.

particular was transformed from a monopolistic market to a free market system open to any interested parties, limited only by ownership structure as mandated by the Philippine Constitution.

The developments in the power generation sector resulted in a new market system as shown in Figure 1.

The National Power Corporation is still presented as a power generator or generating company (GENCO) pending its full privatisation. However, private sector investments in power generation are now in place as evidenced by the growing number of independent power producers (IPPs). Another significant development in the new market system is that electricity distribution companies (i.e. privately owned utilities and electric cooperatives) are now authorised to develop and produce their electric power, thus allowing backward integration opportunities not only for economic but also for technical reasons.

Adding more incentives to both the generators and buyers of electric power is the provision in the EPIRA which mandates the establishment of

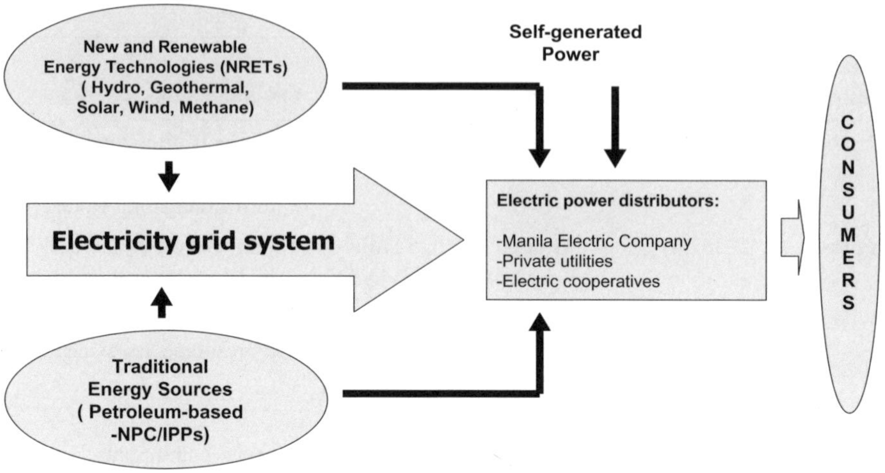

Figure 1 The Electrical Grid and Distribution System in the Philippines

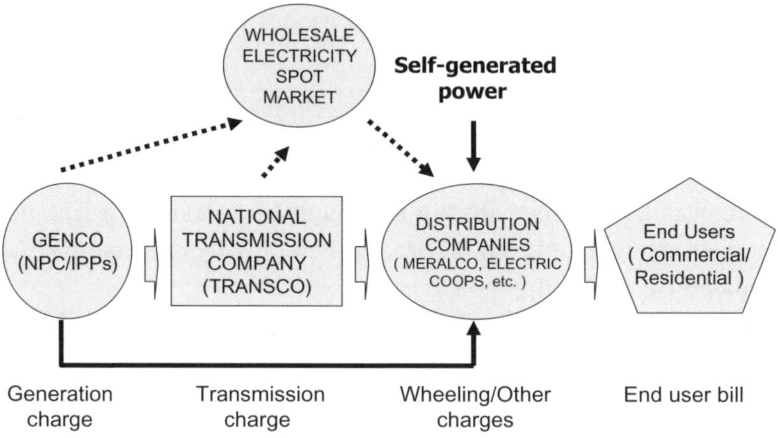

Figure 2 The Power Distribution System and the WESM

the Wholesale Electricity Spot Market (WESM). The spot market is a platform that simulates a free market system that can work to the advantage of both the GENCOs and the distribution companies, or in certain cases, to the contrary. It is hoped that the new market framework illustrated in Figure 2 will result in benefits to end users in the form of affordable or cheaper tariffs for electric power.

The variety of laws and policies set forth by the government ensure and allow the free market system to work thus giving market competition to play and set prices of products in the market. With new and renewable energy technologies (NRET) pitted against petroleum-based power plants, with more incentives favouring the former, it is hoped that new and renewable energy businesses and industry will emerge and flourish.

6.5 THE ELECTRICAL GRID SYSTEM

To ensure connectivity and markets for the output of commercial power generation projects large and small, the country operates an electrical grid system. This grid scheme was in place even at the time when power generation and region-wide distribution was the responsibility of the NPC. There is a grid for the major islands of Luzon, Visayas and Mindanao where provincial-level power distributors (e.g. electric cooperatives) can source their power for retail to institutional and residential consumers.

As mandated by the EPIRA, the grid and Grid Code were put in place. As defined in the EPIRA, the grid refers to the high-voltage backbone system of interconnected transmission lines, substations and related facilities. The EPIRA espouses a Grid Code referring to the set of rules and regulations governing the safe and reliable operation, maintenance and development of the high-voltage backbone transmission system and its related facilities.[3]

Also forming part of the provisions of the EPIRA, a National Transmission Corporation (TransCo) was organised to acquire all the transmission assets of the NPC. TransCo was specifically organised to assume the electrical transmission function of the NPC, and have all the powers and functions granted unto it. TransCo assumes the authority and responsibility of the NPC for the planning, construction and centralised operation and maintenance of high-voltage transmission facilities, including grid interconnections and ancillary services.

With the regional grid system now in place, sufficient infrastructural provisions are also in place for any generation company using renewable energy sources to connect with the electrical grid, thus ensuring a ready market for its output. It is just a matter of the renewable energy power

[3] Electric Power Industry Reform Act of 2001 (RA 9513).

generator delivering an electrical energy output consistent with the voltage levels of the power grid nearest to it or to the specific demand of its buyer/user, should it opt to directly supply its output to the distribution system of the utility company.

The grid system at the regional level allows the transport of indigenous and renewable energy to other parts of island in the country, thus enhancing efficiency and maximising the use of the energy output, and at the same time providing electricity supply to areas with insufficient generation capacity. This is the particular case in Negros island where excess capacity from geothermal plants was transmitted to Cebu island (both in the Visayas region) using the submarine cable that connects these two islands.

Following the mandate under the EPIRA, there is now a Philippine Grid Code promulgated by the Energy Regulatory Commission (ERC) which it approved per Resolution No. 115.

6.6 THE RENEWABLE ENERGY ACT OF 2008

Giving inspiration and impetus to the development of the renewable energy sector of the Philippines are the administrative policies/directives set forth and various laws enacted as earlier mentioned, as well as the political will to undertake the specific programmes and projects.

After a series of programmes, projects and a variety of initiatives to develop, promote and commercialise the use of renewable energy in the country, landmark legislation for the renewable energy sector was put in place by Congress. This was the enactment of RA 9513, otherwise known as the Renewable Energy Act of 2008.

The Renewable Energy Act made a number of significant provisions to address the development, financing and marketing of electricity as well as incentives for renewable energy–based power generation systems. Under the provisions of the Renewable Energy Act, general incentives have been accorded to investors in renewable energy projects as stipulated under Chapter III of the said act. In particular, the said act provides for the following:

> Section 15. Incentives for Renewable Energy Projects and Activities. — RE developers of renewable energy facilities, including hybrid systems, in proportion to and to the extent of the RE component, for both power and

non-power applications, as duly certified by the DOE, in consultation with the BOI, shall be entitled to the following incentives:

(a) Income Tax Holiday (ITH) — For the first seven (7) years of its commercial operations, the duly registered RE developer shall be exempt from income taxes levied by the national government.

Additional investments in the project shall be entitled to additional income tax exemption on the income attributable to the investment: *Provided*, That the discovery and development of new RE resource shall be treated as a new investment and shall therefore be entitled to a fresh package of incentives: *Provided, further,* That the entitlement period for additional investments shall not be more than three (3) times the period of the initial availment of the ITH.

(b) Duty-free Importation of RE Machinery, Equipment and Materials — Within the first ten (10) years upon the issuance of a certification of an RE developer, the importation of machinery and equipment, and materials and parts thereof, including control and communication equipment, shall not be subject to tariff duties: *Provided, however,* That the said machinery, equipment, materials and parts are directly and actually needed and used exclusively in the RE facilities for transformation into energy and delivery of energy to the point of use and covered by shipping documents in the name of the duly registered operator to whom the shipment will be directly delivered by customs authorities: *Provided, further,* That endorsement of the DOE is obtained before the importation of such machinery, equipment, materials and parts is made.

Endorsement of the DOE must be secured before any sale, transfer or disposition of the imported capital equipment, machinery or spare parts is made: *Provided,* That if such sale, transfer or disposition is made within the ten (10)-year period from the date of importation, any of the following conditions must be present:

(i) If made to another RE developer enjoying tax and duty exemption on imported capital equipment;
(ii) If made to a non-RE developer, upon payment of any taxes and duties due on the net book value of the capital equipment to be sold;
(iii) Exportation of the used capital equipment, machinery, spare parts or source documents or those required for RE development; and
(iv) For reasons of proven technical obsolescence.

When the aforementioned sale, transfer or disposition is made under any of the conditions provided for in the foregoing paragraphs after ten (10) years from the date of importation, the sale, transfer or disposition shall no longer be subject to the payment of taxes and duties;

(c) Special Realty Tax Rates on Equipment and Machinery. — Any law to the contrary notwithstanding, realty and other taxes on civil works, equipment, machinery, and other improvements of a Registered RE Developer actually and exclusively used for RE facilities shall not exceed one and a half percent (1.5%) of their original cost less accumulated normal depreciation or net book value: *Provided,* That in case of an integrated resource development and generation facility as provided under Republic Act No. 9136, the real property tax shall only be imposed on the power plant;

(d) Net Operating Loss Carry-Over (NOLCO). — The NOLCO of the RE Developer during the first three (3) years from the start of commercial operation which had not been previously offset as deduction from gross income shall be carried over as a deduction from gross income for the next seven (7) consecutive taxable years immediately following the year of such loss: *Provided, however,* That operating loss resulting from the availment of incentives provided for in this Act shall not be entitled to NOLCO;

(e) Corporate Tax Rate — After seven (7) years of income tax holiday, all RE Developers shall pay a corporate tax of ten percent (10%) on its net taxable income as defined in the National Internal Revenue Act of 1997, as amended by Republic Act No. 9337. *Provided,* That the RE Developer shall pass on the savings to the end-users in the form of lower power rates.

(f) Accelerated Depreciation. — If, and only if, an RE project fails to receive an ITH before full operation, it may apply for Accelerated Depreciation in its tax books and be taxed based on such: *Provided,* That if it applies for Accelerated Depreciation, the project or its expansions shall no longer be eligible for an ITH. Accelerated depreciation of plant, machinery, and equipment that are reasonably needed and actually used for the exploration, development and utilization of RE resources may be depreciated using a rate not exceeding twice the rate which would have been used had the annual allowance been computed in accordance with the rules and regulations prescribed by the Secretary of the Department of Finance and the provisions of the National Internal

Revenue Code (NIRC) of 1997, as amended. Any of the following methods of accelerated depreciation may be adopted:

i) Declining balance method; and
ii) Sum-of-the years digit method

(g) Zero Percent Value-Added Tax Rate — The sale of fuel or power generated from renewable sources of energy such as, but not limited to, biomass, solar, wind, hydropower, geothermal, ocean energy and other emerging energy sources using technologies such as fuel cells and hydrogen fuels, shall be subject to zero percent (0%) value-added tax (VAT), pursuant to the National Internal Revenue Code (NIRC) of 1997, as amended by Republic Act No. 9337.

All RE Developers shall be entitled to zero-rated value added tax on its purchases of local supply of goods, properties and services needed for the development, construction and installation of its plant facilities.

This provision shall also apply to the whole process of exploring and developing renewable energy sources up to its conversion into power, including but not limited to the services performed by subcontractors and/or contractors.

(h) Cash Incentive of Renewable Energy Developers for Missionary Electrification — A renewable energy developer, established after the effectivity of this Act, shall be entitled to a cash generation-based incentive per kilowatt hour rate generated, equivalent to fifty percent (50%) of the universal charge for power needed to service missionary areas where it operates the same, to be chargeable against the universal charge for missionary electrification;

(i) Tax Exemption of Carbon Credits — All proceeds from the sale of carbon emission credits shall be exempt from any and all taxes;

(j) Tax Credit on Domestic Capital Equipment and Services. — A tax credit equivalent to one hundred percent (100%) of the value of the value-added tax and custom duties that would have been paid on the RE machinery, equipment, materials and parts had these items been imported shall be given to an RE operating contract holder who purchases machinery, equipment, materials, and parts from a domestic manufacturer for purposes set forth in this Act: *Provided,* That prior approval by the DOE was obtained by the local manufacturer: *Provided, further,* That the acquisition of such machinery, equipment, materials, and parts shall be made within the validity of the RE operating contract.

In addition to the aforementioned incentives under Section 15 of the law, Section 21 provides incentives for commercialisation of renewable energy technologies to cover all manufacturers, fabricators and suppliers of locally produced RE equipment and components duly recognised and accredited by the DOE (in consultation with DOST, DOF and DTI), and the project duly registered with the Board of Investment (BOI). This particular provision identified the renewable energy sector as a priority investment sector that will regularly form part of the country's Investment Priorities Plan. As such, all entities duly accredited by the DOE under the Renewable Energy Act are entitled to all the incentives such as the following:

(a) Tax and Duty-free Importation of Components, Parts and Materials. — All shipments necessary for the manufacture and/or fabrication of RE equipment and components shall be exempted from importation tariff and duties and value added tax: *Provided, however,* That the said components, parts and materials are: (i) not manufactured domestically in reasonable quantity and quality at competitive prices; (ii) directly and actually needed and shall be used exclusively in the manufacture/fabrication of RE equipment; and (iii) covered by shipping documents in the name of the duly registered manufacturer/fabricator to whom the shipment will be directly delivered by customs authorities: *Provided, further,* That prior approval of the DOE was obtained before the importation of such components, parts and materials;
(b) Tax Credit on Domestic Capital Components, Parts and Materials. — A tax credit equivalent to one hundred percent (100%) of the amount of the value-added tax and custom duties that would have been paid on the components, parts and materials had these items been imported shall be given to an RE equipment manufacturer, fabricator, and supplier duly recognized and accredited by the DOE who purchases RE components, parts and materials from a domestic manufacturer: *Provided,* That such components, and parts are directly needed and shall be used exclusively by the RE manufacturer, fabricator and supplier for the manufacture, fabrication and sale of the RE equipment: *Provided, further,* That prior approval by the DOE was obtained by the local manufacturer;
(c) Income Tax Holiday and Exemption. — For seven (7) years starting from the date of recognition/accreditation, an RE manufacturer,

fabricator and supplier of RE equipment shall be fully exempt from income taxes levied by the National Government on net income derived only from the sale of RE equipment, machinery, parts and services; and

(d) Zero-rated Value Added Tax Transactions. — All manufacturers, fabricators and suppliers of locally produced renewable energy equipment shall be subject to zero-rated value added tax on its transactions with local suppliers of goods, properties and services.

6.7 FEED-IN TARIFF SYSTEM FOR RENEWABLE ENERGY SOURCES

Ensuring a market outlet for the renewable power generation project is vital to the development of the renewable energy sector. To have this scenario and to encourage proliferation of energy from renewable energy sources, particularly those intended for connection with the regional electrical or utility grid, Section 7 of the Renewable Energy Act has made specific provisions as follows:

> Section 7. Feed-In Tariff System. — To accelerate the development of emerging renewable energy resources, a feed-in tariff system for electricity produced from wind, solar, ocean, run-of-river hydropower and biomass is hereby mandated. Towards this end, the ERC in consultation with the National Renewable Energy Board (NREB) created under Section 27 of this Act shall formulate and promulgate feed-in tariff system rules within one year upon the effectivity of this Act which shall include, but not limited to the following:
>
> (a) Priority connections to the grid for electricity generated from emerging renewable energy resources such as wind, solar, ocean, run-of-river hydropower and biomass power plants within the territory of the Philippines;
> (b) The priority purchase and transmission of, and payment for, such electricity by the grid system operators;
> (c) Determine the fixed tariff to be paid to electricity produced from each type of emerging renewable energy and the mandated number of years for the application of these rates, which shall not be less than 12 years;

(d) The feed-in tariff to be set shall be applied to the emerging renewable energy to be used in compliance with the renewable portfolio standard as provided for in this Act and in accordance with the RPS rules that will be established by the DOE.

The Renewable Energy Market (REM) is likewise established to facilitate compliance with the provisions of the law. The Department of Energy is tasked to establish the REM and shall direct the Philippine Electric Market Corporation (PEMC) to implement changes to the WESM Rules in order to incorporate the rules specific to the operation of the REM under the WESM.

6.8 NET-METERING MECHANISM

To have a certain or captive market for the electrical energy output of renewable energy projects, particularly in situations where there is excess power at the level of institutional consumers who ventured into self-generation, there has to be a mechanism to address the possibility of selling extra output to the electrical grid system. This predicament has been addressed by the provisions of the Renewable Energy Act on net metering and this in fact is one of the unique provisions of the law.

The net-metering scheme provided for under Section 10 reads as follows:

> Section 10. Net-metering for Renewable Energy. — Subject to technical considerations and without discrimination and upon request by distribution end-users, the distribution utilities shall enter into net-metering agreements with qualified end-users who will be installing RE system.
>
> The ERC, in consultation with the NREB and the electric power industry participants, shall establish net metering interconnection standards and pricing methodology and other commercial arrangements necessary to ensure success of the net-metering for renewable energy program within one (1) year upon the effectivity of this Act.
>
> The distribution utility shall be entitled to any Renewable Energy Certificate resulting from net-metering arrangement with the qualified end-user who is using an RE resource to provide energy and the distribution utility shall be able to use this RE certificate in compliance with its obligations under RPS.

> The DOE, ERC, TRANSCO or its successors-in-interest, DUs, PEMC and all relevant parties are hereby mandated to provide the mechanisms for the physical connection and commercial arrangements necessary to ensure the success of the Net-metering for Renewable Energy program, consistent with the Grid and Distribution Codes.

The net-metering mechanism stands to benefit electricity distributors and institutional consumers with the potential to generate their own electricity, whose excess power capacity can be sold back to the grid system. The importance of the net-metering scheme lies in the fact that the renewable energy plant capacity can be maximised by users and distributors so that there is a guaranteed market for surplus energy production.

6.9 ROLE OF GOVERNMENT AGENCIES

Under the stated deregulation policy in the energy sector, private investors are given plenty of leeway and privilege in doing their business, particularly with prices of petroleum-based products which are left to market conditions. This is not the case, however, with the electrical power sector where certain controls and regulations are put in place, but still give investors in the power generation and distribution business the opportunity to recoup their investments plus reasonable returns, while at the same time addressing the concerns of end users of electrical power. Concerns are addressed by way of a series of public or consultative hearings whenever there are tariff rate changes.

The Electric Power Industry Reform Act of 2001 (RA 9136) has given government agencies like the Department of Energy and Energy Regulatory Commission a specific mandate. These agencies have substantial authority to protect the various stakeholders, such as the investors in the electrical power sector, including the interests and concerns of the public at large. Generators of power from whatever sources, including renewable energy resources and systems/technologies, have to apply for and be cleared and/or endorsed by the DOE. Final authority (i.e. Certificate of Compliance) to market the output of generation companies as well as distribute the same at certain prices or tariffs is left to the judgment of the ERC guided by the provisions of the EPIRA and its

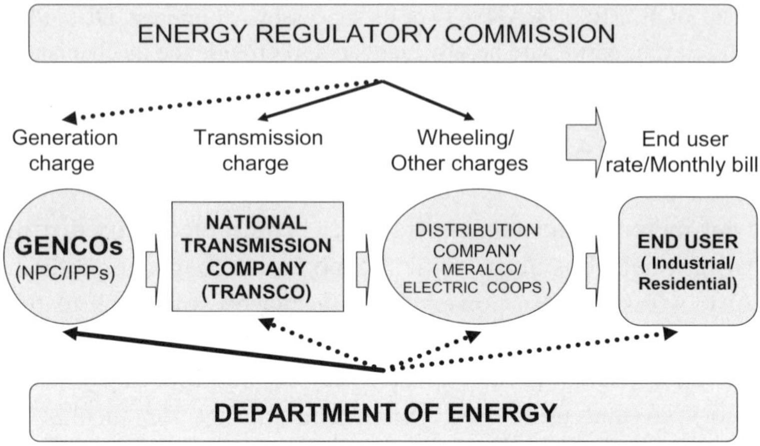

Figure 3 The Electric Power Industry of the Philippines

Implementing Rules and Regulations. Deregulated as it is, the electric power industry is fully monitored by the DOE and ERC as diagrammatically shown in Figure 3.

6.9.1 Role of the ERC in the EPIRA Regime

Among others, the privatisation policy of the government gave the private sector the privilege and right to invest in the power generation sector under the Build-Operate-Transfer (BOT) Law, particularly in the early 1990s when the country experienced acute power outages. This scenario gave the distributors and users of electrical power an option of whom to buy from or source their electricity from, which they will eventually distribute in their respective franchise or service areas. This scenario has also given some power distributors the option to go into horizontal and backward integration, thus making the price of electrical power competitive and hopefully benefiting end users.

Added to this scenario is the creation of the Wholesale Electricity Spot Market which further gives the institutional buyers (i.e. utility companies/ electric cooperatives) the option of where to buy from or source their power from at any given time of day which they believe is advantageous. This scenario is explained by Figure 4.

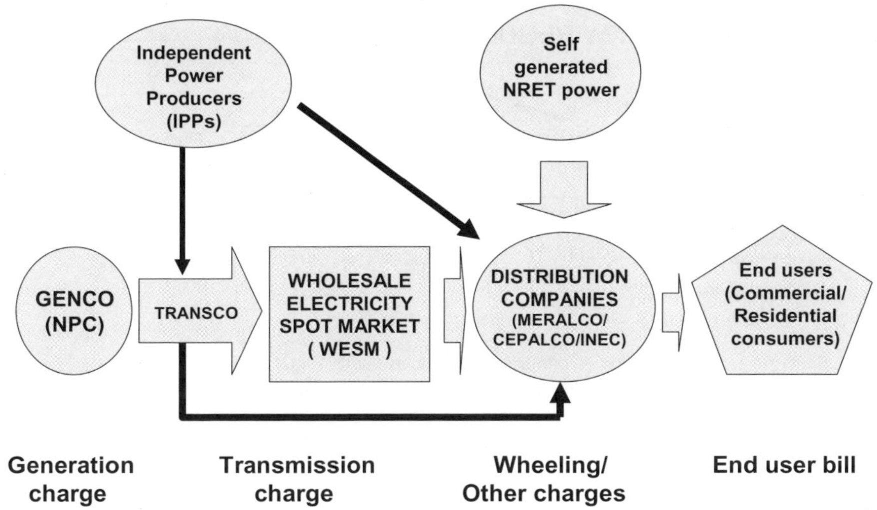

Figure 4 Power Sourcing Options for Electric Power Distributors

Given the liberalised scenario in power generation and the options available to distributors of electricity at the end user level, the ERC plays a critical role given its mandate to address the interest of the consumer — the public at large — without jeopardising the return on investment and profit motives of the generation companies and the investors in general.

Under the EPIRA, prices charged by generation companies are not categorically stated as subject to regulation by the ERC; however, generation companies are required to submit their financial statements (to the ERC) to address market power abuse or anti-competitive behaviour. Unlike generation companies, transmission of electrical power is by regulated common electricity carriers and subject to the rate-making powers of the ERC. The distribution of electricity (by private utilities and electric cooperatives) to end users/consumers is subject to regulation by the ERC, hence tariff rates and other charges have to be approved by the ERC.

The critical role played by the ERC in the electricity rate- or tariff-making process is shown in Figure 5.

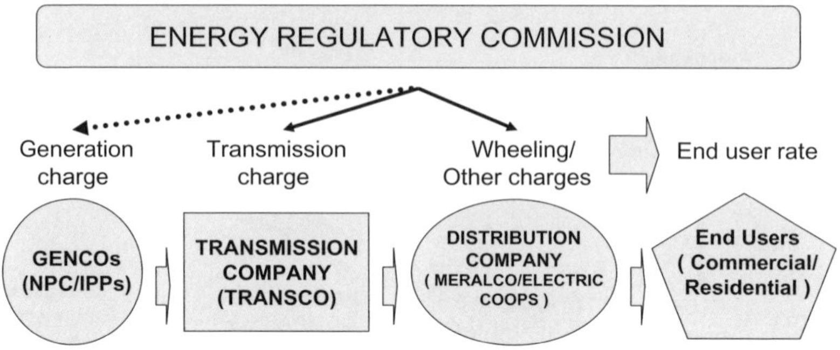

Scenario 1: GENCOssubmits generation rates charges to ERC
Scenario 2: TRANSCO petitions ERC for transmission charges to distributors/utilities.
Scenario 3: Distributors/Utilities petitions ERC for tariff rates to consumers/end users.
Scenario 4: Other stakeholders petitions ERC regarding tariff matters.
Note: In all scenarios, ERC involves all stakeholders in tariff setting process.

Figure 5 Electricity Tariff-Setting Process in the Philippines

6.9.2 Role of the WESM in Electricity Trade

The EPIRA established the Wholesale Electricity Spot Market, giving further options to concerned parties to get the most out of the benefits of a free market enterprise. As referred to under the EPIRA, the DOE is mandated to establish a wholesale electricity spot market composed of the wholesale electricity spot market participants.

As provided for under the EPIRA, the DOE facilitated the creation of the Philippine Electricity Market Corporation (PEMC). The PEMC undertook the preparatory work and initial operation of the WESM. The PEMC was established to maintain, operate and govern an efficient, competitive, transparent and reliable market for the wholesale and purchase of electricity and ancillary services in the Philippines in accordance with applicable laws, rules and regulations. The Articles of Incorporation and By-Laws of the PEMC were finalised in collaboration with the WESM Technical Working Group. The PEMC is a duly incorporated non-stock, non-profit corporation registered with the Securities and Exchange Commission (SEC) on 18 November 2003.

Simply put, the WESM mechanism runs similar to a stock market wherein instead of trading shares of stocks, electricity as a commodity is placed on the trading floor for any interested parties to grab. The WESM shall provide the mechanism for identifying and setting the price of actual variations from the quantities transacted under contracts between sellers and purchasers of electricity.

6.9.2.1 *Membership in the WESM*

To be a player in the wholesale spot market, both generation companies and distributors (private utilities and electricity cooperatives) have to be accredited by the PEMC who run/manage the WESM.

The number of parties directly and indirectly involved in WESM operations to date is given in Table 3. As shown in the table, 30 generators have been accredited to sell their electricity. Seven electric power distributors/retailers including Manila Electric Company (MERALCO) have been accredited to source their power using the WESM system. Four generators and one supplier have expressed their intention to be accredited. Nine organisations have filed their applications with the WESM.[4]

6.9.2.2 *How Does the WESM Work?*

The WESM is a system of electronically connected market players who sell and buy their needs for electricity at any time of day. The WESM does

Table 3 List of Accredited WESM Participants

1. Generators	30
2. Distribution utilities	1
3. Electric cooperatives	6
4. Suppliers	5
5. Indirect participants	16
6. Intending participants	5
7. Applicants	9

Source: Wholesale Electricity Spot Market (www.wesm.ph, 13 March 2009).

[4]Wholesale Electricity Spot Market. www.wesm.ph.

this by scheduling electricity generation and dispatch while balancing demand at all times. A typical trade takes place as follows:

> Step One: Trading participants submit hourly bids stating their price of, and demand for, electricity. Bids are submitted to the Market Operator (MO). Price bids reflect only the energy costs.
>
> Step Two: The MO matches bids using the Market Dispatch Optimization Model (MDOM), which takes into account market requirements and physical system constraints. As such, the MO first dispatches generators with the lowest offers until demand is fully met at the market clearing price.
>
> Step Three: The MO submits the dispatch schedule to the System Operator (SO) for implementation.
>
> Step Four: Suppliers and buyers settle respective payments through the WESM. Under its price determination methodology, the total cost of electricity is computed using the market clearing price (spot price), market fees and charges for ancillary services. In the case of bilateral power supply contracts, however, the involved trading participants have the option of settling directly with their contracting parties.
>
> This system allows for transparency wherein electricity is provided at its true cost, based on the economic principles of supply and demand.

6.10 CAGAYAN ELECTRIC POWER AND LIGHT COMPANY, INC

Cagayan Electric Power and Light Company (CEPALCO) is based in Cagayan de Oro City in Northeastern Mindanao. The company is one of those enterprising and socially conscious organisations which took advantage of the benefits of a deregulated electrical power sector by generating electricity using renewable energy technologies such as hydro as well as solar energy sources.

The company began its operations in 1952 with a modest power-generating capacity of 5,000 kW and a customer base of only 750. The company was granted congressional franchise on 17 June 1961. Today, CEPALCO has over 100,000 residential, commercial and industrial customers within its franchise area that covers Cagayan de Oro City and the municipalities of Tagoloan, Villanueva and Jasaan, all in the province of

Misamis Oriental, including the 3,000-hectare PHIVIDEC Industrial Estate.[5]

CEPALCO is now the third-largest electricity distribution company in the Philippines, behind Manila Electric Company, the biggest distributor. The company's growth in energy consumption has consistently been among the highest in the country. Modern facilities and equipment as well as an efficient service network have made CEPALCO one of the most reliable electricity service companies in the country. The company's distribution network includes 138 kV, 69 kV, 34.5 kV and 13.8 kV systems.

The company is a privately owned company, where the Abaya family is the founder and major shareholder. The four top shareholders (Fullmax Philippine Development, LLC, Abaya Investments Corporation, Breavel, Inc., and the Abaya family) together own 63.1 percent of the company.

6.10.1 CEPALCO's Solar Photovoltaic (PV) Plant

CEPALCO made a major and innovative decision by venturing into investments in renewable energy technology, particularly with its photovoltaic (PV) facility. The site of the PV plant is on a two-hectare site and construction of the PV power plant, which started in August 2003, was handled by Sumitomo Corporation. The PV plant was finished in April 2004. It is this particular project of CEPALCO that drives the publicity of the company, not only in the Philippines but globally, as it puts the country among the major generators of solar power among developing countries.

The plant's 1 MW capacity consists of 6,480 Sharp ND-Q7E6Z PV modules/panels designed to provide up to 1,500 MWh of electricity annually. The solar PV modules are manufactured by Sharp Japan with inverters manufactured by Sansha and all other components made locally.

The PV plant of CEPALCO started its commercial operations on 26 September 2004. After a period of three years of commercial operations, the International Finance Corporation (IFC) of the World Bank reported that the PV plant had operated with greater than expected annual

[5] CEPALCO. www.cepalco.com.ph.

energy production. Since the start of its commercial operations, the plant has exported to CEPALCO a total of 4,169,100 kWh. At its current generating capacity, the PV plant supplies the equivalent requirement of no less than 900 CEPALCO residential customers.

The CEPALCO PV power plant generates 1.1 MW of power and is currently the 133rd-largest solar power plant in the world. The PV plant puts the Philippines at number nine among the countries in the world having the largest solar power plants. The Philippines is behind solar powerhouse Germany (which has 64 out of the top 100 largest solar power lants), Portugal, Spain, Japan, the US, Italy, the Netherlands and South Korea.

6.10.2 Project Cost of the PV Plant

The total project cost of the PV plant of CEPALCO is about US$8 million funded under the Global Environment Facility (GEF) through the International Finance Corporation (IFC) including the US$4 million grant from the World Bank. The GEF support is a loan that turns into a grant after five years of successful operations of the plant by CEPALCO. The co-financing component of the project from CEPALCO is US$3–4 million.

According to the IFC, the purpose of the project was to demonstrate the effectiveness of solar PV (through a conjunctive-use application) in addressing distribution capacity issues. The IFC funds were used to build a 1 MW distributed generation solar PV plant, which is integrated into the 80 MW distribution network of CEPALCO, and operated in conjunction with an existing 7 MW mini-hydro electric plant. The plant has operated without incident since its inauguration in 2004. It appears to have been successful in proving solar PV to be an effective and technically reliable technology to address peak-load energy supply issues. The IFC reported that the solar PV plant operated by CEPALCO is a strong technical case as the project has resulted in a significant reduction in greenhouse gas emissions.[6]

The PV project is categorised by the World Bank's IFC as a Category B project according to the Procedure for Environmental and Social Review

[6] World Bank International Finance Corporation (IFC) Project No. 502486

of Projects, because a limited number of specific environmental and social impacts may result, which can be avoided or mitigated by adhering to generally recognised performance standards, guidelines or design criteria. The project was funded in the context of technical, environmental and social information submitted by the company.

6.10.3 Generation Cost of the PV Plant

The PV power plant is a project of CEPALCO as part of its investment. As such, and having no separate organisation or personnel for the PV plant itself, the generation cost of the PV facility on a per watt or kilowatt basis is somehow difficult to compute or estimate and is confidential. As a commercial organisation, however, it is presumed that the operation of the PV facility is deemed to be profitable, given the fact that the project is to be replicated on a larger scale.

6.10.4 Non-Energy Benefits from the PV Plant

The electrical energy output of CEPALCO's PV plant may be considered small compared with other sources like large-scale hydropower plants and petroleum-based power plants. However, the contribution of the PV plant to the climate change initiatives is substantial. The solar PV plant of CEPALCO is expected to displace 24,000 tonnes of CO_2 over its lifetime.

Being one of a kind, CEPALCO's PV plant has already been visited by over 13,000 students and visitors, both local as well as foreign renewable energy enthusiasts, since it started operations.

The facility was even visited by the judges of the Court of Appeals in the hope that the agency could consider the project one of its models or inputs in the construction of its upcoming building.

6.10.5 Energy Supply Mix of CEPALCO

CEPALCO is making every possible effort to improve the company's independence from its major electricity supplier (NPC) and this is supported by the fact that the company has now four sources of power

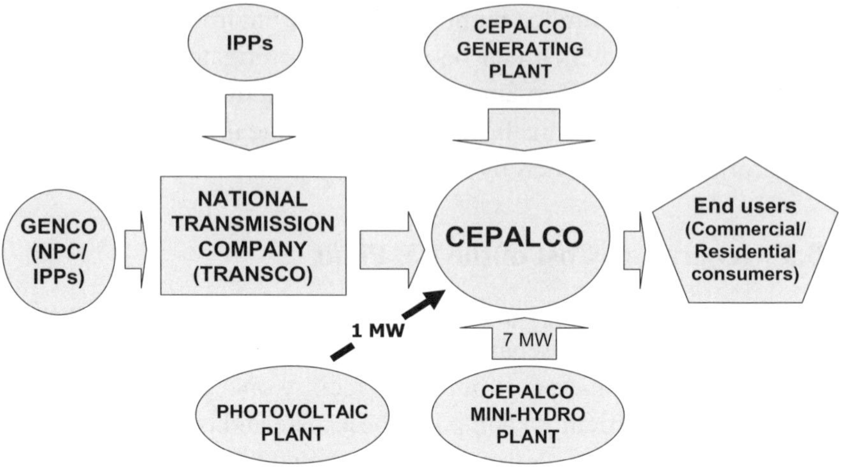

Figure 6 CEPALCO Energy Sources

(see Figure 6), three of which are from their own power plants. The entrepreneurial decision of the management of CEPALCO to venture into the PV project resulted in a variety of energy sources and flexibility. The energy supply mix of CEPALCO is shown in Figure 6. CEPALCO sources its power externally (from NPC/TransCo Mindanao grid) and also internally, from its own electricity-generating facility, mini-hydro plant and the 1 MW PV facility.

6.10.6 Expansion of the PV Plant

Given the positive and encouraging experience from the existing PV facility, CEPALCO now plans to embark on an even larger solar park within its service territory. The envisioned solar park shall make use of a 30-hectare lot within the First Cagayan de Oro Business Park in Villanueva Oriental, some 30 minutes east of Cagayan de Oro City, its base of operation.

A feasibility study of the proposed PV plant expansion indicates that it will be able to supply the CEPALCO distribution network with no less than 14,000,000 kWh of electricity annually, which is equivalent to no less than 30,000 barrels of fuel oil per year. The proposed PV plant, with a total installed capacity of at least 10 megawatt-peak (MWp), shall be constructed over a period of at least five years and shall use the best available solar technology in the market. The phased-in construction strategy will enable CEPALCO to capitalise on the increasing efficiency and decreasing costs of solar cells which currently command no less than 60 percent of the PV plant's installed costs. It will also cushion the impact of generation costs on CEPALCO's customers.

If implemented according to plan, the first phase of the proposed 30-hectare solar park shall be commissioned by 2012 to augment the expected shortfall in firm capacity in the Mindanao grid.

6.11 NORTHWIND POWER DEVELOPMENT CORPORATION (NPDC)

The Philippines has been found to have a potential wind power of 76,600 MW, leading other wind power–producing countries such as Germany (14,000 MW potential wind power), Spain, the US (6,000 MW each), Denmark (3,000 MW) and India (2,100 MW). A wind mapping study conducted by the United States National Renewable Energy Laboratory has found Bangui Bay in Ilocos Norte to be one of the areas across the country where 10,000 km^2 of windy land exists with good to excellent wind resource potential.

The NorthWind Power Development Corporation (NPDC) is a relatively new business organisation involved in power generation, capitalising on wind potential in the Bangui Bay off Ilocos Norte in Northern Luzon. The wind farm project in Ilocos Norte was drawn up in 1996 though a wind resource analysis and mapping study conducted for the Philippines by the NREL. The study showed that various areas spread around the Philippines are receptive to wind power installations. These areas include Bangui and Burgos towns in Ilocos Norte, Batanes and Babuyan islands also north of Luzon and the higher interior terrain of Mindoro, Samar, Leyte, Panay, Negros, Cebu, Palawan and eastern Mindanao.

The NPDC took advantage of the wind power potential of the country, particularly the Ilocos region, by investing in the first wind farm in

Table 4 Specifications of NorthWind Power System

Turbine's hub height	—70 meters
Blade length	—41 meters
Rotor diameter	—82 meters
Windswept area	—5,281 sq. m.
*** Ground level to center of nacelle	
The turbine are oriented facing the sea, effectively eliminating windbreaks and achieving terrain roughness of class 0.	
Annual generation capacity	—74,482 MWh
Wind turbine arrangement	—Single row
Spacing	—326 meters
Orientation	—North
Prevailing wind direction	—Northeast

Source: NorthWind Power Development Corporation, Makati City, 2010.

the country and in Southeast Asia. The wind farm established by the NDPC in Bangui, Ilocos Norte, uses wind turbines arranged in a single row stretching along a 3 km shoreline off Bangui Bay facing the South China Sea. The wind farm uses 1.65 MW Vestas V82 wind turbines supplied by Vestas Asia Pacific A/S, the leading supplier of wind turbines in the world. The turbines are onshore and arranged in an arc spaced about 326 m apart. Other technical details of the wind turbines are shown in Table 4.

Harnessing the strong winds coming from the north-northeast of the country, the wind farm is the largest wind power project in Southeast Asia. A first in Southeast Asia, the wind power plant is now comprised of 20 turbines, each standing at 70 m or equal to the height of a 23-storey building. The wind farm can generate a maximum capacity of 33 MW. The company is considering another 40 MW wind power project in Cagayan province, also in Northern Luzon, in the next two years.

The first phase of the project started with 15 wind turbines in 2000 with an aggregate capacity of 25 MW and a 69 km transmission line to Ilocos Norte Electric Cooperative in Laoag City. In June 2008, the NPDC added five more turbines, raising the wind farm's capacity to 33 MW.

6.11.1 Funding the NPDC Project

Initially, the funding that was provided by the NPDC was for five turbines, which is equivalent to a capacity of 8 MW. Eventually, the Danish International Development Agency (DANIDA) partially funded the first phase of the Bangui Bay project. All 15 wind turbines under the Phase 1 project are connected to the Luzon grid, and have been delivering power to Ilocos Norte Electric Cooperative. The second phase comprising an additional five turbines is funded by an additional investment by the NPDC, amounting to US$13 million, and the total project cost amounts to US$50 million.[7]

In all, DANIDA funded $29.35 million of the $50-million project cost through a zero-interest mixed-credit facility, which was complemented by a guarantee from the Philippine Export-Import Credit Agency. About $10.5 million came from grants, while the balance was put in by NPDC shareholders. NorthWind's major shareholders include Moorland Phils., Phildane Resources Corp. and Fabmik Construction and Equipment Corporation.

6.11.2 NPDC Expansion and Creation of a New Subsidiary

To handle its expansion project, the NPDC has created a new subsidiary to take charge of its expansion programme in the Cagayan area, worth $95 million. The NPDC put up a 40 MW wind farm project in Aparri, Cagayan, in 2009. The company is bullish in expanding their capacity with the passage of the Renewable Energy Act. For its expansion projects, the NPDC may tap the Danish government and other investors and creditors for the Cagayan wind project. The company also expects to tap Japanese and Spanish investors and creditors. Former Energy Secretary Vincent Perez, now of Alternergy, said with the growing interest in renewable power sources, an increase in foreign investment is projected for renewable projects in emerging countries. Perez, who is Chairman of energy advisory firm Merritt Partners and Managing Director of renewable power developer Alternergy, said that investments in renewable energy sources such as wind, hydro and solar power are expected to pick up. After

---

[7] www.northwindpower.com.

an extensive road show in the US, Middle East and Europe, Perez's group were able to source $150 million in an equity commitment to Alternergy from foreign investors primarily, for wind power development.

6.11.3 Sale Price of NPDC Power Output

The only market for now for the electricity output of the NPDC is Ilocos Norte Electric Cooperative (INEC) which has an existing Renewable Energy Sales Agreement (RESA). The distribution system of the NPDC's wind farm is embedded in the INEC grid and thus negates the power-delivery charges of the National Transmission Corporation (TransCo), which is considered a saving for INEC. The NPDC has a pending accreditation with the WESM where, other than INEC as a market, excess power output of the NPDC can be sold in the spot market being administered by the WESM.

As stated in the RESA, the NPDC will extend a 7 percent discount to INEC benchmarked against the rate of the National Power Corporation. This pricing scheme will reduce the power charges being paid by Ilocos residents. The wind energy produced by the Bangui wind farm of the NPDC translates to a 7 percent reduction in power costs from prevailing rates or a 5 percent discount of the weighted average price in the Wholesale Electricity Spot Market.

On top of reduced power rates, the wind farm will pave the way for the entry of additional investment opportunities whose operations depend on good power quality. The province's unstable power would force the Coca-Cola Bottling Company to avoid switching to INEC's power line due to low voltage between 5 pm and 10 pm. The bottling company is one of the few huge power-dependent companies in the province.

The Bangui Bay wind farm project sells electricity to Ilocos Norte Electric Cooperative and it now provides 40 percent of the power requirements of the province of Ilocos Norte, gradually increasing to 70 percent once Phase 2 is completed.

6.11.4 Carbon Credits for the NPDC

The electricity that the NPDC generates will displace greenhouse gas emissions such as carbon dioxide by approximately 65,000 tonnes per year. It is the first to be registered with the executive board of the Kyoto Protocol to the United Nations Framework Convention on Climate

Change. When carbon credits are duly accredited and issued the appropriate Certified Emission Reductions (CERs), the same can be traded in the carbon market. CERs are the carbon offset credits generated under the UN Clean Development Mechanism for emissions reduction investment in developing countries. CERs are bought by developed countries and their firms to count towards their own domestic emissions targets.

The price of Certified Emission Reductions in the global carbon markets ranges from US$10 to US$30 per tonne. In Europe, the carbon price was around €9.60 as of December 2008.[8]

If the CER of the NPDC is sold at a low market price of US$10 per tonne, the annual carbon equivalent production of the NPDC translates to US$650,000 per year or estimated to be US$6.5 million over a 10-year period.

The ERC lauded the NPDC for investing in eco-friendly renewable energy projects for cheaper electricity services as well as a clean and green environment. With its compliance to the technical, financial and environmental standards set by law, electricity consumers in the area are assured that the ERC has carefully reviewed the safety and reliability of the NPDC's wind farm facilities.

6.11.5 Local Government Unit's Efforts Paid Off

The electricity supply from the NPDC was a welcome development by the local government unit and the provincial officials. Already, business developers have started discussing potential industries with the provincial government, ranging from glass to cement plants in eastern Ilocos Norte towns. It was Ilocos Norte Governor Ferdinand Marcos, Jr., who, as a congressman back in the 1990s, aggressively pursued the development of a power plant in the province. The governor had previously disclosed that Ilocos Norte had let loose potential investors in the past due to poor power quality in the province. Governor Marcos had always complained then for the NPC to do something about its power service, but to no avail. At present, Ilocos Norte is most affected during power outages because it is found at the end of the power grid which comes all the way from Bauang, La Union.

[8] Carbon Positive. http://www.carbonpositive.net/viewarticle.aspx?articleID=137.

6.11.6 Contribution of the NPDC to the Grid

The NPDC's aggregate installed capacity of 33 MW is only 0.33 percent and 0.25 percent of the Luzon grid and the national grid, respectively. This share provided by wind energy in terms of generation capacity is way below the current limit set by the ERC. These figures may be considered minuscule but when one looks at the fact that the electricity production of the NPDC supplies 40 percent of the power needs of INEC with the potential to supply up to 70 percent of the province's needs, the contribution of the NPDC is substantial.

The ERC determines the compliance of a generating company to the market-share limitations by determining the maximum load-carrying capability of the facility operated by the generation company on a yearly basis. To prevent anti-competitive behaviour, the ERC ensures that an electricity generation` company does not exceed the market share limitations in the grid where it operates (set at 30 percent) and in the national grid (set at 25 percent).

6.12 ILOCOS NORTE ELECTRIC COOPERATIVE

Ilocos Norte Electric Cooperative is a consumer-level electrical power provider in the northern-most province of Luzon province, which once sourced its electricity from the National Power Corporation. INEC has a power demand of 32.42 kW (substation capacity) with a load factor or 58.76 percent. As of 29 February 2008, INEC has energised all 21 municipalities of Ilocos Norte, including Laoag City and City of Batac, posting a record of 100 percent energisation of the province and 100 percent of the province's 557 villages (barangays).

The electricity cooperative used to source its power from the Luzon grid of the NPC which provides electrical power all over the Philippines. In 2001, INEC linked up with the NorthWind Power Development Corporation — the first wind power producer in the Philippines. At the time of initial link up in 2001, the NPDC had a rated capacity of 24.75 MW from its 15 wind turbines. This capacity increased to 33 MW with the addition of five more turbines. The Bangui Bay wind farm of the NPDC generates power at wind speeds averaging 7 m/s. The NPDC's wind farm can help reduce INEC's system loss by improving its stability and electricity quality and reinforcing its transmission system through a 50 km, 69,000 V line constructed by the NPDC.

6.12.1 Energy Supply Mix of INEC

The availability of wind power–based electricity provided by the NPDC made it possible for INEC to diversify its power sources outside the NPC and its own mini-hydropower plant. The energy supply mix of INEC as of the end of 2005 is shown in Figure 7. From zero contribution in the early part of 2005, the contribution of wind power rose to 25 percent by year-end 2005. As power from INEC sourced from wind resources increased to 25 percent, electricity power sourced from the NPC was reduced to only 71 percent from 93 percent in early 2005, as shown in Table 5.[9]

The details of the energy supply mix of INEC are shown in Table 5. The energy sourced from its own mini-hydropower plant appears to be fluctuating, and in fact reducing in terms of share. Clearly increasing in terms

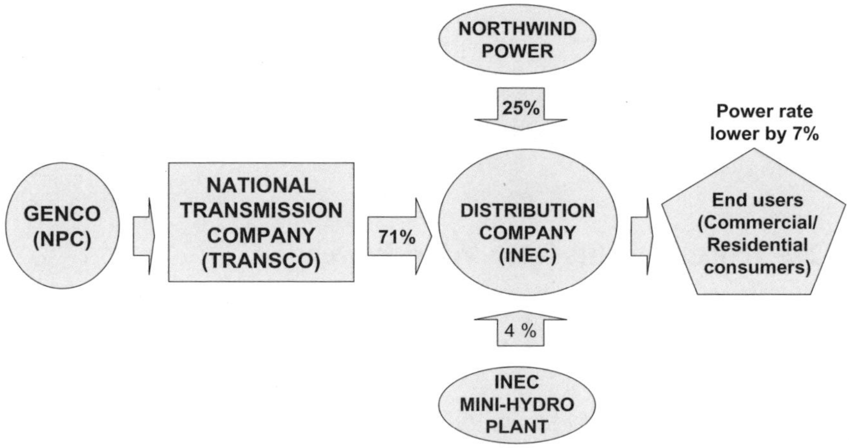

Figure 7 The INEC Energy Supply Mix (As of December 2005)

[9] Energy Regulatory Commission. www.erc.gov.ph. ERC Case No. 2005 019 RC, p. 9.

Table 5 Energy Supply Mix of INEC (2005)

Month	Mini Hydro (kWh)	% share	NPC (kWh)	% share	NorthWind (kWh)	% share	Total (kWh)
Jan	906,220	7%	11,961,974	93%	0	0.00%	12,868,194
Feb	587,200	4%	12,743,614	96%	0	0.00%	13,330,814
Mar	657,670	5%	11,943,508	95%	0	0.00%	12,601,178
Apr	450,060	3%	15,762,013	97%	20,789	0.13%	16,232,862
May	249,180	1%	15,660,217	93%	849,165	5.07%	16,758,562
Jun	201,600	1%	14,500,913	91%	1,268,114	7.94%	15,970,627
Jul	138,600	1%	13,738,983	87%	1,850,940	11.77%	15,728,562
Aug	195,300	1%	13,487,345	87%	1,769,442	11.45%	15,452,087
Sep	174,300	1%	12,795,817	86%	1,826,552	12.34%	14,796,669
Oct	137,600	1%	11,176,063	78%	3,037,368	21.16%	14,351,031
Nov	319,200	2%	11,497,740	76%	3,404,884	22.37%	15,221,824
Dec	621,600	4%	9,930,433	71%	3,442,196	24.60%	13,994,229
Total	4,638,530		155,198,620		17,469,450		177,306,600
Average		2.75%		87.51%		9.74%	

Source: Energy Regulatory Commission (www.erc.gov.ph)

of magnitude and percentage share is the energy supplied by wind power through the NPDC, indicating the critical role played by wind energy technology.

6.12.2 INEC Benefits from Wind Power

It is indeed a blessing for INEC to be the beneficiary of the electricity from wind sources, owing to the following benefits:

a) It is a source of electricity cheaper in acquisition costs by about 7 percent than its usual source of energy (i.e. National Power Corporation). This lower rate is passed on to the consumers of INEC's electricity power.

b) Savings on the part of INEC on account of transmission costs usually budgeted or paid to TransCo. The NPDC's power output is embedded into the INEC transmission system, thus negating TransCo fees. The connection and power sourcing from the wind farm project generated savings of approximately \$2.54 million for the consumers of INEC in 2006 and 2007. The savings occurred since the NPDC was embedded in the INEC grid and thus negated the power-delivery charges of TransCo.

c) The assurance of a localised energy source with the potential to distribute up to 70 percent of INEC's power demand, which hopefully means more long-term monetary benefits to INEC and its customers.
d) The energy from the wind farm of the NPDC supplies the energy needed by INEC, thus addressing the voltage fluctuation problem in the INEC service area which in the past they complained about.

6.12.3 INEC's Concerns about the Spot Market

The EPIRA called for the establishment of the Wholesale Electricity Spot Market wherein a fraction of the electricity requirements of electricity cooperatives have to be purchased from the spot market through electronic bidding. In its initial implementation, INEC has applied to be one of the pilot electricity distribution utilities and the first electricity cooperative to participate in the WESM. However, INEC appears not to be so excited about this possibility.

As per the WESM Rules, electricity cooperatives are required to purchase at least 10 percent of their energy requirements from the spot market. At present, INEC's energy requirements are purchased from the NPC and the NPDC as well as INEC's own mini-hydropower plant. During the trial operation by INEC personnel with the WESM system, it was observed that there are times when the price of electricity in the spot market is higher than the NPC price but there are also times when the price of electricity is lower. In the WESM operation, distribution utilities are required to submit their bids for their energy requirements one hour ahead, thus the price of electricity that INEC purchases from the spot market will change every hour. To monitor closely the prices of electricity in the spot market, there is a need to man the INEC Energy Trading Office 24 hours a day. This project is a new concept in the Philippine electricity industry but it aims to reduce the rate of electricity because of the competitive bidding. To date, several assets of the NPC have already been privatised, the most recent of which is Magat Hydroelectric in the province of Isabela acquired by the Aboitiz Group of Companies. Given this scenario, it is possible that the 7 percent discount rate from the NPDC and the spot market prices as well as renewable energy sales agreements with the NPDC may have complications that can potentially jeopardise the concern of INEC to serve its customers at affordable prices.[10]

According to the ERC legal office, there is now a legal case filed by the NPDC regarding the refusal of INEC to settle the entire bill submitted by the NPDC to INEC.[11]

6.13 MONTALBAN METHANE POWER PROJECT

Other than the solar photovoltaic plant of CEPALCO and wind-powered generation system of the NPDC, the Philippines takes pride in the methane-powered facility that is connected to the distribution utility (MERALCO). In previous years, the country had a number of biogas/methane projects considered commercial in scale but none of these projects was ever connected to the electrical grid. The Montalban Methane Power Corporation (MMPC) is a project of First Balfour, Inc., one of the power/energy companies belonging to the Lopez Group. The project makes use of the garbage from Metro Manila that is dumped at the landfill facility located in Montalban, Rizal. The MMPC has secured an agreement with the local government of Rizal province to build the country's first waste-to-energy power plant at the Rodriguez (formerly Montalban) landfill site. The MMPC will capture the landfill gas or methane from the 14-hectare landfill to produce enough electricity to provide 15,000 households with power. The methane-powered facility began operations in July 2008 and President Gloria Macapagal Arroyo launched the project.

The project is a build-own-operate (BOO) project and Monark Equipment Corporation (MEC) was commissioned to put up the power plant for the project. First Balfour will be responsible for the installation of nine units

---

[10] Ilocos Norte Electric Cooperative. http://www.inec.gov.ph

[11] Phone conversation with Atty Adriano of ERC Legal Office, 23 March 2009.

of generator sets with 2 MW capacity each but derated at 850 kW using methane as fuel. The project scope included construction of the powerhouse building, equipment foundations, piping works for fuel/gas header, condensate and cooling water, cabling works, small power and lighting, plumbing, ventilation system and monitoring system.[12]

Methane-based projects in the Philippines are not really new but this particular scale and type of project is the first of its kind in the Philippines and one of the largest in Asia. With an estimated construction cost of $30 million, it is expected to generate 15 MW of power over 10 years. MMPC officials said that at least 1,500 metric tonnes of garbage would be needed to sustain the plant's operations. Increasing the volume of trash to 2,500 metric tonnes can extend production to 10 years instead of just five years.

The company plans to sell its power to Manila Electric Co. and the Wholesale Electricity Spot Market. The project expects to generate an income of US$50 million. In addition, it can earn more once it qualifies as a Clean Development Mechanism project under the United Nations Kyoto Protocol, and will generate at least 500,000 Certified Emission Reductions.

The methane gas facility of the MMPC follows the Kyoto Protocol of the United Nations Framework Convention on Climate Change (UNFCCC) initiative and provides carbon credits for developed countries under a category of projects that reduce emissions in developing economies under the Clean Development Mechanism. Furthermore, the power plant project is a candidate for Gold Standard Clean Development Mechanism status.

6.14 MORE WIND POWER PROJECTS

San Carlos Wind Power Corporation, a Filipino-Danish joint venture, is investing P2.987 billion for the construction of a 30 MW wind power project. This is the third new and renewable energy project approved by the Board of Investments. The project will be located around Mount Malindog in Barangays, Linubagan and Prosperidad, San Carlos City, Negros Occidental, which is 700–800 m above sea level. The Board of Investments

[12] First Balfour. www.firstbalfour.com.

approved pioneer status for the project, it having met the minimum investment requirement for wind technologies at $1.25 million.

For the development of the project, the partnership between Smith Bell Wind Technologies, Inc., and Global Renewable Energy Partners was put together to establish and organise the San Carlos Wind Power Corporation. The San Carlos wind farm will comprise 16–20 wind turbine generators each with a capacity of 1.5–2 MW, with a total rated capacity of 30 MW. When operational, San Carlos intends to sell the generated power to the electric distribution facilities in the Negros and Panay sub-grids. Of the total cost, the firm intends to spend P1.7 billion for the acquisition of turbines, while the rest will be used for the construction and development of the facilities. The bulk of the cost at P2.2 billion is expected to come from loans, while the rest from equity. The project is also seeking Danish foreign aid in the form of grants on interest payments, and from European banks.

San Carlos is the third wind power project to be registered with the Board of Investments. The other two projects, also granted with pioneer status by BOI, are the 40 MW project of Northern Luzon Wind Power Project of PNOC Energy Development Corporation (PNOC/EDC) and another project by NorthWind Power Development Corporation.

6.15 WIND POWER CONTRACTING ROUND

To further entice investors in renewable energy technologies, the Department of Energy has employed creative means fashioned after the oil concession system. The DOE launched the Wind Power Contracting Round that offered 16 wind sites. Three companies that were earlier awarded pre-commercial contracts (PCCs) to harness the country's wind energy are now conducting actual wind assessments under their respective work programmes. Philippine Hybrid Energy Systems, Inc., was awarded three PCCs for wind projects in Marinduque; Baleno, Masbate; and Tablas, Romblon; with a combined capacity of 30 MW. Trans-Asia Renewable Energy Corporation was also awarded a contract for a potential 30 MW wind project in Sual, Pangasinan, and San Carlos Wind Power Corp. for a 25 MW wind farm in San Carlos City, Negros Occidental.

Companies that bid for the 11 other sites are now in the process of securing PCCs from the Department of Energy.[13]

6.16 FINANCIAL SUPPORT MECHANISM FOR NRETS

With many renewable energy technologies now in the mature and commercial stage, particularly solar and wind technologies, the next constraints and obstacles to their widespread use are more financial and economic considerations.

It is therefore important to provide a financial support scheme and incentive to address investors' concerns. It is along this premise that renewable energy development programmes in the Philippines have put substantial emphasis on the financial support scheme, particularly on credit availability, as well as incentives in the form of duty-free imports and tax holidays. Aside from the pre-operating incentives, renewable energy projects in commercial operations are given additional incentives when the project is covered by the Incentives Act or the Investment Priorities Plan (IPP) being administered by the Board of Investments.

These concerns are given even more emphasis in the form of financial support schemes, as well as incentive measures enshrined under the Renewable Energy Act of 2008. The following are some elaborations in this regard.

6.16.1 Financial Support Under the Renewable Energy Act

To encourage investors to venture into renewable energy projects, the Renewable Energy Act made specific provisions on financing commercial projects under Section 29 as follows:

> Section 29. Financial Assistance Program. — Government financial institutions such as the Development Bank of the Philippines (DBP), Land Bank of the Philippines (LBP), Phil-Exim Bank and other government

[13] Department of Energy, 2008.

> financial institutions shall, in accordance with and to the extent allowed by the enabling provisions of their respective charters or applicable laws, provide preferential financial packages for the development, utilisation and commercialisation of RE projects as duly recommended and endorsed by the DOE.

The Development Bank of the Philippines has financing packages under its Wind Energy Financing Program, RE Project Preparation Revolving Fund, Rural Power Project for Type A Beneficiaries, Rural Power Project for Type B Beneficiaries and CDM Initiatives.

Philippine Export-Import Credit Agency (PhilExim), for its part, provides loan guarantees to selected wind power projects such as the Bangui Bay wind farm.

6.16.2 Available Financing from the Private Sector

Even prior to the enactment of the Renewable Energy Act, the commercial banking system in the Philippines made available commercial loans and financing schemes, given the fact that products of energy-based projects are always in demand.

It is a matter of practice among private commercial banks to support and finance renewable energy projects that are bankable or whose cash flow and income stream support the business venture.

6.16.3 Financial Support from External Parties

Large-scale or commercial renewable energy-based power generation technologies are expensive and come with techno-economic apprehensions. Hence, the support of external parties, both from bilateral and multilateral sources, is considered of great help.

Other than the availability of domestic funds from the banking and financial system, international or foreign-based sources also offer financial assistance such as the Global Environment Facility (GEF) and International Finance Corporation (IFC) of the World Bank which provided the funds for the photovoltaic power plant of CEPALCO in Cagayan de Oro City.

The United Nations Development Programme GEF also offered assistance in project preparation and in securing loan guarantees for the project.

Developed countries and donor organisations noticed the growing energy demand, hence the Asian Development Bank (ADB) and its development partners are setting up a facility that would provide seed capital for renewable energy and energy efficiency projects in the Asia-Pacific region.

The ADB said it would develop the Seed Capital Assistance Facility that would be initially funded by a $4.2-million grant from the GEF, a global partnership established in 1991 to help developing countries fund projects that protect the global environment. The Seed Capital Assistance Facility would be jointly managed by the ADB and United Nations Environment Programme. The ADB said the facility would

> provide technical assistance to private equity fund managers and entrepreneurs to develop sustainable clean energy funds and financing for the early stages of such projects, share in the costs of development and transactions, and encourage taking riskier portfolios through a seed capital return enhancement offered on a per-project basis.

It further noted that the facility would increase access to financing at the early stages of sustainable energy enterprises and projects around the Asia-Pacific region. With increased experience among financiers in investing in small-scale renewable energy and energy efficiency projects, mainstream energy investors would be encouraged to invest more in clean energy enterprises and projects.[14]

6.17 TECHNICAL AND ECONOMIC EFFICIENCY

Renewable energy technologies in general suffer the perception of relatively low technical efficiency and hence low economic/financial efficiency. The technical efficiency of a solar PV system stands at just a little above 10 percent, with wind energy conversion systems limited by the

[14] Asian Development Bank. www.adb.org.

Betz coefficient that leads to a maximum theoretical efficiency below 60 percent. Adding demerit to this low technical efficiency is the fact that these systems produce a direct current (DC) type of electricity as opposed to the alternating current (AC) type demanded by grid and system loads. Outputs of solar PV and wind power systems have to be converted to AC electricity, thus increasing initial system costs and thus affecting financial/economic efficiency computations even though the inputs (sun and wind) are available for free.

The policy of the Philippine government, as enshrined in the Renewable Energy Act and other laws earlier enacted provide a venue for investments deemed attractive for energy system generators and providers. Outputs of renewable energy systems can be connected to the regional electrical grids, hence allowing the supply of NRET-generated power to be distributed or sold elsewhere too far away from the point of power production — realities which could have been too costly for alternative/renewable power generation systems due to technical losses. This interconnection scenario, therefore, takes care of the limitations and low competitiveness of the NRETs vis-à-vis the traditional petroleum-based power generation system. It is in this light that renewable energy-based power generation systems become somehow competitive as they can even serve to balance voltage instability in some areas served by the grid, as in the case of the situation of Ilocos Norte province.

With the output of the PV plant of CEPALCO forming part of the power supply and distribution lines of the company, as well as the electric power output of the NPDC embedded in the distribution grid of INEC, the question of low technical efficiency is now a foregone conclusion as, in fact, the outputs of these facilities serve as voltage stabilisers besides the financial/economic benefits they provide, on top of saving some operating expenses on account of savings from wheeling charges from TransCo.

6.17.1 Margin Advantage for NRET Electricity

Unlike tariff rates charged by distribution utilities and electric cooperatives which are explicitly regulated under the provisions of the EPIRA and other ERC regulations, electricity outputs or rates of power generators from renewable energy sources are treated differently though they are regulated under the rate-setting mandate of the ERC. As such, the profitability of operations of renewable energy-based companies is not controlled or curtailed, and hence is very attractive and motivating for investors. It can be said then that, potentially or in reality, financial/economic attractiveness or efficiency is expected to be relatively high on account of the expected higher return on investment levels that can be set as compared to electricity distribution businesses, a scenario that favours the investors in NRET-based projects.

This notion is explained by the current situation of both CEPALCO and INEC. The PV system of CEPALCO is part of its power plant's distribution utility as well as its generating utility. The company owns and operates hydro and PV plants whose output is part of the electricity it supplies to its institutional/residential consumers. This being the case, CEPALCO is not necessarily required to divulge the costs and returns of the PV generation facility, hence there is really no way of knowing whether the price charged by the PV facility is too high or not. The same is true with the electric power from the NPDC which is sold to INEC by way of an Energy Sales Agreement (ESA). The ESA ensures for the NPDC a market outlet and guaranteed price benchmarked against the NPC rate at a discount rate of 7 percent. It was INEC which filed the petition with the government's Energy Regulatory Commission (ERC) and the ESA between INEC and NPDC that is valid for 20 years is deemed clear to both parties. When the NPC is fully privatised, the same discount rate will apply but benchmarked against the going electricity rate in the province as the buyer of NPC interest inherits the provisions in the ESA. What is not factored in the determination of the cost of electricity sold by the NPDC to INEC is the money equivalent of the CERs which the NPDC can sell to the carbon market. This is somehow a grey area, which in the view of the author is favourable to the renewable energy generators like CEPALCO and the NPDC.

A very important aspect and motivating factor in constructing and operating a renewable energy–based company is that aside from sales from electricity, the generator can earn a substantial income from the sale of carbon credits if the firm is duly certified by appropriate bodies to be qualified for Certified Emission Reductions. These credits are substantial and more than enough to offset whatever inefficiencies NRET technologies may have. This appears to be an advantage that provides economic or financial efficiency and advantage as it steps up early recovery of investment apart from helping the host country improve its contribution to the Kyoto Protocol.

6.18 MORE INVESTMENTS IN RENEWABLE ENERGY NEEDED AND EXPECTED

Envisioning a goal of having a 4,500 MW capacity of new renewable energy in the next 10 years, the renewable energy sector will need some $8.5 billion in fresh investments. This investment required is an estimate on the conservative side. Director Mario Marasigan of the Department of Energy's Energy Utilization and Management Bureau expressed confidence saying that investors would find the renewable energy sector quite lucrative, particularly when the Implementing Rules and Regulations of RA 9513, or the Renewable Energy Act of 2008, are finalised.

Right now, the DOE may not have an exact handle on the number of investors that are seriously interested in investing in renewable energy projects. What the department knows at this point is that the renewable energy projects are most attractive to potential investors. Most of these investors are looking at wind, hydro, geothermal and biomass, including solid waste-to-energy concepts, and biofuels. At least one company is interested in ocean energy thermal conversion.[15]

The finalisation of the Implementing Rules and Regulations of the Renewable Energy Act should prompt potential investors to finalise their investment plans in the sector. The Implementing Rules and Regulations are expected to be completed by June 2009, ahead of the July deadline set by the law. The law is widely expected to spur investments in the renewable energy sector, due mainly to incentives that are offered to potential investors. Some of these incentives are exemptions from tariff duties and zero-rated value-added tax for the importation of machinery and equipment for the first 10 years of an operating contract, as well as tax credit on domestic capital equipment and services.

[15] Ho, A. "$8.5B in renewable energy investments needed", *Philippine Daily Inquirer*, 23 March 2009.

Special realty tax rates will also be imposed on equipment and machinery to be used for renewable energy development. An income tax holiday will also be granted to potential investors for the first seven years of operation.

6.19 SUCCESS FACTORS IN THE PHILIPPINE NRET PROGRAMMES/PROJECTS

Whatever experiences and successes as well as failures the Philippines may have had in NRET matters is a combination of products and results and political will in developing the continually updated National Energy Plan. This would have been impossible were it not for a variety of legislations and administrative provisions to support the attainment of the vision set forth in the energy plan.

The global development and volatility of the global markets for petroleum products was a dilemma but in some ways served as a reminder of the need to continually pursue efforts in developing the potential of renewable energy sources as a component of the projected generation capacity and eventually the energy supply mix. The efforts made in the area of commercialising the gasification technology, commercial experiences in biogas technology, the progress made in developing coconut-based fuel from a pure CNO-diesel fuel mix to coconut methyl esters (biodiesel), the initial failures in small-scale wind power projects as well as the pilot projects in the area of PV all contributed to the initiation of and commercial-scale ventures in solar and wind power projects that are now generating megawatt-level capacities already connected to the grid system.

The following factors may have greatly contributed to the commercial use and megawatt-level power generation projects using renewable energy sources:

a) Availability and abundance of natural resources (e.g. solar, wind, biomass).
b) Political will and government policy pronouncements on private sector participation in the area of power generation, resulting in a privatised power generation system.

c) Commitment to pursue research and development as well as promotional development efforts to popularise and commercialise the use of renewable energy sources.
d) Existence of a number of laws and administrative interventions, principally incentive schemes, thus favouring investments and private business ventures in the power sector.
e) Availability of foreign/local financing support schemes (e.g. loans and grants from DBP, LBP, IFC, DANIDA) to augment local financial limitations.
f) Existence of guaranteed or captive markets as well as government assurance to ensure reasonable returns to private investors.
g) Support of local government units in cementing the intents and purposes built into the national energy plan.
h) External pressures in terms of volatile global markets and environmental concerns (e.g. Kyoto Protocol) that favourably offset the economic disadvantages of some renewable energy technologies.
i) Existence of mature and commercial technologies using renewable energy sources.
j) Willingness of local and foreign investors as well as concerned entrepreneurs who care about clean energy and environmentally friendly power generation technologies.

6.20 SUMMARY AND CONCLUSIONS

If there is any success in the development of renewable energy technologies in the Philippines resulting in the establishment of megawatt-level capacity power plants, this can be traced to a number of incentives and mandatory provisions of laws as well as a series of efforts made by the government commencing in the late 1970s to the present date. The variety of laws, for example the Investment Act, BOT Law, Biofuels Law, EPIRA, Clean Air Act, Ecological Solid Waste Management Act, and most recently, the Renewable Energy Act, are indications of the commitment of the Philippine government to make renewable energy take on a role in the country's energy generation capacity down to the energy supply mix. These efforts appear to have been well received by the private sectors, such that ownership and management of power generation is now largely in the hands of the private sector. A number of investments have been made by foreign or international organisations, including the World Bank's International Finance Corporation which supported the CEPALCO PV project and DANIDA which partly financed the NPDC's wind power project.

The 33 MW production of the NPDC using the wind energy potential of Bangui in Ilocos Norte is the biggest in Southeast Asia and the first venture accredited with Certified Emission Reductions. Its connection to the electrical grid with a potential to supply up to 70 percent of the electricity demand of the province of Ilocos Norte is worth noting and encouraging for prospective investors. The company's plan to put up more wind generators of 40 MW in Cagayan province, also in Luzon, is proof that the wind energy conversion system is indeed a mature technology and one that is now tested successfully in the Philippines.

For solar energy technology by PV, the 1 MW solar PV plant is another first of its kind in Southeast Asia. It is also connected to the grid and is now playing a key role in supplying the electricity needs of the service area of CEPALCO. No less than the World Bank's IFC has given a positive endorsement to the project for its success. The plan of CEPALCO to put up a much bigger solar park capable of generating 10 MW is an indication of encouraging financial returns to the company.

Being a new project and unique in the sense that power generation is part of CEPALCO's business activities and with the RESA scheme to guarantee a market for the electricity output of the NPDC, the true costs and returns of the two NRET power plants (by CEPALCO and the NPDC) remain confidential, given that these organisations are private commercial ventures. Nonetheless, the expansionary attitude these companies have is indicative of a bright future for these ventures, given that outputs of their plants can be easily sold or disposed through the electrical grid system.

The annual climate change mitigation contribution of the three major projects mentioned is 65,000 tonnes of carbon equivalent for the NPDC. Throughout the project's lifetime, the MMPC expects to produce an equivalent of 500,000 tonnes with CEPALCO which stands to produce 10,000 tonnes equivalent. When traded in the carbon exchange market, it means additional income for the three companies which also means compliance to the Kyoto Protocol on the part of the Philippines. Investment wise, it meant an investment of about US$88 million for the three NRET-based power projects alone.

All three renewable energy projects (CEPALCO, NPDC, MMPC) connected to the electrical grid are supported by private investors with funding support from international financing institutions (e.g. IFC and DANIDA) and local investors as well. This is an indication that even without financial support from government financial institutions as mandated by the Renewable Energy Act, renewable energy projects connected to the electrical grid can take off, and in fact, the existing projects are expansionary ventures.

In the meantime, the full implementation of the Renewable Energy Act with its Implementing Rules and Regulations are now being discussed, and given the fact that the law mandates government financial institutions to make available its financial resources along with a variety of incentives to private investors, there is a reason to be optimistic for local and foreign investors, and the government as well.

REFERENCES

Anonuevo, E. P. "ERC approves Montalban methane-fed plant operation", *Manila Times*, 13 February 2009.

Cahiles-Magkilat, B. "Filipino-Danish JV to invest P3 B in wind power project", Manila Times, 25 October 2004. www.manilatimes.net/national/2009/jan/06/yehey/business/20090106bus11.html.

Callangan, R. B. "Wind Energy Development in the Philippines", Department of Energy, Makati City, Philippines.

Finance Manilla, "Solar and wind power in the Philippines", 3 August 2009. http://financemanila.net/2008/08/solar-and-wind-power-in-the-philippines/.

First Balfour. http://www.firstbalfour.com/projects.php?proj_id=22&page=&filter _catcat_catpc_id=1&filter_catcat_catpc_id=1&sub=power.

http://ipb2000.com/index.php/enviroment/1707-regulator-approves-northwind-proposal-to-sell-wind-farm-output-.

Ho, A. "DOE to award 4 wind projects", *Philippine Daily Inquirer*, 21 December 2008. http://business.inquirer.net/money/breakingnews/view/20081221-179246/DOE-to-award-4-wind-power-contracts.

Ho, A. "$8.5B in renewable energy investments needed", *Philippine Daily Inquirer*, 24 March 2009. http://business.inquirer.net/money/breakingnews/view/20090324-195823/85B-in-renewable-energy-investments-needed.

Humphrey, K. "Giant windmills power Northern Philippines", *UnpluggedLiving*, 13 October 2005. www.unpluggedliving.com/giant-windmills-power-northern-philippines.

Karunungan, E. "Renewable Energy Fuels: Key to Energy Independence and Security", Department of Energy, Makati City, Philippines, 2008.

Kho, M. "Philippines may soon become wind farm powerhouse", *Philippine Daily Inquirer*, Manila, Philippines, 30 January 2009.

Linao, G. "Philippines hopes northern wind farm the first of many", *Philippine Daily Inquirer*, Manila, Philippines, 8 March 2007.

Remo, R. "ADB to fund renewable energy firms", *Philippine Daily Inquirer*, 14 March 2009.

Remo, A. R. "DOE expects 8 power plants to go on stream", *Philippine Daily Inquirer*, 2 June 2009, p. B1.

Romulo, B. "Stable power supply in the Visayas", *Manila Bulletin Online*.

CHAPTER 7

THE LIQUEFIED NATURAL GAS (LNG) BUSINESS: FROM EVOLUTION TO REVOLUTION

Steve Puckett and Tony Regan

ABSTRACT

This chapter charts the history of liquefied natural gas (LNG) from its earliest discovery and evolution over a period of 50 years, through to its current phase of revolution, which has major implications for the size and profile of the industry. It concludes with an outlook for the industry to 2020.

7.1 INTRODUCTION

Natural gas liquefaction dates back to the 19th century when British chemist and physicist Michael Faraday experimented with liquefying different types of gases, including natural gas.

German engineer Karl von Linde built the first practical compressor refrigeration machine in Munich in 1873. The first liquefied natural gas (LNG) plant was built in West Virginia in 1912 and began operation in 1917. The first commercial liquefaction plant was built in Cleveland, Ohio, in 1941. The LNG was stored in tanks at atmospheric pressure. The liquefaction of natural gas raised the possibility of its transportation to distant destinations. In January 1959, the world's first LNG tanker, The Methane Pioneer, a converted World War II liberty freighter containing five 7,000-barrel aluminum prismatic tanks with balsa wood supports and insulation of plywood and urethane, carried an LNG cargo from Lake Charles, Louisiana, to Canvey Island, United Kingdom. This event demonstrated that large quantities of LNG could be transported safely across the ocean.

Over the next 14 months, seven additional cargoes were delivered with only minor problems. Following the successful performance of The Methane Pioneer, the British Gas Council proceeded with plans to implement a commercial project to import LNG from Venezuela to Canvey Island. However, before the commercial agreements could be finalised, large quantities of natural gas were discovered in Libya and the gigantic Hassi R'Mel field in Algeria, which are only half the distance to England compared to Venezuela. With the start up of the 260-million-cubic-feet-per-day (MMcfd) Arzew GL4Z or Camel plant in 1964, the United Kingdom became the world's first LNG importer and Algeria the first LNG exporter. Algeria has since become a major world supplier of natural gas as LNG.

In 1970, the Marsa El Brega liquefaction plant came on stream in Libya and gradually other European countries and the US became LNG importers (Barcelona, Spain, in 1969; La Spezia, Italy, and Everett in the US in 1971; and Fos, France, in 1972).

7.2 EVOLUTION

The development of an LNG business in the Atlantic Basin was slow due to competition from cheaper US domestic and North Sea gas production and pipeline supply but the LNG business came of age with the development of an Asian market. Japan, with very little indigenous energy supply, was a major importer of oil and coal and was keen to gain access to natural gas. Tokyo Gas and Tokyo Electric opened the first Japanese LNG terminal at Negishi in 1969, followed by Osaka Gas's Senboku terminal in 1971. The first supply to Japan came from the Kenai plant in Alaska but an Asian LNG business was born when Brunei LNG brought on stream the first Asian LNG train in 1972.

Japan, Korea and Taiwan were all potentially large gas markets. Unlike Europe and the US they had no indigenous or piped supply and it was this factor that underpinned the rapid development of LNG in Asia. Indonesia brought on stream the Bontang LNG plant in 1977, followed by Malaysia LNG in 1983 and Australia's North West Shelf in 1989. The Bontang LNG facility was expanded to eight trains and, until the recent development of Qatar, was by far the largest LNG liquefaction plant in the world. Korea opened its first LNG terminal in 1986 and Taiwan in 1990, and when total sales of LNG hit 100 million tonnes in 2000, 73 percent was going into Asia (Figure 1).

Strong Asian demand and the potential of significant US demand led to another phase of LNG liquefaction development with Atlantic LNG in Trinidad and NLNG in Nigeria coming on stream in 1999, followed by Oman LNG in 2000.

Sales grew steadily but slowly, reaching 50 million tonnes in 1990 and 100 million tonnes in 2000. Gas price increases and technological

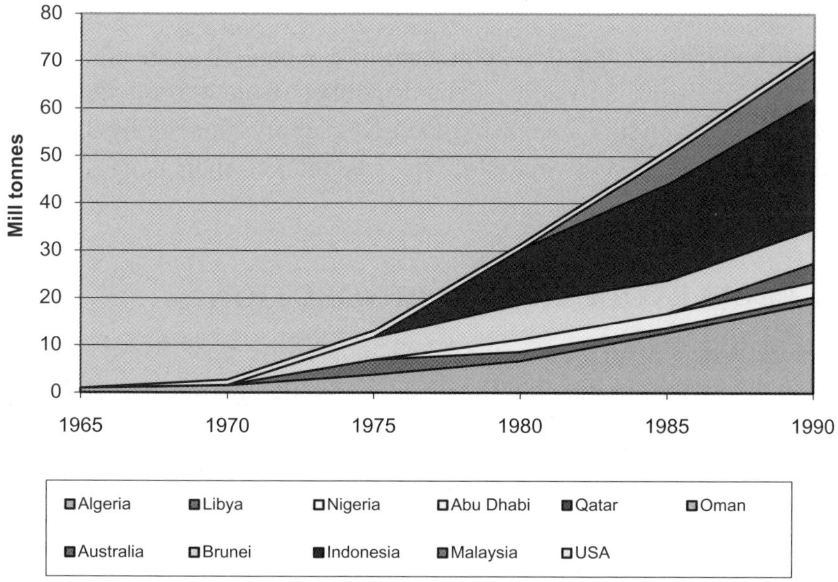

Figure 1 LNG Sales (Billion cubic metres) 1965–1990.

Source: Cedigaz.

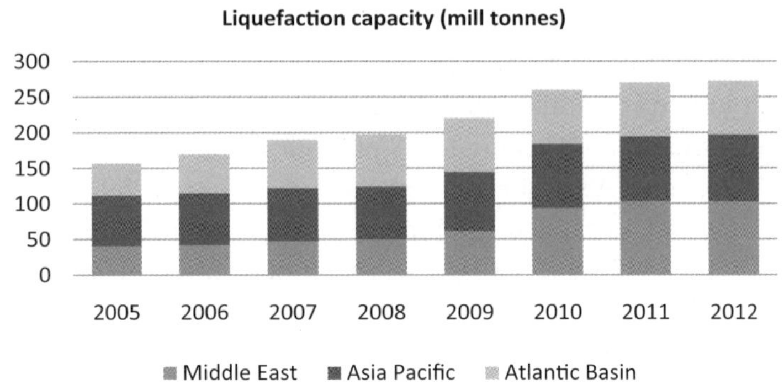

Figure 2 Global Liquefaction Capacity (Million Tonnes)

Source: Cedigaz.

advances that drove down liquefaction costs increased the attractiveness of LNG to gas producers but cross-border piped supply grew faster, reducing the call for LNG outside Asia. Thus, although LNG supply doubled between 1990 and 2000, the share of LNG in the total gas market remained very small, rising from 3.5 percent in 1990 to about 5.6 percent by 2000.

This suddenly changed in 2009 and 2010, when, 50 years after the first commercial cargo, an unprecedented number of new LNG liquefaction plants came on stream, increasing the LNG supply capacity by 32 percent and leading to LNG's share of the gas market increasing to almost 10 percent (Figure 2).

7.3 FROM EVOLUTION TO REVOLUTION

After 50 years of evolution the LNG industry is now going through a period of revolution which will substantially change the size and profile of the industry. Dramatic change is occurring.
LNG liquefaction:

- Liquefaction trains double in size — but mini trains also introduced
- Mega producers — Qatar and shortly Australia
- Floating LNG will speed up project implementation and enable the development of small gas fields

LNG receiving terminals:

- Re-gasification vessels radically speed up entry of new buyers
- Huge expansion of re-gasification capacity with new terminals in South America, Europe and the Middle East

Massive expansion of the LNG fleet:

- Vessels double in size — introduction of the Q-Max
- Surplus vessels — spurs conversion to storage or re-gasification

New entrants:

- 20 new players enter the business
- Multinationals make further major commitments to LNG

New gas supply:

- CBM/shale gas to LNG — from 0 to 40 million tonnes in five years!
- Very significant potential from unconventional gas

A look back at the LNG market of 2005 compared to the likely market of 2015 puts this revolution in perspective. In 2005 14 countries imported LNG, with just four really significant players. In 2010 21 countries were importing LNG and re-gasification capacity had almost doubled. With the industry focusing on supply, it is often not appreciated just how fast the customer base is growing and just how dramatic the changes that are underway. If current plans and ambitions are fulfilled, by 2015 40 countries, including Singapore, will be importing LNG and the LNG liquefaction capacity is expected to be about 360 million tonnes compared with 157 million tonnes in 2005 (Figures 3 and 4).

7.4 REVOLUTION: INTRODUCTION OF MERCHANT TRAINS

Traditionally the LNG business was integrated from wellhead to burner. A producer only committed to develop an LNG project if they had firm off-take commitments from buyers who simultaneously made commitments to build

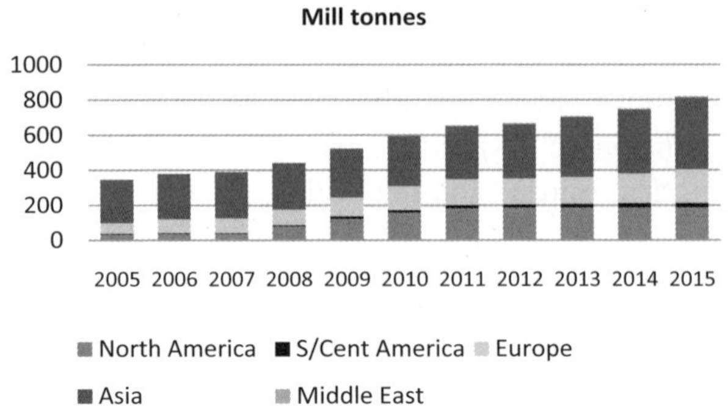

Figure 3 Global Re-gasification Capacity, 2015 vs. 2005.
Source: Cedigaz/Tri-Zen International.

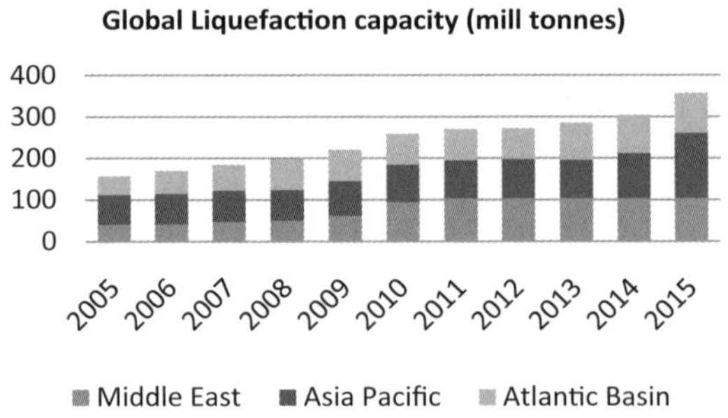

Figure 4 Global Liquefaction Capacity, 2015 vs. 2005.
Source: Cedigaz/Tri-Zen International.

the receiving facilities and entered into long-term sales contracts to supply the power, industrial or city gas markets. This changed in 2005 when Atlantic LNG in Trinidad and Egypt LNG brought on stream LNG trains without having off-take agreements and established the principle of "merchant" trains.

The first spot sales of LNG were made in 1993 but, as most production had been committed to term contracts, there were very few spot transactions until about 2000 when about 4 percent of LNG was traded on the spot market. Merchant trains created far more "liquidity" in the market; and led to a sharp increase in the number of spot transactions, taking the spot market from about 10 percent of LNG transactions in 2005 to 21 percent by 2010 (Figure 5).

In addition to stimulating an embryonic LNG spot market, it led to the globalisation of the trade, with LNG cargoes moving from Norway and

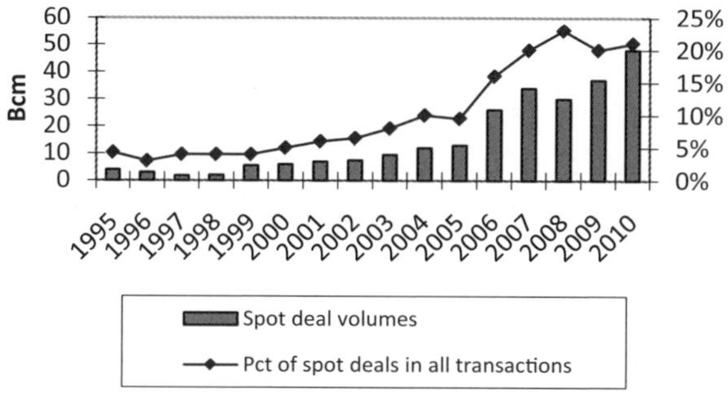

Figure 5 Percentage of Spot Transactions.

Source: Cedigaz.

Trinidad to Japan and from Sakhalin to the Middle East, and increased availability encouraged more buyers to enter the market. In 2011, 61 million tonnes of LNG was sold under spot or short term contracts, 26% of the market.

7.5 REVOLUTION: INTRODUCTION OF MEGA VESSELS

The first LNG vessels had carrying capacities of 50,000 to 70,000 m^3 and a typical modern LNG vessel has a carrying capacity of 135,000–140,000 m^3 and costs about US$200 million.

Nakilat (Qatar) has recently introduced vessels that are referred to as Q-Flex and Q-Max vessels and have capacities of between 209,000 and 266,000 m^3 (and cost US$250–285 million each). Nakilat did not exist in 2005 but they now own 54 LNG vessels, making it the largest LNG ship owner in the world.

7.6 REVOLUTION: HUGE EXPANSION OF LNG RE-GASIFICATION CAPACITY

Between 2005 and 2015 the LNG re-gasification capacity at import terminals is set to almost treble to 930 million tonnes. This is being driven by the following:

- US natural gas production was declining and on the assumption that additional demand would be primarily met by importing LNG, new import terminals were built and earlier ones expanded. Re-gasification capacity rose from 38 million tonnes in 2005 to reach 163 million tonnes in 2011, by which time it had become clear that very little LNG was going to be needed due to rising production of domestic shale gas. Only 3.5 million tonnes of LNG was imported in 2012, utilising less than 2.5 percent of terminal capacity.

- The UK has turned to LNG to replace declining North Sea production and two large terminals were commissioned in 2009 at Milford Haven. Phase 3 of the Grain LNG terminal expansion was completed in 2010 and there is now sufficient LNG re-gasification capacity to meet almost 50 percent of the UK's gas demand. Capacity has grown from three million tonnes in 2005 to 37 million tonnes in 2012.
- Concern about long-term gas supply security has led most European countries to consider an LNG option. Fifteen countries have built, or are planning to build, LNG terminals. The Rotterdam terminal in the Netherlands and the Nynashamn terminal in Sweden came on stream in 2011 and Poland, Croatia, Estonia and Lithuania, are all planning to start importing LNG within the next five years.
- The introduction of floating re-gasification vessels in 2007 has had a dramatic impact on the market by significantly reducing the time taken to build import capacity. Argentina, Brazil, Chile and Kuwait have all been able to bring on stream import capacity within about 18 months. Other Central and South American countries are considering LNG imports and this region has the potential to become a significant market (Figure 6).

7.7 THE GAME CHANGER: FLOATING RE-GASIFICATION VESSELS

Floating re-gasification terminals are either vessels (LNG carriers that have been converted by installing re-gasification equipment on the bow of the vessel) or purpose-built floating platforms such as Adriatic LNG, off Rovigo in Italy, that was commissioned in August 2009.

The attraction of floating re-gasification vessels is that they enable a speedy low-cost entry as they can be brought on stream in less than a year compared with 3–4 years for a conventional onshore terminal. They also

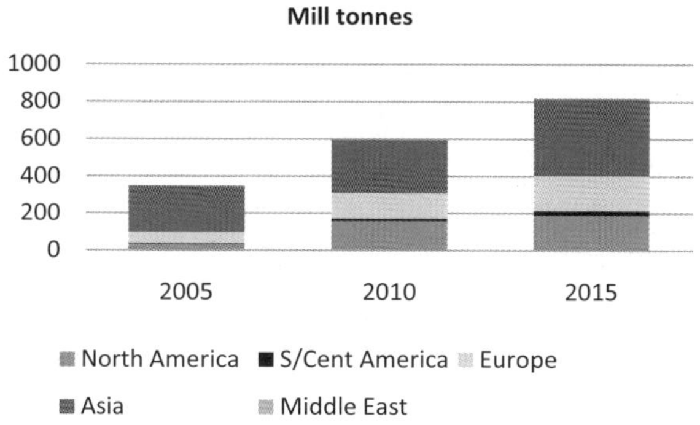

Figure 6 Revolution – Huge Expansion of Re-gasification Capacity
Source: Tri-Zen International.

enable LNG to reach smaller markets that may only need 0.5–1.0 million tonnes per annum and can be a "get you started" solution whilst a larger onshore terminal is being planned and built.

The main proponents of floating re-gasification vessels have been Excelerate Energy and Energy Golar LNG and Hoegh LNG. The first floating re-gasification terminal, Excelerate Energy's Gulf Gateway in the US, was commissioned in 2005 followed by Teesside GasPort in the UK in 2006. There are two main concepts: Excelerate Energy's "Energy Bridge" concept has re-gasification vessels discharging offshore via a submerged turret loading buoy, with the re-gasified LNG being dispatched onshore via submarine lines. The other concept has the vessels going to a port and either discharging over the berth directly into gas trunk lines or via another moored storage and re-gasification vessel.

During 2009, floating re-gasification vessels went into service in Brazil (Petrobras Pecam, January 2009; Petrobras Rio, March 2009), Kuwait (operates during the summer to support peak generating demand) and the US (Northeast Gateway, April 2009). Golar/Shell provided a floating re-gasification vessel in Dubai in 2010 and Malaysia and Indonesia became LNG importers in 2012 using floating storage and re-gasification units (FSRUs). There are now 13 floating terminals in operation and although the initial concept was based on the conversion of LNG carriers, 15 new build FSRUs have been ordered for delivery between 2013 and 2015 by Excelerate, Golar and Hoegh LNG and BW.

The fast pace of re-gasification terminal development is unprecedented in the 50 years of history of the industry. Having moved from only six significant LNG importing countries five years ago, the industry has gone global with South America and the Middle East joining the club and most Asian and European countries now seeking to import LNG.

Seventy percent of re-gasification capacity was in Asia in 2005; in 2010 it looked as if it could drop to less than 40 percent with the Atlantic Basin becoming the larger market by 2015. However, low domestic gas prices in Europe and greater use of coal in power generation has led to interest in LNG waning and several import terminal projects in Italy and Germany being cancelled. Europe switched from being the fastest growing LNG market in 2010 to the one with the largest decline in demand in 2012.

Potentially there could be 930 million tonnes of re-gasification capacity in operation by 2015, which is vastly more than the LNG supply capability.

Unfortunately for LNG liquefaction sponsors, re-gasification capacity does not correlate directly with LNG demand. For example, Japan imported 87 million tonnes of LNG in 2012 and has a re-gasification capacity of 220 million tonnes a year. However, the rapid expansion of re-gasification capacity gives a very clear indication of the significant potential LNG demand.

7.8 EVOLUTION TO REVOLUTION: LNG LIQUEFACTION CAPACITY

A steady focus on capturing economies of scale led to gradual increases in train size over the first 40 years of the LNG business. Typical LNG liquefaction train capacities were 1.3 million tonnes in early plants (Kenai) and then 2–3 million tons per year during the 1990s.

This suddenly changed and liquefaction train sizes doubled over the five years from 2004 to 2009. Five-million-tonne trains were introduced at Atlantic LNG (Trinidad) and SEGAS (Egypt) in 2005 and Qatar brought on stream six mega trains of 7.8 million tonnes per year in 2009/10.

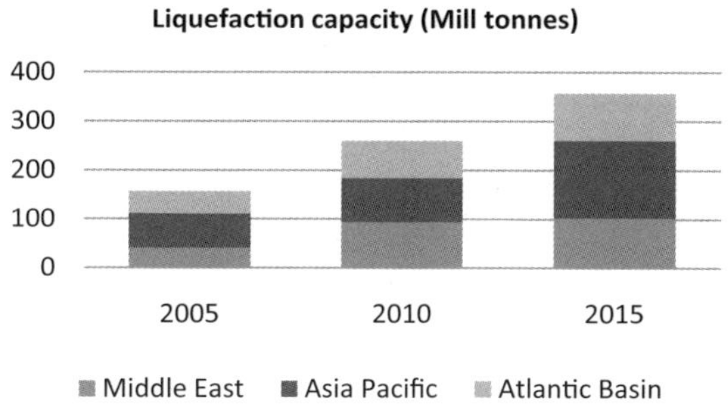

Figure 7 Huge Expansion of Liquefaction Capacity

Source: Tri-Zen International.

LNG liquefaction capacity grew gradually from less than 1 million tonnes in 1965 to 132 million tonnes in 2004 but then expanded by 100 million tonnes between 2005 and 2010 with new greenfield projects coming on stream in Australia (Darwin LNG), Russia (Sakhalin LNG), Indonesia (Tangguh LNG) and Yemen. Of particular significance was the expansion of Qatargas and RasGas in Qatar which lead to the country becoming the largest LNG supplier. In 2010 Qatar completed the construction of all its trains and now has 77 million tonnes of LNG liquefaction capacity making it the largest LNG exporter. (Figure 7).

An unprecedented 75 million tonnes of new liquefaction capacity came on stream in 2009/10, increasing global liquefaction capacity by 38 percent. Although this led to surplus capacity in 2010/2011, no new capacity came on stream in 2011 and there is now insufficient new capacity coming on stream. The final investment decisions (FIDs) for both PNG LNG in Papua New Guinea and Gorgon in Australia was made in 2009 and six more projects in Australia took FID between 2010 and 2012. In addition, Mitsubishi took FID on Donggi Senoro in Indonesia in 2011 and Cheniere Energy sanctioned the first four trains at Sabine Pass in 2012. These will increase LNG liquefaction capacity by about 30 percent and although this will mean LNG liquefaction capacity will have increased from 157 million tonnes in 2005 to 370 million tonnes in 2016 it is unlikely to be sufficient to meet all demand. (Table 1)

Table 1 Liquefaction Capacity Under Construction 2013

Project	Country	mtpa	Start Up	Operator
Skikda replacement	Algeria	4.5	2012	Sonatrach
Arzew	Algeria	4.7	2013	Sonatrach
PNG LNG	Papua New Guinea	6.3	2014	ExxonMobil
Qld Curtis	Australia	8.5	2014	BG
Donggi-Senoro	Indonesia	2	2014	Mitsubishi
Australia Pacific T1	Australia	4.5	2014	Origin/CP
Pacific Rubialas FLNG	Colombia	0.5	2014	Exmar
Gorgon T1	Australia	5	2015	Chevron
Gladstone LNG	Australia	7.8	2015	Santos
Gorgon T2	Australia	5	2015	Chevron
Sarawak FLNG	Malaysia	1.2	2015	Petronas
MLNG Train 9	Malaysia	3.6	2015	Petronas
Gorgon T3	Australia	5	2016	Chevron
Prelude	Australia	3.6	2016	Shell
Wheatstone	Australia	8.6	2016	Chevron
Ichthys	Australia	8.4	2016	INPEX
Australia Pacific T2	Australia	4.5	2016	Origin/CP
		83.7		

Source: Tri-Zen International Pte Ltd.

7.9 REVOLUTION: LNG LIQUEFACTION GAME CHANGERS

Just as re-gasification ships have changed the game with respect to LNG terminals there are also some "change the game" cards that are about to be played on the liquefaction side:

CBM to LNG:

- Coal bed methane (CBM) production in Queensland has increased rapidly over the past few years and as reserves are far in excess of Australian gas demand, a number of producers considered exporting CBM as LNG.

This attracted the interest of international LNG players and five CBM-to-LNG projects have been proposed based around the port of Gladstone. It is most unlikely that five separate projects will go ahead. Three are under construction and LNG Ltd hopes to reach FID on its Fisherman's Landing project in 2013. Shell/PetroChina are developing the fifth project, an eight million tonnes per annum plant (mtpa) and they also hope to take FID in 2013 for a 2018 start-up. By 2015, 25 mtpa of LNG could be exported from Gladstone from the first three projects.

CBM is also going into LNG in Indonesia. VICO (BP/ENI) is supplying CBM from the Sanga-Sanga block in East Kalimantan into the existing Bontang LNG plant.

Small CBM-to-LNG plants are already operating in China where they provide a way to quickly monetise early CBM production ahead of completion of pipelines to the local markets.

Shale gas to LNG:

- The U.S. Energy Information Administration projects U.S. natural gas production to increase from 23.0 trillion cubic feet (tcf) in 2011 to 33.1 tcf in 2040, a 44 percent increase. Almost all of this increase in domestic natural gas production is due to projected growth in shale gas production, which grows from 7.8 tcf in 2011 to 16.7 tcf in 2040.

  Canadian natural gas production is forecasted to decline — from 5.3 tcf a year in 2012 to 4.8 tcf/year in 2019 due to declining demand from the USA. However potential demand from LNG projects is leading to increased investment particularly in the shale gas reserves in the Montney Basin, Horn River and Laird Basin in British Colombia and Alberta. Five shale gas-to-LNG projects are under development on the British Colombia coast which could lead to the production of about 48 million tonnes of LNG by 2020.

  In the US, sixteen liquefaction projects have been proposed that could potentially produce 180 million tonnes of LNG from shale gas. Not all of these will go ahead.

  Australia has huge shale gas resources, development of which is just starting. Production could rapidly exceed Australian demand and therefore it is expected that some of this will be exported as LNG.

Floating LNG production:

- Floating re-gasification units were an industry game changer that enabled LNG buyers to install LNG receiving facilities at a fraction of the cost of building conventional onshore LNG terminals and to be operating in months rather than years. Floating liquefaction will be another game changer of potentially even greater impact. In May 2009 Shell took the Final Investment Decision on a huge FLNG facility to develop the Prelude field and has an agreement with Samsung to build a further nine. The massive structure weighing around 600,000 tonnes, roughly six times as much as the largest aircraft carrier, will be located over 450 km northwest of Broome, Western Australia to process gas initially from seven subsea wells in the Prelude field in the Browse Basin and, in a second phase, from the Concerto field. Later in the project life, gas is also expected to come from the Crux field.

  Shell's FLNG plant will produce about 3.6 million tonnes per annum of LNG. About 1.3 million tonnes of condensate and 400 million tonnes per annum of LPG will also be produced. The LNG will then be transferred to conventional LNG carriers for delivery to customers across Asia. Analysts estimate that the capital cost of Shell's Prelude FLNG facility will be just over US$6 billion or about US$1,700 per tonne of capacity. This compares favourably with conventional onshore projects and the sponsors of the smaller vessel based FLNG units are forecasting capital costs below US$1,000 per tonne of capacity for their units.

  FLNG will be an industry game changer. It will enable the development of stranded gas reserves and by locating the facilities above the field; it reduces cost by removing the need for gas compression stations; long subsea pipelines to shore; a jetty for loading vessels and onshore facilities including roads, storage yards and accommodation facilities.

  Floating LNG is now gaining traction with greater variation in scope than originally envisaged. Originally offshore, there is now growing interest in inshore and even berthed facilities and smaller units.

  Exmar recently announced a 0.5 mtpa Floating Liquefaction Re-gasification & Storage Unit (FLRSU) for Pacific Rubialas in

Colombia. This will be a static liquefaction unit, a floating storage vessel with 140,000 cubic metres of storage and a second vessel able to act as a floating re-gasification vessel delivering LNG to Caribbean markets. Start up is scheduled for Q4 2014 and this could be the first FLNG unit to go into commercial production.

Petronas has sanctioned its first FLNG unit that will be located 180 km off Bintulu in Sarawak. An EPCIC contract has been awarded to Technip and DSME for a 1.2 mtpa unit that is scheduled for start up in late 2015. Petronas is developing a second 1.5 mtpa FLNG unit for use off Sabah and this could be in operation by 2016.

The attraction of floating liquefaction plants is that they offer developers a lower-cost alternative for gas field development and faster monetisation of assets. They also enable the development of small stranded gas reserves that would otherwise be uneconomical to develop. There are circa 90 gas fields in the 1–3 Tcf range that are suitable for development by small LNG FPSOs and about 30 in the 3–10 Tcf range suitable for large-scale LNG FPSOs.

A particular issue with small-scale LNG FPSOs is the need to reduce the weight and footprint aboard ships. This requires some compromises and simpler liquefaction processes and leads to another significant differentiator between the classes — having to use simpler processes (single mixed refrigerant, dual expander processes) compared with the larger class which can use baseload-type liquefaction processes adapted for offshore applications (e.g. Shell or APCI's dual mixed refrigerant, a single mixed refrigerant or the mixed fluid cascade technology).

Three FLNG units are under construction and another six projects hope to take FID shortly. Potentially almost 20 million tonnes of LNG production could be coming from FLNG units by 2018. The total volume of firm, planned and proposed FLNG projects has now reached 36 million tonnes from 14 projects.

7.10 LNG LIQUEFACTION: THE GREAT LEAP FORWARD

Having factored in capacity currently under construction there will be about 370 million tonnes of LNG supply from 2016 compared with 273 million tonnes today. An unprecedented number of 47 projects are expecting to reach Final Investment Decision in the next couple of years. Many will not be sanctioned but if all were to go ahead they would add a further 390 million tonnes of liquefaction capacity by 2020. In addition, there are a considerable number less advanced or speculative proposals. If all the proposed projects were to go ahead liquefaction capacity would exceed 700 million tonnes. This won't happen, but potentially there could be 500 million tonnes of liquefaction capacity by 2020.

Australia has taken the great leap forward and North America is poised to follow.

Also unprecedented are the number of projects under construction in Australia and, if all are completed on schedule, Australia will overtake Qatar as the largest LNG producer in 2017. 60 million tonnes of new capacity is currently under construction. The list includes three projects that will utilise coal bed methane as the feedstock and Shell's first floating LNG vessel at Prelude (Figure 8).

In addition, Australian project sponsors are offering a further 50 million tonnes by the end of this decade but not all of the proposed projects will go ahead. A particular issue in 2012 has been the huge cost overruns of several of the projects under construction in Australia and Papua New Guinea, whilst considerable progress has been made in developing

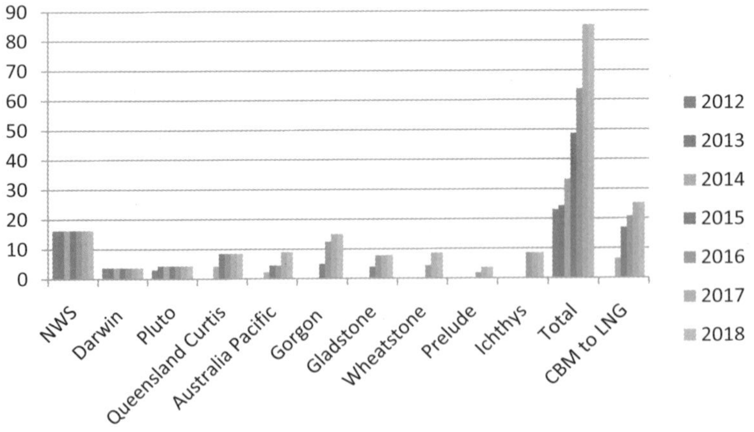

Figure 8 Australian LNG Liquefaction Capacity (mpta)

Source: Tri-zen International Pte Ltd

what are expected to be substantially cheaper major LNG projects in Canada and East Africa. This has drawn attention to the fact that Australia stands out as a particularly expensive location to build liquefaction plants and led to doubts about whether any of the proposed future LNG projects in Australia will go ahead.

When several of the projects listed above took FID in 2010/11 they were almost the "only show in town" as the recession had lead to sponsors of other projects putting the brake on sanctioning projects. Since that time the world has changed dramatically with a flood of new offerings from the USA, Canada and East Africa.

New LNG capacity is also under construction in Malaysia, Indonesia and Papua New Guinea and brownfield expansion is being considered in Brunei, Indonesia and Russia (Sakhalin). Two major new LNG sources, Canada and East Africa, could also be supplying Asia Pacific demand before the end of the decade.

The LNG world needed Australian supply in 2010–11 but looking further out, buyers have vastly more choice and it looks increasingly difficult to make the case for a second phase in Australia.

Bonaparte LNG will be FLNG, so will be lower cost than conventional onshore projects, and Gorgon Train 4 and Wheatstone Train 3 will be Brownfield expansion projects, so these may go ahead. However Browse and Shell/PetroChina's Arrow LNG project looks particularly vulnerable unless they can find a way to substantially reduce cost. Potentially this could be done by turning Browse into an FLNG project and for Shell/PetroChina to seek hospitality from one of the three projects under construction at Curtis Island rather than building a separate green-field plant at the same location.

Can North America make a great leap?

Of particular significance are developments in North America. Low gas prices and the availability of a large number of underutilised LNG receiving terminals have triggered an interest in building liquefaction capacity. Not all of these will go ahead but already three Canadian projects have received export licences and hope to move to Final Investment Decision this year. In the USA, Cheniere has received permission to export to non-FTA countries and has taken FID on the first phase (two trains) of its Sabine Pass liquefaction project.

The sheer scale of what is proposed is unprecedented with about 260 mtpa of new capacity being proposed from North America. This is greater than current global LNG production.

In Canada, declining natural gas exports to the USA are driving gas producers to seek new markets. Six export projects have been announced all of which are in British Colombia; except for one proposed in Nova Scotia, utilising US shale gas. The BC projects will be targeting the premium price North East Asia LNG market.

The projects have been particularly successful in attracting the leading LNG players/buyers as investors and are located reasonably close to some of Canada's prime shale gas resources in the Montney Basin and Horn River.

Potentially Canada could be exporting about 40 mtpa of LNG by 2020 for an expenditure of about $100 billion (liquefaction, pipelines and upstream CAPEX).

The total volume of proposed US LNG projects has now reached 210 million tonnes. The submission of a report to the US DoE by NERA forecasting, that LNG exports would not have a significant impact on domestic gas prices, has raised expectations that the DoE will shortly start issuing licences to export LNG to non FTA countries, clearing the way to rapid development of the proposed projects.

However, the focus on export applications and the comparison of US costs with those of the Australian projects has led to unrealistic expectations regarding the potential for US LNG exports. To be viable, a project needs far more than an export licence, in particular it needs customers. So far, there is buyer interest in less than 20 percent of the proposed capacity and only one project has been sanctioned. Many of the projects will not go ahead but the USA could be exporting about 40 million tonnes of LNG 2020.

7.11 REVOLUTION: THE INDUSTRY PLAYERS

In 2005 there were 17 liquefaction projects, 39 players and a global capacity of 157 million tonnes. The market was dominated by national oil companies and multinational companies such as Shell and ExxonMobil. By 2015 there are expected to be 40 liquefaction projects with a global capacity of 360 million tonnes, including 42 million tonnes from unconventional gas. The number of companies with investments in LNG will have increased substantially to 64 participants.

Although the market will still be dominated by national oil companies with Qatar Petroleum at the top of the list, some of the NOCs have dropped down in the ranking in the face of strong growth by the multinational oil companies (NOCs). Shell is the dominant multinational with about 8.5 percent of global LNG capacity (39 operating trains) and

Table 2 Liquefaction Capacity by Equity Share — Top 20 Players

Million tonnes	**2005**		**2015**
Sonatrach	20.30	Qatar Petroleum	50.96
Petronas	18.83	Shell	29.05
Qatar Petroleum	16.21	Sonatrach	28.80
Pertamina	15.46	Petronas	27.86
Shell	10.78	Chevron	23.55
BP	8.71	ExxonMobil	21.43
ExxonMobil	6.98	Cheniere	18.00
BG	5.62	BG	16.32
ENI	5.21	Total	16.18
Total	5.17	NNPC	14.29
Oman Govt	5.07	BP	12.49
Mitsubishi	5.00	ConocoPhillips	7.51
NNPC	4.66	Mitsubishi	7.51
JILCO	4.22	Woodside	6.55
ADNOC	3.99	ENI	6.43
Brunei Govt	3.60	Inpex	6.37
Mitsui	2.65	Pertamina	6.08
Repsol	2.29	Oman Govt	5.10
Union Fernosa	2.23	Gazprom	4.80
Woodside	1.98	Mitsui	4.52
	148.96		**313.80**

Source: Tri-zen International Pte Ltd.

both Chevron and ConocoPhillips have entered the top 20, with Chevron becoming the sixth-largest producer when it brings Gorgon and Wheatstone on line (Table 2).

7.12 OUTLOOK

The pace of change and development in the LNG industry is unprecedented compared with the first 40 years and there is every likelihood that the business in 2020 will look considerably different from that foreseen in current forecasts. It is unlikely that all of the currently proposed LNG liquefaction plants will go ahead and that those that do go ahead will start up as currently scheduled.

The customer base is substantially larger than just a couple of years ago and therefore future growth will be built on a much larger base. LNG is moving away from being a modest contributor to total gas supply and by 2015 might represent about 15 percent of global gas supply.

Although global LNG consumption fell slightly in 2012 compared with 2011 we forecast that demand will double between 2010 and 2020 and reach 450 million tonnes.

Asian LNG consumption is growing strongly and almost every country in Asia is becoming an LNG importer. We forecast that Asian LNG consumption will double by 2020 reaching 310 million tonnes, substantially more than current LNG production capability. Actual consumption will depend on the speed of infrastructure development and progress towards market pricing of gas.

South East Asia is emerging as a significant new market. PTT opened the 5 mtpa Map Ta Phut LNG terminal at Rayong in Thailand in 2011 and forecasts demand of 20 million tonnes by 2020. Indonesia became an importer in May 2012 when Nusantara Regas (an FSRU) came on stream in West Java. Pertamina is converting the Arun liquefaction plant to a receiving terminal and a second FSRU is scheduled to start up Lampung in South Sumatra in 2014, under a contract between Hoegh LNG and PGN.

Petronas will shortly commence commercial operations of its first import terminal at Malacca and is proposing to build one with a capacity of 3.8 mtpa at Pengerang in Johor. Vopak and the Dialog Group are also proposing to build a terminal at Pengerang. This will be smaller at 0.7 mtpa and both terminals hope to be completed by 2016. Petronas has also proposed import terminals at Lahad Datu, Sabah and Lumat.

The 3.5 million tonne capacity Singapore LNG terminal on Jurong Island is scheduled to come on stream in 2013. When a third tank is completed in 2014, capacity will increase to 6 mtpa and then 9 mtpa in 2017 when a fourth tank is completed.

Vietnam and the Philippines also have plans to import LNG and by 2015 South East Asia could be importing as much as 20 million tonnes of LNG.

Demand is also growing in South America and the Middle East but there is considerable uncertainty about European demand. Natural gas demand fell in 2011 and 2012 and the IEA forecast that European demand will remain below 2010 levels until 2017. There is potential for faster growth in Europe but this looks unlikely whilst coal prices remain much lower than natural gas. Generators have been attracted to cheaper coal, and imports have increased considerably from the US, Colombia and South Africa. LNG imports fell in 2012 to 52 million tonnes compared with 67 million tonnes in 2011, with the biggest drop in the UK where imports fell by 44 percent. Sweden opened its first terminal in 2011 and the Gate terminal in Rotterdam came on stream in 2012. Poland's first import terminal is scheduled to be completed in 2014 and Croatia, Cyprus, Estonia, Lithuania and the Ukraine all have plans for import terminals. Potentially Europe could be importing 90 million tonnes of LNG by 2020 but there is probably a plus/minus 25 percent sensitivity around this number particularly whilst the energy policy of the European Community remains uncertain.

Potentially global demand could be considerably higher than the 450 million tonnes that we are forecasting for 2020. Rising gas prices have obscured the fact that both gas and LNG are very competitive when compared with competing petroleum fuels. Term LNG contract prices in Asia tend to be linked to the Japanese Crude Cocktail or Brent and the formula used guarantees that LNG will be priced slightly lower than crude and considerably lower than petroleum products. LNG is cheaper than fuel oil and products such as diesel and LPG can be about 60 percent more expensive than the landed cost of LNG. This point is just beginning to be appreciated by industry and the transportation fuel sector.

America's Natural Gas Highway® (ANGH), a network of liquefied natural gas truck fuelling stations to support long-haul trucking along major interstate corridors throughout the United States is going into place. Clean Energy Fuels has completed 70 new LNG truck fuel stations and plans to build a further 70 to 80 LNG fuel stations adjacent to long-haul trucking routes and around major warehouse distribution centres in North America. Shell has agreed with Travel Centres of America, the largest full service truck stop operator in the US, to install more than 200 LNG fuel lanes at about 100 Travel Centre sites and Petro Stopping Centers throughout the US interstate highway system.

In Canada, Shell is working on the Green Corridor project with Flying J Inc. to supply 250,000 tons of LNG a year to trucks along the 1,600 kilometre highway from Alberta to the Pacific coast in Canada. However this is dwarfed by China where by 2015 the number of LNG filling stations is expected to reach 3,000 and 220,000 heavy trucks are expected to be LNG fuelled. Australia is also starting to show interest and we may now be seeing the emergence of a significant new market for LNG as a truck and marine fuel.

LNG is being introduced as a marine fuel across northern Europe and we expect to see a significant increase in demand for LNG after Europe and North America phase out fuel oil from their bunker markets in 2015 and ship owners are faced with a choice of LNG, or much more expensive diesel.

Whilst the number of LNG liquefaction projects under construction and expecting to be sanctioned in the next couple of years looks impressive, we anticipate that it will be insufficient and there will still be unmet demand in 2020.

We expect Australia to bring on 60 million tonnes of new capacity by 2018, the US and Canada about 40 million tonnes each by 2020, and East Africa about 20 million tonnes. East Africa is emerging as a major new gas source. Reserves in Mozambique and Tanzania already exceed 100 tcf and potentially these two countries could support LNG exports of 50–60 million tonnes per annum in the longer term.

An additional 160 million tonnes by 2020 is not enough and therefore there remains a considerable incentive to bring on LNG from projects proposed in other countries such as Brunei, Indonesia, Nigeria and Russia.

7.12.1 What about China and India?

Both countries imported about 14 million tonnes of LNG in 2012. Chinese LNG demand is increasing only slowly due to low domestic gas prices. Domestic natural gas and LNG production is rising, imports from Central Asia will exceed LNG imports in 2012 and China is about to start importing gas from Myanmar. Synthetic gas production from coal is forecast to reach 80 Bcm by 2020 and production of coal bed methane and shale gas could be significant by 2020. China has a wide choice of gas sources and is not going to be as dependent on LNG as Japan, Korea and shortly, India. Despite this we anticipate that China will be importing 45 to 50 million tonnes per annum by 2020. China's gas market has huge potential for further growth so there is further upside to these figures.

There is far greater uncertainty about Indian demand due to policy uncertainties and far greater price sensitivity than China. Despite that, gas demand is expected to continue to grow at about 4.5 percent per annum. Distribution infrastructure has improved significantly over the last few years and a number of new LNG terminals are under development. However, perhaps the main driver behind increased LNG imports has been the unexpected decline of domestic gas production since 2010. It is hoped that domestic production could recover post 2015 but LNG imports are expected to increase from 14 million tonnes in 2012 to reach 25 million tonnes in 2020. Potentially they could reach as much as 40 million tonnes but this depends on a significant degree of price liberalisation and regulators accepting the principal of market pricing.

7.13 CONCLUSION

Thus whilst in the early days it was demand from Japan and Korea that underpinned the early development of the LNG industry it will be China and India that support "the great leap forward" and the huge expansion in supply proposed for 2015–2020.

Asia Pacific is regarded as the cradle of the LNG industry and although we now have three production zones (Asia Pacific, Middle East and Atlantic Basin) the pendulum will swing very much back to Asia Pacific with about 50 percent of global liquefaction capacity and about 60 percent of demand being in the Asia Pacific by 2017.

CHAPTER 8

DEVELOPING RENEWABLE ENERGY AND CARBON ABATEMENT PROJECTS IN ASIA

William I. Y. Byun

ABSTRACT

For a range of differing policy reasons from energy security to industrial development, national goals in various Asian countries now emphasise developing renewable energy power generation. However, the form of the renewable energy projects being developed, such as wind or biomass, reflects the specific characteristics of the national policies which favour certain forms over others. Also, there are practical challenges in developing renewable energy projects due to their specific geographic and size profiles, in particular due to the smaller nature of each individual project. As a result, renewable power development tends to be very local in outlook and the more successful programmes have tended to reflect local climate as well. Finally, the current development of renewable energy projects is now seen as intimately tied to the global markets for carbon offsets and the additional revenue streams from such offsets. Looking ahead, the direction of such carbon markets in turn influences the future direction and nature of the implementation of renewable energy projects in Asia. The picture then becomes much more fragmented and again tied to individual countries' policy frameworks rather than to broad market-based drivers or global carbon initiatives.

8.1 OVERVIEW OF RENEWABLE ENERGY

Renewable energy is now often in the news and, despite the current global economic downturn, has been recession-resistant, with governments across the region and globally using the renewable energy sector as one of the main fiscal drivers for economic pump-priming. In addition to these various national recession-specific stimulus packages for renewables, across Asia, for differing policy reasons, national goals in various Asian countries have emphasised developing renewable energy power generation, be it in financing for wind farms, subsidies for solar energy plants, or incentives for promoting various upstream "clean" technologies.

Renewable energy is simply defined as energy generated from resources that are naturally replenished. Within renewable energy, the sources can be further divided into the conventional renewables which have traditionally been utilised, such as hydroelectric, biomass, and geothermal, and the new cleantech sources, such as solar, wind, and ocean/wave. Other individual renewable segments include waste-to energy (municipal solid waste incineration) and recovered gas from landfills or coalmines.

However, the form of the renewable energy projects being developed, such as wind or biomass, depends significantly in turn on the specific characteristics of the national policies which favour certain forms over others. Rather than following global trends, each national policy is inextricably tied into and organically derived from the specific characteristics of each nation's economic characteristics rather than from its inherent suitability for different renewable fuels. Therefore, solar energy promotion is a policy priority in relatively sunless Korea as opposed to biomass, while the opposite holds true in Thailand.

Also, because there is the very practical challenge of developing renewable energy projects due to their specific geographic tie-in and small size, a necessary adjunct to the way such renewable energy project developments are being pursued is that they are now inextricably tied into the global markets for carbon offsets and the additional revenue streams from such offsets.

Looking ahead, the direction of such carbon markets in turn influences the future direction and nature of the implementation of renewable energy projects in Asia. The picture then becomes much more fragmented and the various uncertainties in such global carbon frameworks mean that renewable energy projects are again being primarily driven by each individual country's policy frameworks rather than broad market-based drivers or global carbon initiatives.

8.1.1 The Challenges of Renewables

Renewable energy development is fundamentally different from that of other electricity generation fuel sources. While its market behaves differently from the other fuel sources, the initial, visibly stark distinction is due to its very different size profile. The overwhelming majority of global electric power generation is provided by the fossil fuels of coal, oil, and gas. As a rule of thumb, 1 megawatt (MW) of power supplies electricity to about 10,000 homes. Coal plants typically produce around 1,000 MW and China adds about 50,000 MW of capacity every year. Taken together, that points to a heavy dependence on coal for power generation, particularly in non–Organisation for Economic Co-operation and Development (OECD) Asia where coal is cheap, high in calorific value (energy), and plentiful.

As shown in Figure 1, the actual implementation of renewable energy is a tiny fragment compared to the political and media hype. At present, only 8 percent of global energy comes from renewable sources.

Even within the overall category of renewable energy, a closer look reveals that despite the disproportionate visual emphasis on wind turbines, solar farms, and other aesthetically politically correct imagery in the media, the bulk of renewables is comprised of hydro and biomass which, by definition, encompass the masses of "backward" burning of traditional biowastes and small dams or water mills.

Then, looking beyond the media glamour and high-tech imagery and marketing terms such as "cleantech", etc., renewable energy as a sector for electric power generation is still fairly embryonic (Figure 2).

Worse still, renewable energy in comparison to fossil fuels is generally not cost competitive and, without a specific policy subsidy for the feed-in tariff, is not a financially viable investment alternative. Whereas coal-fired power plants can generally achieve break-even at a tariff revenue of about 3–4 US cents/kilowatt hour (cents/kWh), biomass would usually require about 6–8 cents/kWh to break even, with wind higher and solar significantly higher. These numbers deceptively narrow the gap

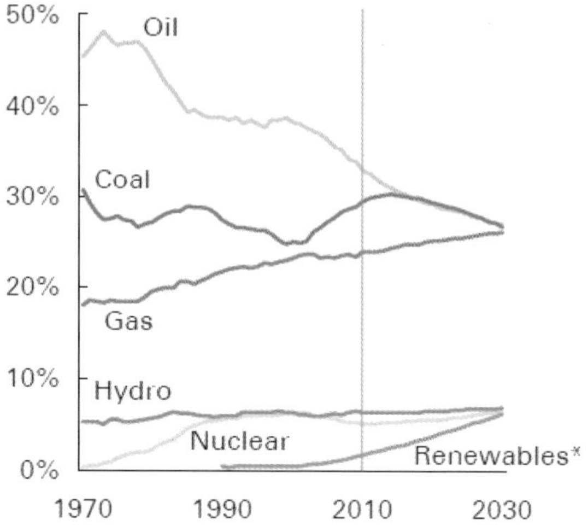

Figure 1 Shares of World's Primary Energy Supplies
Source: BP Energy Outlook 2030.

further in that in terms of overall capital expenditure (CAPEX), the economies of scale from a 1,000 MW coal plant are not possible for renewables projects which tend to be much smaller. While costs are coming down for technologies such as solar or wind, without a specific policy tariff accumulator to the purchase price of electricity generated, renewables-fueled electric power plants currently are not financially viable. This is especially significant in the current global economic downturn where government budgets are strained by financing the necessary fiscal stimulus and additional spending for such feeder tariffs may seem a luxury.

However, coal production and utilisation is increasingly difficult, due to both domestic political and social opposition and global criticism from anti-pollution and anti–global warming activists. Following places such as California where there has not been a new fossil baseload power plant in over 20 years due to social resistance, increasingly, it is becoming practically impossible to obtain local licensing for large coal baseload plants in places such as Korea and Thailand where the environmental non-governmental organisation (NGO) movements are taking hold, and even more so in China.

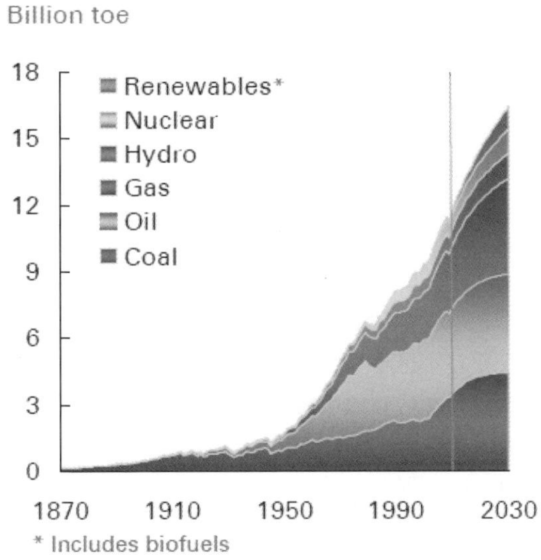

Figure 2 World Commercial Energy Use

Source: BP Energy Outlook 2030.

Gas and oil usage is equally challenging for most Asian countries due to their energy security issues, since access to such fuels is often by import from distant, possibly unreliable sources or due to other policy needs and uses. Because each country faces different fuel security profiles and different economic profiles, their approaches to policies for renewable energy incentives also differ. We now look at three different renewables markets in Asia for a comparative overview.

8.1.2 Overview of Energy in Asia: Selected Country Case Studies

In reviewing the renewable energy landscape in Asia, it may be helpful to take a couple of countries as illustrative examples of how their policy formulations reflect specific local issues and concerns as opposed to broader global trends. Here, Indonesia, Thailand, and Korea are compared.

Examining population compared to installed electricity capacity in many of these countries highlights the oftentimes limited availability of energy in Asia. It is also a strong indicator of the quality of life and the development economics of the country. Specifically, Indonesia has a population of 245 million people — four times that of Thailand's 65 million people — yet it has about 17 percent less installed electricity capacity (25 gigawatts (GW) versus 30 GW). This highlights both the less developed economic status of Indonesia and also what may be a key inhibitor to such development due to the distinct electricity supply shortages that currently exist in Indonesia.

Indonesia has rather diversified potential energy sources because it is very rich in natural resources. Although it is now a net oil importer, it was historically an OPEC country due to the volume of oil produced. In a pure assessment, the proportion of renewables seems comparatively large in the electricity generation fuel mix, occupying 13.8 percent of the fuel mix. However, this outlook is also somewhat distorted due to several large hydroelectric power plants on the remote island of Papua (Figure 3).

Thailand is heavily reliant on gas as an energy source (due to the availability of offshore sources in the Gulf of Thailand) and because of this imbalance in its energy portfolio, the government has been driving investment into and drafting policies to encourage alternative energy sources (Figure 4).

Korea (reflecting its relatively developed status as an OECD country — although it is not classified as a developed country for the purposes of the Kyoto Protocol) has 25 percent less people than Thailand (49 million compared to 65 million) yet twice the installed capacity. Korea has over

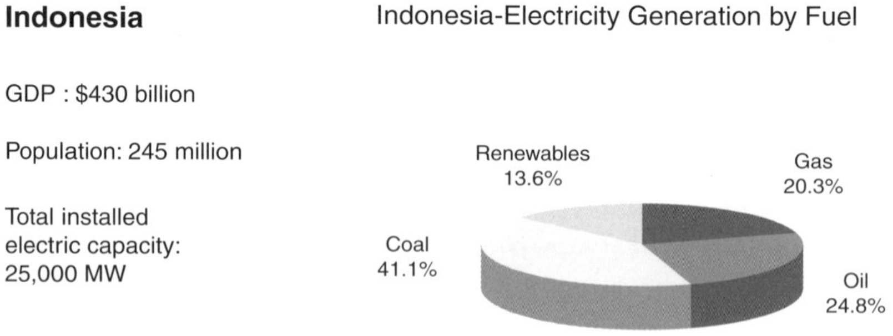

Figure 3 Indonesia: Electricity Generation by Fuel

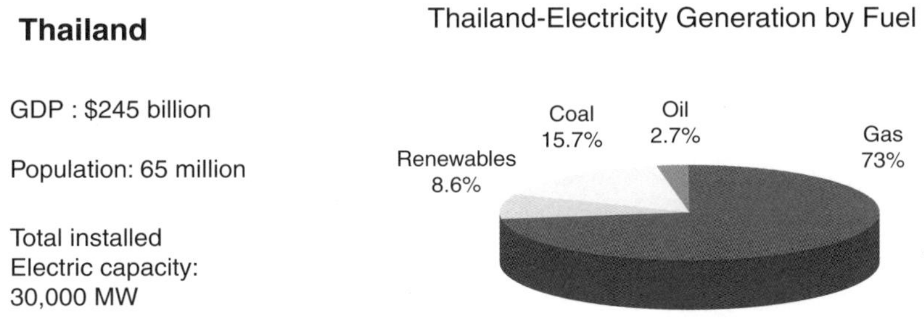

Figure 4 Thailand: Electricity Generation by Fuel

66 GW installed whereas Thailand only has 30 GW. However, Korea lacks its own energy sources — it is the fifth-largest importer of oil and the second-largest importer of liquefied natural gas (LNG), behind Japan in the Asia-Pacific region.

Hence, the government has invested heavily in securing their energy supply, oftentimes sending companies overseas to gain control of different energy commodities. Another result of the limited domestic energy sources has been a funneling of investments into building nuclear power plants. The chart in Figure 5 for Korea is distorted by the inclusion of nuclear into the renewables sector as nuclear accounts for 97 percent of all installed renewable energy capacity.

Looking deeper into each country's profile, the direction of their renewable energy policy then becomes clearer as a reflection of the local economic profile.

8.1.2.1 *Renewable Energy Development in Indonesia*

Indonesia's geography creates certain challenges to central electrification — the country is composed of hundreds of thousands of tiny islands, with roughly half of the national population living on the main island of Java. This has led to a concentration on increasing supply on the Java-Bali grid, which makes up 77 percent of the installed national electricity capacity (Table 1).

Indonesia has an installed electric capacity of 25 GW, with renewable energy making up only 2.7 GW of that pie. The actual renewable energy potential has been measured at over 140 GW.

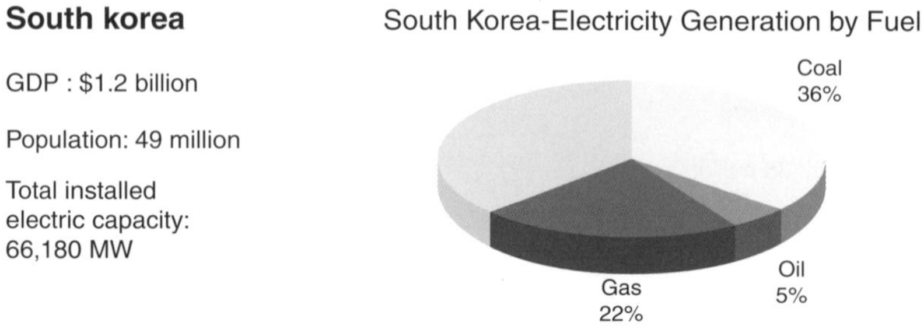

Figure 5 South Korea: Electricity Generation by Fuel

Source: Asia Renewables.

Table 1 Composition of Power Capacity on Major Islands in Indonesia (MW)

Composition of power capacity on major islands (MW)				
	Outer Islands	%	Java-Bali grid	%
Renewables	644	11	2751	14
Non-renewables	2617	46	16626	85
Diesel	2441	43	109	1

Source: Asia Renewables.

Indonesia has passed some legislation to support renewable energy development, including legislation which in theory has PT PLN (Persero), the national utility company, entering into power purchase agreements with renewables producers at a premium. The following laws provide such a framework:

1. Ministerial Decree No. 1122/2002 outlined new Power Purchasing agreements.
2. Law No. 27/2003 allows for private sector development of geothermal energy projects.
3. Regulation No. 3/2005 allows for private sector partnerships with PLN.
4. Ministerial Decree No. 002/2006 defines pricing for renewable energy Independent Power Providers (IPPs).

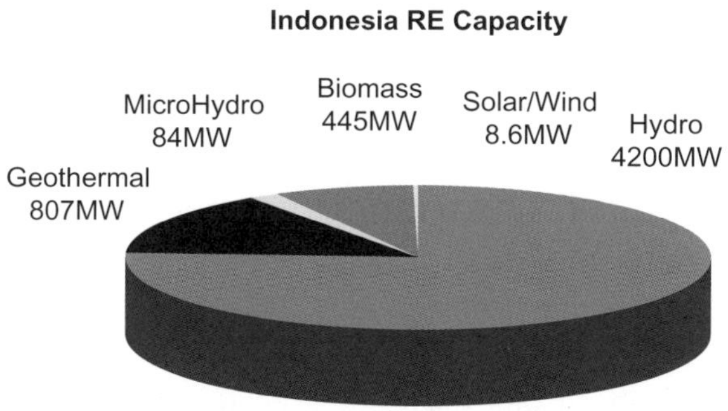

Figure 6 Indonesia's Renewable Energy Capacity

The initiatives in 2005 and 2006 sought to allow private players to develop smaller-scale projects (under 10 MW) quickly by providing for a "short-form" Power Purchase Agreement (PPA) template, faster approval time, and a PLN obligation to purchase. The PPAs are to have an extendable 10-year contract for projects under 10 MW with a guaranteed electricity off-take. Such laws were exactly what the market needed to help the development of renewables in Indonesia where much of the demand is spread across a vast geography and dovetails well with having many small plants to serve the distributed island populations (Figure 6).

However, at the same time, these new investment laws also managed to effectively stall any actual implementation of the law by prohibiting foreigners from taking an equity stake in any projects smaller than 10 MW. Such a prohibition not only directly limits foreign investment equity from going into a sector in need of such funds, but also casts a chilling pall over any foreign financing for such projects. Since financing often requires recourse against a project's equity, by closing such an option, debt financing is also affected. Especially in an environment where such projects are already challenging due to their small size and country risk, such new uncertainty adds another factor to encourage investors and financiers to invest elsewhere. Presently, while such a prohibition is under review, the uncertainty of such a review and timeframe has, in effect, stalled all such small-scale power projects in Indonesia.

Already, the exacerbations from government legislation have meant that the scoreboard for new electricity generation (Greenfield IPPs) in

Indonesia — for all power, not just for renewables — has been zero since 1997. Given that neither economic growth nor population growth had been at a standstill since 1997, such a lack of new capacity classically illustrates how economic growth is hobbled by a lack of sufficient infrastructure capacity, resulting in breakdowns and severe strains in supply.

Because of the huge shortfalls in capacity, the national government and PLN have been focusing their attention and resources on bolstering the main demand located on Java Island at the expense of the demand from the thousands of other islands with their scattered populations. To compound the frustration of logic, it is exactly in those scattered "outer islands" that there is significant untapped renewable energy potential that could be developed to satisfy just such unmet demand (Figure 6).

8.1.2.2 *Renewable Energy Development in Thailand*

Thailand is perceived in the markets as having the most comprehensive and investor-friendly renewable energy framework in Southeast Asia and has been the most successful in utilising policy instruments to incentivise private investment to implement projects. There are set PPAs for small-scale (less than 10 MW) plants and 5–25-year PPAs for projects between 10 MW and 80–90 MW. There are also Board of Investment (BOI) incentives such as temporary income tax exemption to ease cost of capital, subsidies to cover capital costs, and clear, high attractive tariffs under the Governments subsidized feed-in tariffs under their VSPP and SPP programs. Based on these factors, renewable energy projects have taken off in Thailand more than in any other Southeast Asian country.

Overall, Thailand has a 97 percent electrification rate, no acute shortage of energy, and a good grid network for transmission and distribution. However, there are also implementation difficulties. Specifically, the sale of energy is to the provincial authorities and not the national authority, which creates pricing and deal execution issues as there is no standardised process. This form of PPA is also not flexible for deal specifics, which rules out more creative deal structuring. Lastly, tariff resets add risk because they increase the risk and unpredictability of revenue.

However, the overall market perception is that the existence of such specific issues itself reflects the level of specificity in the legislative framework and is a challenge to the project itself rather than a structural roadblock. Finally, too, the sale being to the provincial authority, the Provincial Electricity Authority (PEA), rather than to the national utility, the Electricity Generating Authority of Thailand (EGAT), actually helps renewables projects in that it keeps the oversight and management of renewables at the provincial level where the demand for such small-scale electricity and other stakeholders such as biomass providers are centred, rather than at the "distant" national utility level where the focus and attention may be on huge 1,000+ MW plants rather than the 10 MW plants.

8.1.2.3 *Renewable Energy Development in Korea*

As an OECD country, South Korea is at a higher level of economic development, but also shares with other Asian countries the policy emphasis on renewable energy. Korea is an extreme example of the pressure for renewable energy due to the almost complete lack of domestic fuel sources for power.

South Korea has the highest installed capacity at 66.18 GW, with renewables only making up 1.32 GW (solar, wind, mini-hydro, biomass/biogas), excluding nuclear. Due to the lack of natural resources, the government has been very proactive in building nuclear power plants and nuclear capacity is estimated to be around 22 GW or one third of total installed capacity, with many more plants planned in the next five years. South Korea's renewable energy potential is estimated to be 80 GW (Figure 7).

Unlike Indonesia, given its compact size and homogeneous infrastructure, South Korea's national government targets are easily implemented. Unlike Thailand, its government has one of the largest current account surpluses in the world and therefore has a tremendous amount of room to deploy financial support and incentives.

Korea currently has a renewable energy target of 5 percent by 2011 (currently 2.5 percent) and the government has proactively passed legislation and provided funding to support the achievement of this goal. Specifically, the government manages a Carbon Fund and Credit Fund that develops renewable energy projects and buys and sells those credits on the secondary market, respectively. The funds invest in renewable energy projects in the region in addition to domestic markets. Other legislation support includes differentiated feed in tariffs, with solar being the

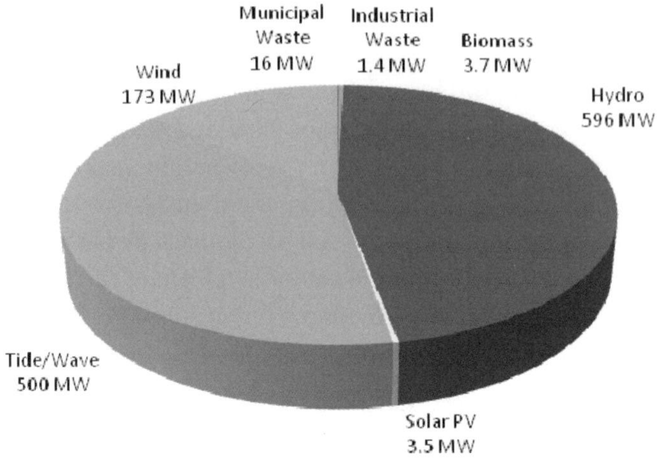

Figure 7 South Korea's Renewable Energy Mix

Source: South Korea's Renewable Energy Mix

highest at 0.70 cents/kWh, subsidies and tax incentives (which are up to 100 percent of costs for solar thermal/photovoltaics (PV)), and other national initiatives such as the Renewable Portfolio Standards and Voluntary Agreements. Current PPAs guarantee fixed rates for five years for small hydro and biomass/waste projects and for 15 years for solar PV and wind projects (Figure 7).

The implementation difficulties in Korea have reflected those overall for investments into Korea, namely technical specifics such as a cap on distributed feed-in tariffs (250 MW for wind and 20 MW for solar projects) and a lack of resources and land to build renewable energy projects. There has been progress on the second challenge that includes ongoing feasibility research with regard to the tidal and wind resources along the coast.

Despite these implementation difficulties, the programmes implemented thus far have had some results and, moving forward, there are also opportunities for private investors in the green tech sector. The government has declared that it wants to position itself as a green tech manufacturing export leader in Asia and has announced that it wants to invest 107 trillion Korean won (KRW), $85.77 billion or 2 percent of the annual GDP, in green sectors. With regard to results, the differentiated feed-in tariffs that were implemented in 2002 have led to the installation of 110 MW from over 40 power plants. The government has paid out KRW 11.7 billion so far (2006 Est.). The Voluntary Agreements Program implemented in 1998 to the present, which allows companies to voluntarily commit to limiting carbon emissions and increasing energy efficiency in return for tax breaks and other accounting benefits, has seen the participation of 1,288 companies, saving over 1.76 million tonnes of oil equivalent (MTOE) through energy efficiency programmes. The government has spent KRW 645.2 billion on incentives for the energy efficiency incentives under this programme. Overall, the commitment, especially financial, of the government is clear and has been a strong source of comfort to the investment community.

8.1.3 Practical Challenges to Developing Renewable Energy Projects

The reality is that while renewable energy has positive attributes for both the environment and energy security, there are clear reasons too why it is not more readily prevalent. There are a couple of key bottlenecks that often prevent the implementation of projects.

Renewable energy is considered a more "diluted" form of energy, for example it requires roughly four truckloads of biomass to achieve the same amount of energy that could be extracted from one truckload of coal. Such a challenge also means that sourcing and fuel supply chains are more dilute, for example many more truckloads of biomass would need to be brought in than for a comparable amount of coal-fired power generation.

Scale is also a challenge in that renewable energy projects tend to be small and thereby lose the economies of scale that large fossil fuel plants achieve. Large billion-dollar turbine orders for fossil fuel plants do clearly achieve preferential queue places for orders over a small 10-million-dollar order, resulting in months of delays (and lost revenues). For financial institutions, the same transaction costs for paperwork etc. apply for the billion-dollar-coal plant as for a 10-million-dollar biomass plant. Size matters.

Environmental safety and impacts are not neutral. Although renewable energy is generally thought of as "clean", there are some adverse environmental impacts that can occur when building power plants. For example, the Three Gorges Dam has led to the displacement of people and destruction of much of the ecosystem in the rivers. Even wind farms are meeting increasing community resistance due to their visual impact on the landscape.

Renewables also tend to be much more tied into geographical and seasonal factors. Renewables cannot generate electricity 100 percent of the time because the resources themselves are intermittent. Renewables are weather and geography dependent and not consistent. For example, wind farms cannot function on calm days and solar plants cannot generate electricity on cloudy days.

Finally, the overwhelming barrier is economic. Renewable energy is much more expensive than traditional fossil fuel plants. Even if costs per installed MW can be similar over the lifetime of the plant (such as coal and geothermal), the upfront or front-load nature of the costs for renewable energy development is much higher in terms of financial risk. For example, geothermal energy has virtually no fuel costs for the lifetime of a plant. On the other hand, all the fuel-related costs are upfront, including the roughly US$3 million per drilled well (including dry wells) in sourcing the steam. Hence the financial expenditure profile for geothermal is far more expensive than a coal-fired plant where fuel costs are spread over decades. Hence, globally, renewables are overall not as economical, in terms of a developer's or investor's bottom line, as fossil fuel plants. While there are some debates about how the full social cost of fossil fuels is not included in the pricing of fossil fuel plants, nonetheless, for current developers and investors, the total expenditure is less economical for renewables.

8.1.4 Climate Change as a Driver of Renewable Energy Development

A recent development in the global renewable energy markets has been the rise of climate change considerations, namely the global market for climate change–related carbon offsets. The largest of these markets is that related to the United Nations Kyoto Protocol–related carbon credits, the Clean Development Mechanism (CDM) markets. All of these markets are tied to the various regulatory regimes in the world and the prices for tonnes of carbon in such markets. The price per tonne in the various markets ranges from US$1 to US$20 per tonne. Since 1975, there have been roughly 150 billion tonnes of carbon released into the atmosphere, with

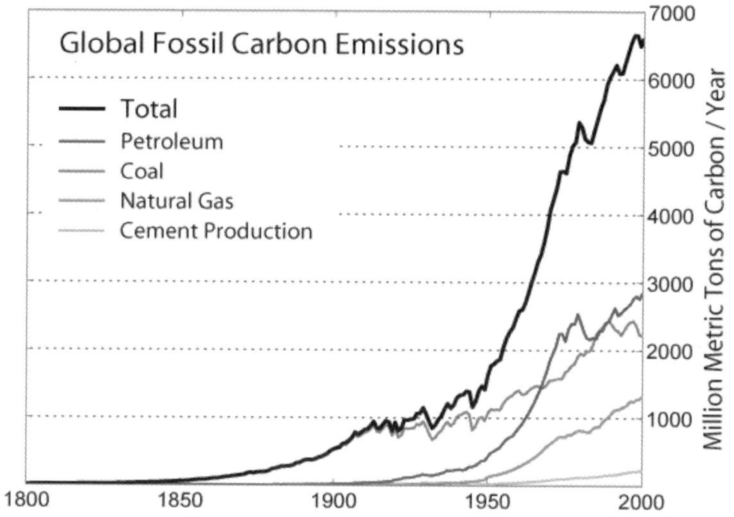

Figure 8 Global Fossil Carbon Emissions

Source: Wikipedia (2004), Global Carbon Emission by Type.

over 2 billion tonnes of carbon emitted from fossil plants yearly in the United States alone (Figure 8).

The Kyoto Protocol took effect in February 2005 and required certain countries classified as developed (Annex I) to meet certain targets, reducing their carbon output to below 1990 levels. Countries classified as developing countries, covering most of Asia excluding Japan, do not have to meet specific reduction targets, but for projects which generate reduction units, they can sell them to developed countries. There are six gases that are designated as greenhouse gases:

1. Carbon dioxide (CO_2)
2. Methane (CH_4)
3. Sulfur hexafluoride (SF_6)
4. Nitrous oxide (N_2O)
5. Hydrofluorocarbon (HFC)
6. Perfluorocarbon (PFC)

The Kyoto Protocol in effect created a cap-and-trade greenhouse gas market between the developed (Annex I) and developing (non-Annex I) countries where units of carbon are traded, measured in tonnes of carbon equivalent. Practically, it created a mechanism for developed countries to invest in carbon reduction projects (energy efficiency, renewable energy projects) in developing countries and to translate the carbon saved from those projects into measurable carbon credits called Certified Emission Reduction (CER) units (1 tonne of carbon) that can then be exchanged in the markets for monetary gain (current prices at year-end 2009 are about US$15 per tonne). The Protocol essentially transformed carbon into a commodity and created a marketplace for these CERs where companies that emit more than their allowance can buy and those that emit less can sell their allowance.

The impact on renewable energy projects has been that whereas previously such projects were deemed small, localised investment projects, a whole new category of potential developers and investors saw them as potential sources of CERs and their revenue streams. For finance purposes, the CERs are revenues from a global source rather than local ones which helps to make the revenue streams less risky as well.

Since 2005 when the Kyoto Protocol entered into force as international law, there has been a significant rise in global interest in small, localised renewable energy projects in Asia. As a rule of thumb, 1 MW of renewable energy generates roughly 5,000 tonnes of CERs. For a 10 MW renewable energy project then, it means roughly 50,000 CERs or, at 2009 prices, an additional revenue stream of US$750,000 per year. Considering that a 10 MW project would cost roughly US$15–20 million, the additional revenue source is a material one. As a result, developers have made CER generation considerations an integral part of any renewable energy project review in Asia.

8.2 "ON THE GROUND"

To look closer at how the various national systems and incentives and the CER markets are affecting renewable energy development in Asia, we will consider as an example one of the most popular forms of renewable energy in the region — biomass.

Biomass is especially relevant to most of Asia since it is often tied in a close relationship to large national agricultural sectors. Biomass is a strong example for the renewables sector because of such tie-ins, rather than other renewables which are much narrower in terms of such national and societal tie-ins in Asia. For example, in Korea, solar has been highly supported due to its emphasis on technology, a priority policy area for the Korean government's growth policies. Wind is supported in China due to the presence of strong wind-related manufacturers but those same sectors are not well supported in other countries which do not have such a tie-in with national policy. Biomass generally cuts across all Asian geographies due to its ability to affect significant populations of agricultural producers and farmers as well.

Example: Biomass (Landscape)

Global biomass electricity capacity is 47 GW and makes up 7 percent of total renewable energy investment.

There has been a proliferation of small biomass projects in emerging Asia. This has been driven by several factors:

1. Strong economic growth and power demand.
2. Abundant resources, with more than 30 percent of the world's total biomass resources in Asia.
3. Governments across Asia have set ambitious targets which lead to funding and legislation support.
4. Large untapped potential, given that this is a growing and emerging sector with many of the opportunities yet to be tapped.

For example, there has been roughly 3,000 MW of biomass for power utilised in Southeast Asia and 2,200 MW utilised in China. While these numbers may look poor as they are out of a potential of 56,000 MW for Southeast Asia and 24,000 MW for China, because biomass plants tend to be small (less than 10 MW each), these utilisation numbers actually mean that there are large absolute numbers of plants.

8.2.1 Investment Considerations

In order to determine if a project is suitable, there are a couple of key factors that need to be checked. First, there needs to be a partner with knowledge of the local business environment. Second, the utilisation of existing and proven technologies decreases risk. The project must also qualify for a stable PPA so that cash flows are less risky. It is also beneficial to have potential Kyoto Protocol financing (money from the sale of CERs) to help boost and stabilise investment returns. Lastly, the project should enjoy support from the local community and government to ensure that there are no implementation complications.

If those conditions are met and there is a solid project base, a private sector developer can then proceed to develop and invest in a renewable energy project. The project should yield revenue from three channels: 1) electricity sales, 2) fly ash sales (post-burning/fertiliser), and 3) CER sales. There is upward pressure on tariff prices and revenue generated from electricity sales in Asia because of the high economic growth and supply shortage. Indonesia's forecasted energy demand is 7–9 percent and Thailand's is around 6–8 percent. With regard to variables that can affect revenue from CER sales, one has to look at supply/demand and regulation which essentially controls demand in the market. Current CER demand is around 788 million to 1.1 billion tonnes of carbon dioxide equivalent per year.

Case Study: Biomass Power

Biomass combustion is one of the oldest and simplest forms of energy production. It is considered renewable and carbon neutral as it prevents the methane release that would have occurred had the waste been left to rot rather than be burned.

A typical illustrative biomass project is now shown.

Greenfield 12 MW Power Plant

Location: Southern Thailand
Fuel source: coconut residue
Fuel: at project site, owned by project owner
Technology: circulating fluidised bed boiler

Its financial projections are given in Table 2. Key assumptions in this project are as follows:

1. There is no alternative use for the fuel, no fuel transport costs, no grid connection costs.

Table 2 Financial Projections and Metrics

Financial Projections & Metrics	
Total CAPEX	US$ 20 mil
Post –Tax NPV@12%	US$430,000
Post –Tax IRR	26%
Average annual electricity revenue	US$ 7 mil
Average annual CERs	57,300
Average annual CER revenue	US$ 1 mil

Sensitivity Analysis: Change (%) of NPV @ 12%		
	10% Improvement	10% Deterioration
CER Price	3.9%	-3.9%
Power Sale Price	26.0%	-26.0%
Fuel Cost	5.6%	-5.6%
O&M Cost	8.3%	-8.3%

Source: Asia Renewables, internal financial model template.

2. No problems in issuing CERs.
3. PPA is renewed for 20 years.
4. Energy Performance Certificate (EPC) per MW is US$1.4 million.
5. Operations and maintenance is 1.5 cents/kWh.

In terms of timing, running costs[1], permitting, etc., are expected to take 1–1.5 years; construction will take 16 months.

There are numerous underlying variables that are assumed and controlled in the financial analysis but generally the internal rate of return (IRR) is relatively high at 26 percent and there are opportunities to generate gains in this sector if projects are implemented properly.

[1] "Running costs" are those which are incurred every month during construction. In other words, before there is any revenue. Therefore, having a longer construction period means there is a longer period of uncovered running costs which means more difficulty in staying afloat until the plant can actually run and generate revenues.

8.2.2 Practical Choke Issues

While there are no major specific hurdles to such a small-scale project and the financial profile looks attractive, actual implementation (the actual build-up of the plant) is often difficult and, with the majority of projects under development in the emerging markets of Asia, tends to be quite low. Development timelines which should be a matter of months often stretch to several years, if the projects are even completed.

Figure 9 demonstrates all the issues at each stage of the project implementation value chain that need to addressed. If such issues are not secured, they can "choke" or prevent the project from being implemented. As can be seen, the main challenges for a biomass power plant are not necessarily technology-specific ones or matters tied to the nature of biomass itself, but rather those related to any implementation of smaller-sized projects in developing markets.

The main choke point is financial. The financial considerations are not unusual and at first glance the project appears financially attractive with a high IRR of 26 percent and a positive net present value (NPV). However, these numbers may be more fragile than they appear, in that fuel prices are

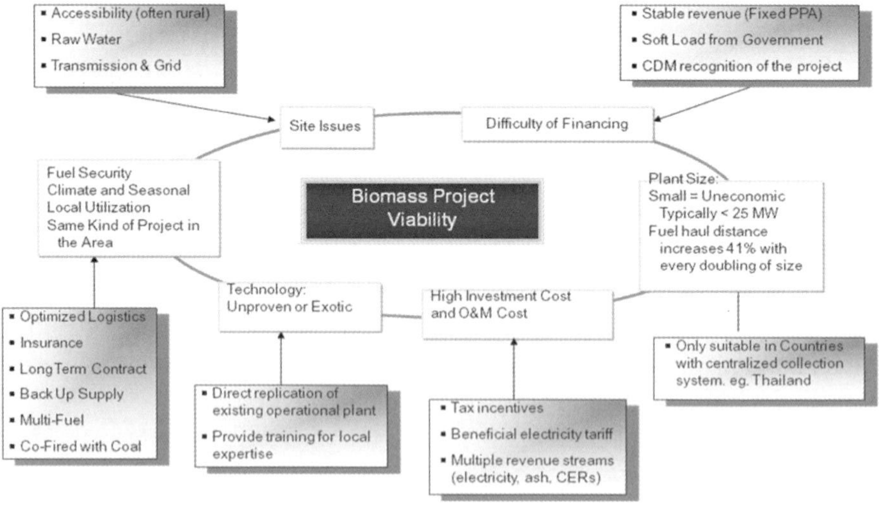

Figure 9 Biomass Project Viability

Source: Asia Renewables.

volatile and their logistics are delicate. Since biomass is more diluted than, say, coal, a much larger quantum of biomass is needed and the shipping and transport then becomes a critical issue. Also, most biomass plants tend to be located near their fuel sources, i.e. in the countryside, which poses additional difficulties of remoteness from supporting infrastructure, and the need to put up expensive grid connections to the nearest suitable transmission lines.

Finally, the nature of the financing required also poses a challenge in that whereas for a larger fossil fuel plant, project financing is an option, for such smaller plants where the capital expenditure (CAPEX) is US$20 million or less, bank financing becomes difficult. Whereas a larger plant may only need to put up 30 percent of the CAPEX as equity and rely on 70 percent bank financing, for smaller plants all US$20 million may need to be put up as equity, thereby making the cost of the smaller plant much dearer in terms of equity. This is especially so for smaller companies which may be engaged in such a sector rather than larger companies engaged in larger fossil fuel plants. These smaller companies already facing a higher cost of equity would now have to face an even higher threshold as the smaller biomass plant would require all equity financing from the company's own balance sheet rather than through non-recourse bank financing.

As is, while projects such as this particular biomass one looks financially attractive, since a snapshot of metrics such as NPV and IRR and the challenges of implementation and build-out do not highlight any one crippling hurdle, the reality is that due to the insufficient financial structure (how to finance the building of the plant and being able to get to the point where IRR and NPV are actually being generated), this project and others like it across emerging markets in Asia are simply not being built and are being regularly rejected by financial institutions and investors. In turn, notwithstanding the grand rhetoric of policy targets, the reality of renewable energy development reinforces the tiny sliver of the overall electricity markets being held by renewables. Simply, renewables are a small market segment for good reason.

8.3 CARBON NEXUS

As seen earlier, the main deterrent to the development of more renewable energy projects is structural in nature, i.e. financial returns are not sufficiently attractive for small-scale projects, country risk in emerging markets, and renewable energy characteristics such as diffuse and sensitive fuel supply considerations. For governments, the main tool against such hurdles has been to provide a higher tariff for electricity sales and to try to streamline taxes and other regulatory hurdles. Thus far, individual national incentives and systems for renewables have been generally insufficient in generating more renewable energy project developments in Asia. To achieve the policy aims for renewables development and other objectives such as fuel security, the national governments in Asia then face the challenge of further increasing tariffs and improving other incentives. However, in a time of global economic challenges and downturns which put pressure on fiscal budgets everywhere, and with the inward-turning orientation by the developed nations to focus on their own economic issues and renewables challenges, a further systemic boost from outside their national confines may be needed. Coupled with such tools at a national level are the new carbon-related ones, which are seen in the emerging markets of Asia as possibly being an additional boost.

The CER markets under the Kyoto Protocol were specifically structured to provide an additional boost to a project's financials by introducing an entirely new revenue stream and also a whole new class of potential investors with international risk profiles.

8.3.1 Overview of CER Generation Mechanism

To simplify the process, there should be an underlying project whose activity generates CERs. Then there is a documentation procedure to certify the CERs and this step spans local government approval, third-party confirmation, and then UN approval. The CER generation process is an administratively long and complex procedure, and depending on the type of renewable energy project it is (unproven methodologies can take up to two or three years to get approved), there is a range of timeframes for carbon financing that can be secured.

This lengthy process has given rise to the carbon consulting industry, which is composed of firms that purely consult developers with regard to the process of certifying their carbon emissions. There are currently 1,785 projects registered, with only 7.3 percent of those projects from Southeast Asia.

Table 3 Southeast Asia: Average Annual CER Reductions and Registered Projects by Host Party

South East Asia: **Average Annual CER Reductions**		South East Asia: **Registered Projects by host party**	
Indonesia	3,337,551	Malaysia	46
Malaysia	3,111,479	Philippines	27
Philippines	1,367,251	Indonesia	24
Thailand	1,287,486	Thailand	17
Viet Nam	889,577	Viet Nam	5
Singapore	15205	Singapore	1
SE Asia Total	10,008,549	**SE Asia Total**	120
% of global	3.316712768	**% of total**	7.303712721

Total projects registered:	1,909 projects 325 million CERs
Average number of projects approved:	200 projects per year
Average size of CER per project:	170,326.5 CERs
Estimated 2012 annual global demand:	2 billion metric tonnes

Source: United Nations Framework Convention on Climate Change, http://www.unfccc.org.

A look at Table 3 highlights Southeast Asia's relatively small market share of annual CER reductions. Table 4 shows the number of projects in validation compared to registered (far outnumbered) and also highlights the administrative bottleneck and the subsequent long queue of projects.

While the CDM system is therefore working mechanically, these numbers of projects highlight that the raw, absolute numbers of projects

Table 4 State of the CER Pipeline (2005 to March 2009): Number of Projects at Each Stage

State of the CER pipeline, 2005-March 2009
number of projects at each stage

Data:
Units: number of projects

Year	Issuing	Registered	At validation
2005	4	64	494
2006	104	471	870
2007	281	898	1734
2008	441	1325	2709
2009	473	1421	2766

Source: New Carbon Finance.

qualifying as CDM projects and thus providing a supply of CERs is still rather low and potentially inadequate to meet the demand.

8.3.2 Reality of the CDM Universe

Is the CDM market sufficiently robust then to satisfy the need of the renewable energy development sector in Asia to boost overall construction and build-out levels? Due to a variety of bottlenecks, including the CER generation mechanism and other challenges to developing renewable energy projects listed previously, there has been a very limited increase in the supply of carbon credits to the primary market. At the same time, governments are passing more ambitious carbon emission and renewable energy targets, driving up demand for these credits. These two forces — driving supply down and demand up — have increasingly widened the gap between supply and demand in the carbon credit market.

Worse still, the Kyoto markets have inherent systemic faultlines. A sample of various countries' positions highlights how far countries are from meeting their Kyoto Protocol targets (Table 5).

Countries such as Canada and Spain are far from being able to meet their 2012 targets and have even indicated that they would not be able to meet such targets. As there is no punishment mechanism under the Kyoto Protocol, failure to meet targets does not carry specific and meaningful risks. Further, due to a historical quirk whereby many former Soviet bloc

Table 5 Sample of Projected 2012 Positions for Various Countries

Sample of Countries' Positions projected 2012	
EU-15	–5.1% (–217 Mt Co2 equiv)
Russia	–33.8%
Italy	–0.2%
Spain	–0.4%
UK	–9.6%
Canada	32.2%
Japan	15.1%

countries are below their 2012 target levels due to a deterioration of their own economies after the collapse of the Soviet Union, there is actually a large supply overhang of carbon offset units (called Assigned Amount Units or AAUs) which could, on paper, satisfy all CER demand globally without making any impact on actual carbon reductions. Due to the lack of CERs, critics have derided AAUs as "hot air", citing a massive global surplus and arguing most were generated through restructuring in Eastern Europe in the 1990s, when polluting industries in ex-communist countries were shutting anyway, rather than through new investment. This is directly evident in Ukraine's and Russia's positions which are both in the negative.

Currently, the average annual demand for CERs is about five times more than the annual supply estimated in Phase 1 of the Kyoto Protocol. At current rates, the UN would need to approve 1,000 projects per year to meet the demand. However, currently only 500 projects per year are approved. As seen in Figure 10, the current rate of project approval (i.e. market supply) is far less than would be needed by 2012 and any straight-line projection between them would be quite an optimistic one.

The reality in the UN's Kyoto carbon markets has been the opposite: waiting times, project uncertainty in the approval process, and rejection rates with no recourse or even explanations, have all increased, thereby further depressing prices for carbon. Further, the continuing uncertainty over the nature of the successor to the Kyoto Protocol (expiring in 2012) has also cast a pall on how to judge any future revenue stream

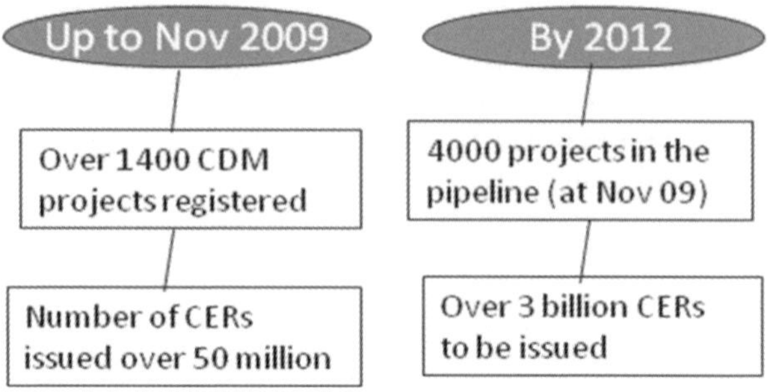

Figure 10 CER Projections

Source: United Nations Framework Convention on Climate Change and Author's Projections.

post-2012. The gaps and uncertainties exacerbate the reality that the carbon markets are failing to provide assurances to the renewable energy development market that carbon revenues could be the boost it needs to overcome its own challenges of insufficient renewable energy project build-outs.

8.4 CRYSTAL BALL

8.4.1 Looking Ahead

Looking ahead in the renewable energy sector, while there is strong policy support at present among the various countries in Asia, the current systems of industry, regulatory, and financial supports have not been adequate to significantly increase the number of projects being actually built out. The challenge is not in technology but rather finances. The challenge of supporting small-scale projects has not been sufficiently dealt with to overcome the hurdle of reluctance among financial investors to invest in such a sector when there are many other sectors in the same emerging markets which may seem more attractive. The emphasis on cleantech as a solution to the lack of actual project construction is misguided. Indeed, new or advanced technology presents more of a hurdle in providing financial comfort to investors who prefer tried-and-tested technologies to anything new and potentially unworkable. Even in the carbon markets, any new technologies require additional methodology review procedures which add several years of approval uncertainties and investment delays to a project. The problem remains that to actually build out a project requires more financial support, especially at the construction phase.

In terms of the global carbon markets, there had been strong expectations that such markets could provide the boost that the renewables sector required to overcome the initial hesitance about projects to be funded during construction. Since carbon buyers and investors are international ones, their risk and funding profiles are expected to be different from those local financing options which have thus far been reluctant to fund local small-scale infrastructure. However, the long lead times and increasing levels of uncertainty in the Kyoto market system itself have meant that the carbon markets are as yet not ready to bridge that financing comfort gap.

Although there has been an enormous amount of expectations about positive synergies between the Asian renewable energy development market and the global carbon offset (Kyoto) market, to date they have not yet been realised and both are now at a crossroads where several additional questions arise.

On the carbon market side, there is still the need for further clarity on how a post-2012 carbon offset market will look and how it could be structured. While there are specifics still to be sorted out, major conceptual changes would also need to be addressed, such as coupling more systems of carbon offset generation with the need to promote small-scale project challenges and reducing timeline uncertainties which hurt any financial benefits which the carbon revenues could potentially provide.

From the local perspective, rather than waiting for global carbon markets to provide an external solution, national governments must continue with the unglamorous but necessary steps to tighten and strengthen their policy frameworks, not only increasing tariffs, but lessening red tape, increasing local financial support and bank loans, speeding up various permits and licensing steps, etc. In Asia already, some of these steps have worked such as localised approvals and PPA processes in Thailand, the high solar tariff structure in Korea, the new legal framework for renewables in the Philippines, and, with some revision on foreign investment, the new regional small-scale renewables framework in Indonesia.

As yet, renewable energy development in Asia remains small, but with a continued, disciplined approach, there are no critical hurdles which should prevent a deepening of the growth of that market.

PART II
NUCLEAR ISSUES IN ASIA

CHAPTER 9

POWER DEVELOPMENT PLAN AND STATUS OF NUCLEAR POWER PLANT (NPP) DEVELOPMENT IN INDONESIA

Djoko Prasetijo

ABSTRACT

Electricity demand in Indonesia has been growing rapidly, and to meet the future demand, large scale power plants have been planned, mostly coal power plants for baseload generation along with considerable amount of geothermal and hydro power. The national electricity company, however, has yet to plan any nuclear energy, as the government's national electricity general plan did not indicate any nuclear power. The paper reports the efforts that have been made by Indonesia over the years to develop the nuclear industry, including to prepare nuclear power projects. The paper also provides some highlights from the media coverage, which act as exhibits as to whether Indonesia will develop nuclear power. The paper reports the preparedness of Indonesia in preparing nuclear infrastructure for pre-project phase as per the IAEA's INIR evaluation.

9.1 INTRODUCTION

Indonesia is recognised as one country in the Association of Southeast Asian Nations (ASEAN) that could embark into nuclear power, and this paper will report the status of nuclear power plant development in Indonesia. The paper will first highlight the current situation of the country's electricity supply and demand, followed by a brief description of the power development plan that has been prepared by PT Perusahaan Listrik Negara (PLN) Persero (the national electricity utility). The paper will then revisit the historical efforts by Indonesia over the years to develop the nuclear industry as well as to prepare nuclear power projects, along with some highlights from the media coverage. Finally, the paper rounds off with a summary and conclusion of the International Atomic Energy Agency's (IAEA) integrated nuclear infrastructure review (INIR) mission conducted in 2009.

9.2 THE "THREE A'S" SITUATION OF THE ELECTRICITY SECTOR

The vast geographical condition of Indonesia's archipelago which spans three time zones and comprises many thousands of islands presents Indonesia as a unique country in terms of electricity provision. Almost 60% of the population resides in Java Island, where most of the economic activity of the country is concentrated; hence about 75% of the national electricity provision is located in the most populous island of Java, as shown in Figure 1. Java's Bali power system has now developed into a mature and modern power system which has a large power grid and large-scale power plants.

Typically for a developing country, the electricity demand in Indonesia is growing very fast. It is estimated that for the gross domestic product (GDP) to grow by 1% annually, the economy will need electricity input to grow by 1.5–2%. Therefore when the government set the target of GDP growth at 6–7% annually, it is expected the electricity demand will grow at 9–11% per year. Consequently, the electricity demand for western Indonesia, eastern Indonesia and Java-Bali will grow from 21 terawatt hours (TWh), 11 TWh and 115 TWh respectively in the year 2010 to 54 TWh, 28 TWh and 252 TWh, as shown in Figure 1.

Borrowing the World Energy Council's criteria of "three A's", i.e. Availability, Accessibility and Acceptability, Indonesia's current situation in its power sector is markedly challenged.

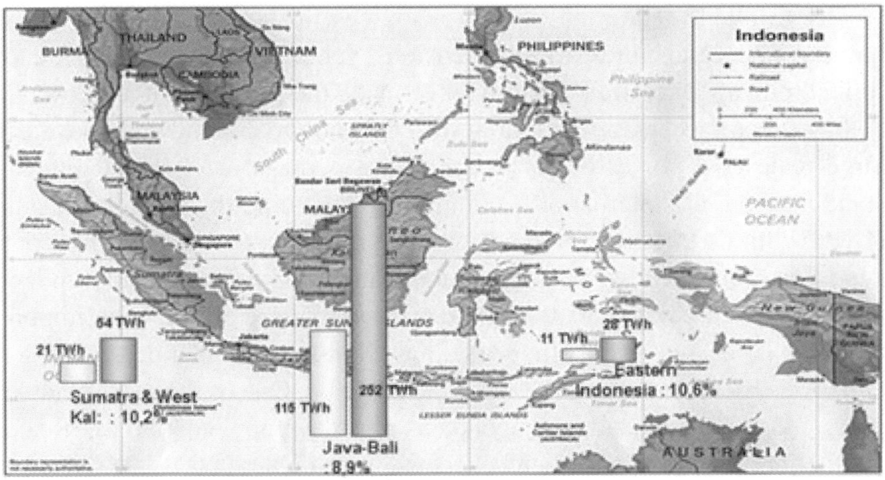

Figure 1 National Electricity Provision: Centred around Java Island

Source: PT PLN (Persero), *Rencana Usaha Penyediaan Tenaga Listrik PT PLN (Persero) 2010–2019*, Jakarta, 2010, ISBN 978 979 1203 14 2.

In terms of availability, electricity supply in many islands, especially those outside Java and Bali, has been constrained along the years due to capacity shortages. Those capacity shortages have been mainly caused by insufficient capacity development due to under-investment, especially since the East Asian economic crisis in 1997 that caused cancellations and delays of many power projects. Only in 2006 did the government initiate a fast-track programme to build 10,000-megawatt (MW) coal power plants to overcome the electricity crisis happening across the country, as well as to replace costly oil combustion for power generation with coal. This was recently followed by the second phase of the fast-track programme in which Indonesia is to add another 10,000 MW in capacity, comprising coal, geothermal, gas and hydropower projects.

In terms of accessibility, only about 65% of people currently have access to electricity, while the remaining 35% or approximately 80 million people have yet to enjoy electricity. The vast geographical coverage of the country contributes to the slow progress of the rural electrification programme, especially in remote areas and outer islands. The government and PLN have strived to increase the electrification ratio by developing locally available renewable energy resources, installing numerous solar home systems and building grid extensions, yet the insufficient budget and limited power generation capacity have made the progress rather slow.

In terms of acceptability, Indonesia's decision to continuously develop large-scale coal power plants in the future perhaps needs better understanding from the international community regarding the greenhouse gas (GHG) emissions. However, the decision is quite natural, considering coal supply is domestically available in abundance. Indonesia actually understands and addresses climate change seriously; therefore in some important climate change events Indonesia has expressed its intention to cut its emissions by a certain amount from the baseline. One of the most notable programmes in the national agenda is the development of large-scale geothermal power plants wherever they are available.

9.3 POWER DEVELOPMENT PLAN

Endowed with quite large coal reserves and geothermal potential and some gas reserves as well as hydropower, Indonesia has intentions of developing a mix of energy for power generation, as shown in Figure 2.

One can see from the figure that Indonesia is going to utilise renewable energy wherever it is available and whenever it is ready, especially geothermal and hydropower. Still, coal will largely dominate the fuel mix for baseload generation.

One can also see in Figure 2 that nuclear power is not included in the power development plan prepared by PLN, because in the planning process PLN is required by the regulations to refer to the national electricity general plan Rencana Umum Ketenagalistrikan Nasional (RUKN) issued by the Ministry of Energy and Mineral Resources, and this planning document does not contain any mention of nuclear power plants.

9.4 NUCLEAR POWER DEVELOPMENT IN INDONESIA

Indonesia has come a long way in the use of nuclear technology for peaceful purposes. It started almost 60 years ago when in 1954 the government set up a committee for radioactivity, as shown in Table 1.

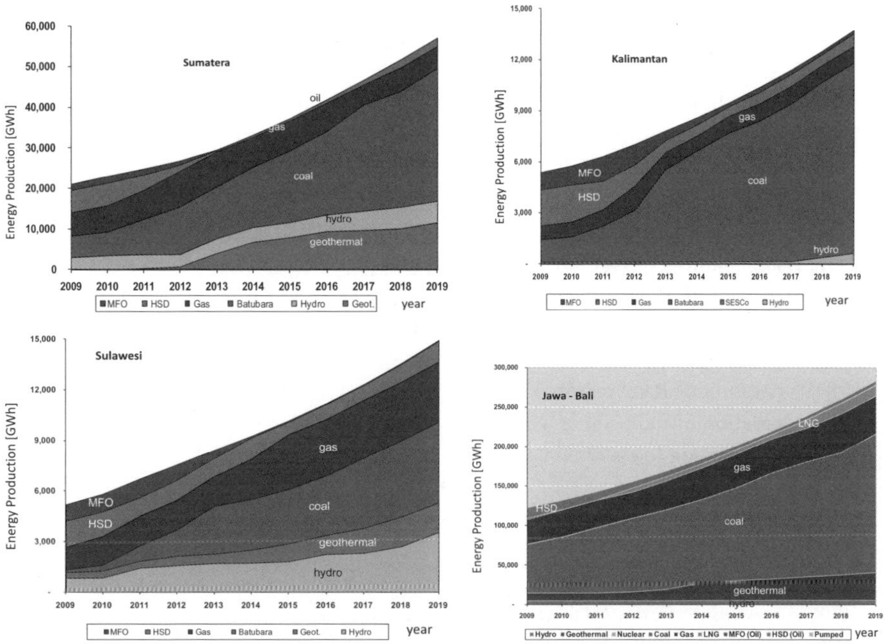

Figure 2 Projection of Fuel Mix for Major Power Systems in Indonesia 2010–2019

The milestones that signify the development of nuclear power plants are shown in italics in Table 1. It was in 1991 when the government assigned BATAN (the National Nuclear Energy Agency of Indonesia) to conduct a feasibility study (FS) of a nuclear power project located in Jepara regency of Central Java province, and the FS was completed in 1996. Then in 1997, Law No. 10 regarding nuclear energy was enacted in the midst of the economic crisis. Under this law, the Nuclear Energy Control Board (BAPPETEN) was established, and BATAN as we know it today was also established.

A comprehensive energy planning study called CADES (Comprehensive Assessment of Different Energy Sources for Electricity Generation in Indonesia) was carried out between 2000 and 2002 involving many stakeholders in the energy sector, namely the Ministry of Energy, Agency for the Assessment and Application of Technology, Directorate General of Oil and Gas, Directorate General of Electricity,

Table 1 History of Nuclear Industry in Indonesia

1954: Establishment of State Committee for Radioactivity
1958: Establishment of Atomic Energy Council and Atomic Energy Agency
1964: Establishment of BATAN (National Atomic Energy Agency)
1975: Operation of Triga Mark II research reactor (250 kW)
1970: GOT signed NPT
1971: Operation of Triga Mark II research reactor (1 MW)
1972: Establishment of Commission for preparation of NPP construction
1978: Ratification of NPT by Parliament
1979: Operation of Kartini research reactor (100 kW)
(1986: Chernobyl)
1987: Operation of RSG research reactor (30 MW)
1988: Operation of radioactive waste management facility
1989: GOI decision to build NPP
1991*: Start of NPP FS*
1995: Whole Indonesian core of 30 MW research reactor
1996: FS completed
1997: Nuclear Energy Act No. 10 of 1997 (also start of Economic Crisis)
1998: Economic crisis continued, establishment of BATAN and BAPETEN
2000: Operation of Triga Mark II reseaich reactor (2 MW) advanced SI reactor
2000: Start of comprehensive assessment of national energy planning
2002: Study completed, NPP was feasible in 2016, submitted to the President in 2003
2005: NPP was included in the RUKN 2005–2025 by MEMR
2006: National Energy Policy 2005–2025 Presidential decree 6/2005(nuclear energy will be a pait of national energy mix)
2007: National Long-Term Development Planning 2005–2019, Law No. 17/2007 (NPP maybe utilized in a period of 2015–2019)
2008: RUKN 2009–2027: NPP not included.
2010: National Mid-term Development Plan 2010-2014, Presidential Decree No. 5/2010 (BATAN to carry out FS of NPP at new sites and to conduct socialization).

Source: Adiwardoyo, *Energy Situation and Nuclear Power Development in Indonesia*, presentation material at Tsuruga Summer Institute on Nuclear Energy 2008, Tsuruga, Japan, September 2008.

State Electricity Company, Bureau of Statistics, non-governmental organisations (NGOs) and IAEA. It is in this study that nuclear power plants were said to be feasible to be introduced in 2016, and subsequently nuclear power plants were included in the RUKN, the national electricity general plan, for 2005–2025.

Another milestone is Law No. 17 of 2007 about national long-term development planning in which nuclear power may be utilised in the period between 2009 and 2019. However, we are now already in the year 2010, and the government has yet to announce or appoint the entity that will assume responsibility for building and running nuclear power projects. Considering the long lead time in the preparation and construction of nuclear power projects, it is considered no longer possible for Indonesia to have its first nuclear power plant running earlier than 2021.

There are at least two current documents showing the intention of Indonesia to build nuclear power projects. One is Law No. 17/2007 regarding National Long-term Development Plan 2005–2019 and the other is Presidential Decree No. 5/2010 regarding National Mid-term Development Plan 2010–2014. In the first document it is said that Indonesia might use nuclear energy from 2015–2019. In the second document the government assigned BATAN to conduct new feasibility studies of nuclear power plants at new sites, and to carry out socialisation and public awareness campaigns, with both assignments being supported by a considerable state budget.

9.5 HIGHLIGHTS OF MEDIA COVERAGE OF NUCLEAR POWER DEVELOPMENT

In general there has not been a clear statement made by the national leaders on whether Indonesia will develop nuclear power. Every now and then one can only find scattered media reports on statements made by government officials in seminars, NGOs or ministers. The following are some examples of media coverage of nuclear power development in Indonesia.

Government indecisiveness in deciding who would own and run nuclear projects was highlighted in a seminar in March 2010, as seen in Figure 3. As will be discussed in another section of this paper, an IAEA integrated nuclear infrastructure review mission which took place last November also noted the need for Indonesia to establish a nuclear energy programme implementing organisation (NEPIO).

Indonesia's plan to establish nuclear power plants remains unclear due to govern ment indecision over who should operate them. BATAN admitted the absence of a definitive decision on operators had hampered discussions on the plants.

"No decision has been made on which organization will be responsible for owning and operating nuclear power plants," BATAN chairman, Hadi Hastowo, told a seminar on the prospects of nuclear electricity in Indonesia on Thursday.

Authorities have long argued that, nuclear plants are needed to tackle expected energy shortages as the country's fossil fuels continue to decrease.

However, a coalition of activists, including Greenpeace Indonesia, the Anti-Nuclear Society (Manusial) and the Civil Society Forum (CSF) have rejected the proposal, saying the projects are too risky in a country that lacks the technology to treat hazardous waste.

(The Jakarta Post, Fri, 03/19/2010).

Figure 3 Government Indecision Hampered Nuclear Power Discussion

Source: Adianto P. Simamora (2010), *Plans for nuclear power stalled due to govt 'indecisiveness'*, The Jakarta Post, March 19.

This indecision would have definitely delayed the timing of the first nuclear power plant in Indonesia (see Figure 4). It is now no longer possible for Indonesia to keep the previous schedule of having the first unit running in 2016.

In February 2010, five pro-nuclear NGOs organised an event in Jakarta, during which they declared their support for the government's effort to build nuclear power.

A postitive support from the parliament was apparent when Commission VII, which is in charge of energy policy, urged the government to speed up the development of nuclear power (Figure 5). In another media article, it is reported the first nuclear power project in Indonesia might be situated outside java island, with Bangka — Belitung area cited as one of the safest site for nuclear power projects in Indonesia (Figure 6).

The examples mentioned in this paper give some understanding of the discourse happening between the government, politicians, NGOs and public in general about nuclear power. One can observe from the media reportage that a firm declaration from the national leaders that "Indonesia is going nuclear" is lacking. In fact, the government seems quiet.

Indonesia is now definitively planning to have a nuclear power plant some time between 2018 and 2020, instead of in 2016 as previously scheduled, National Nuclear Power Agency (Batan) chief Hadi Hastowo said.

"It has been postponed to 2018–2020 because it is not possible to build it in 2016," Hadi said at a discussion themed "Remembering the Chernobyl Disaster 24 Years Ago" here Friday.

He said the Indonesian public should know that the country's need for electricity is to soar drastically in the future and that building a nuclear power plant must be included in the national energy development plan if future electricity shoitages would be prevented.

"A nuctear power plant will not negate other alternative energy sources because it will only be a supplement to ensure the constant availability of electricity. All the other alternative energy sources such as geothermal, hydro, wind, solar and biomass will remain in the national development plan," he said.

(Antara News, May 1, 2010)

Figure 4 Nuclear Power Development in 2016 is No Longer Possible

Source: *RI nuclear power project's timeframe pushed back to 2018–2020*, Antara News, 1 May 2010, Jakarta.

In a major new policy direction, an important parliamentary panel in Indonesia has strongly recommended that the government move toward speedy development of nuclear power plaints as part of the country's efforts to reduce oil dependency.

'The Indonesian parliament's Commission VII, which focuses on energy and mining sector policies, Wednesday said it was in favor of developing nuclear power as an alternates energy source. "It's a promising energy

[source] amid Indonesia's oil and gas shortage. It's urgently needed, so the feasibility study should be done as soon as possible," commission member Satya Widya Yudha told reporters Wednesday.

[businessweek.com/asian-energy-17 Mar 2010].

Figure 5 Politicians in Parliament Support Nuclear Power Development

Source: Anita Nugraha (2010), *Indonesia Parliamentary panel urges speedy move into nuclear power*, http://bx.businessweek.com/asian-energy-business/, 17 March.

Indonesia probably will build a nuclear plant in outside Java islands.

Indonesia will build nuclear plant electricity in outside Java island, one of the safeties place were Bangka-Belitung and Kalimantan islands, sources in Jakarta on Thursday, April 29, 2010.

The first plan of Indonesian nuclear electricity plant was in Muria Mount areas in Central Java, but the plan were opposed by local peoples, and other Green activist that Java islands is a populated and dangerous areas.

The only islands in Indonesia that could not have a negative impact from the earthquake is Kalimantan (Bomeo) Islands.

"The International Atomic Energy Agencies (IAEA) was did the possibility studies in Bangka-Belitung areas for the next Indonesian Nuclear electricity plants. But we will see the result next 6 years in order to know weather the Bangka-Belitung islands provinces are the most safeties places for Indonesian first nuclear plants or not," Indonesian Mineral and Energy Resources Ministry Bangka Belitung branch Chief Noor Nedi said in Pangkalpinang.

http://www.allvoices.com/contributed-news/5700848-indonesia-probably-will-builld-a-nuclear-plant-in-outside-java-islands.

Figure 6 Indonesia Considers Building Nuclear Power Outside Java

Source: Allvoices.

9.6 PREPAREDNESS OF INDONESIA IN NUCLEAR INFRASTRUCTURE ISSUES

As shown in Table 1 earlier, Indonesia's nuclear industry has come a long way since the 1950s, and many infrastructure issues in nuclear power have been addressed over the years. Nevertheless Indonesia needs to examine the preparedness of the development of national infrastructure for nuclear power according to the IAEA's 19 milestones, as described in the IAEA's document NG-G-3.1. Therefore the government of Indonesia, represented by BATAN, in 2009 requested the IAEA to send an INIR mission to evaluate the status of nuclear infrastructure issues and to identify areas needing further attention during the building of national infrastructure, as well as to assist Indonesia in preparing plans of action to address areas for further improvement. The INIR mission took place between 23 and 27 November 2009, and the Agency sent a team of IAEA and international experts.

The scope of the mission was to review the current status of infrastructure development in Indonesia, discuss actions from previous missions, and consider an Indonesian action plan and possible international assistance.

The INIR mission evaluated the progress in each of the 19 infrastructure issues for Phase 1 (pre-project) and Phase 2 (project decision making), with respect to the specific guidance. The following are some of the conclusions made by the INIR mission:

- **National position:** There is national understanding that nuclear power is a part of the future energy mix and that considerable activities have been completed to prepare the infrastructure needed for a nuclear power programme. Yet the mission could not see "the overall picture as to what extent the activities were well coordinated". The mission reckons Indonesia needs to establish a well-coordinated implementation programme and identify the role and responsibilities of the different organisations involved in the nuclear power programme. The mission proposed a national team be established with the following tasks: i) creation of an action plan for infrastructure building; ii) coordination, oversight, monitoring and steering in order to ensure balanced and coordinated development of national infrastructure; iii) defining the responsibilities by clarifying "who is responsible for what part of the nuclear energy programme"; and iv) full development of policy and strategy over the 19 issues of the milestone document.
- **Nuclear safety:** Milestone 1 was achieved for nuclear safety.
- **Management:** Indonesia has taken into account in great detail the different management issues, such as studies on national energy strategy and the possible role of nuclear power, including assessing national criteria and general specifications for an NPP, but these studies need to be updated. Ownership options and operational responsibilities have been considered, but no decision has been made on which organisation will own and operate the NPPs. Identification of the owners/operators of NPPs and determination of their responsibilities in the development of the nuclear power infrastructure are recommended by the mission.

- **Funding and financing:** Indonesia understands fully the different funding and financing aspects, but no decision has been made, because there has not been a decision on the owners/operators. The mission recommends that Indonesia identify the appropriate funding scheme for the selected owner/operator, and develop a funding method for long-term waste and decommissioning liabilities.
- **Legislative framework:** Indonesia understands the international legal regime concerning nuclear power, and has plans to review the national laws governing its nuclear power programme. They recommend that Indonesia review the nuclear and relevant non-nuclear legislation that will affect the nuclear power project, and finalise the ratification process for the Joint Convention on the Safety of Spent Fuel Management and on the Safety of Radioactive Waste Management.
- **Safeguards:** Indonesia understands the safeguards requirements concerning nuclear power. No further recommendation is made.
- **Regulatory framework:** The regulatory framework is in place and no major gaps were identified with respect to Phase 1. The mission recommends an IAEA integrated regulatory review service (IRRS) mission to be considered at an appropriate time.
- **Radiation protection:** Indonesia is well prepared in the field of radiation protection, consistent with the level of development of the NPP project.
- **Electrical grid:** The considerations of the grid for the nuclear power project are well understood by PLN. PLN considers itself to have the capability to analyse the implications of installing NPPs in its network, including alternative sites.
- **Human resources:** Indonesia has done human resource development (HRD) for Phase 1, and has a solid foundation for preparing for Phase 2. The HRD Blueprint has not been developed. The mission recommends involving owner/operator candidate organisations as soon as possible in planning for HRD.
- **Stakeholder involvement:** Stakeholder involvement and communication is a weak point in the preparations for a nuclear power programme in Indonesia and there is a need to strengthen these activities.
- **Site and supporting facilities:** The site selection process is consistent with the level of development of the programme, but certain questions

remain. The team concluded that Indonesia has a good understanding of the issues.

- **Environmental protection:** Work has been initiated in a manner consistent with the development of the nuclear power programme.
- **Emergency planning:** Indonesia understands the need for emergency planning but that additional coordination with local and governmental authorities needs to be conducted.
- **Security:** Indonesia is well positioned to meet the security requirements for Phase 1. Implementation of the recommendations in the Integrated Nuclear Security Support Plan and the report from the sustainability mission in 2009 should provide a solid nuclear security foundation in Indonesia, meeting the requirements of Phase 1 and preparing it to move substantially toward meeting Phase 2 security requirements.
- **Nuclear fuel cycle:** The planning for fuel cycle activities is consistent with the level of development of the programme.
- **Radioactive waste:** The actions are consistent with the development of Indonesia's nuclear power programme. Waste management for the research reactor is well developed. Some activities normally covered in the next phase have already been done, including defining a national waste management organisation and some preliminary site investigations for low-level waste disposal.
- **Industrial involvement:** The actions in this area are consistent with the development of the national nuclear power programme.
- **Procurement:** The actions in this area are consistent with the development of the national nuclear power programme.

9.7 CONCLUSION

Driven by economic and population growth as well as the extension of access to the people, the electricity demand in Indonesia has increased strongly in the past few decades. The Java-Bali power system has now developed into a mature and modern power system having a sizeable power grid with large-scale power plants. To meet the future demand, PLN has made a comprehensive long-term power development plan. In the plan, Indonesia is going to build a large number of coal power plants for baseload generation, and also to utilise renewable energy wherever it is available and whenever it is ready, especially geothermal and hydropower. Nuclear power is not included in the power development plan, because PLN is required to refer to the government's electricity master plan which did not indicate any nuclear power.

Interestingly, in Law No. 17/2007 regarding the National Long-term Development Plan 2005–2019, there is a line saying that Indonesia might use nuclear energy from 2015–2019. Also, in Presidential Decree No. 5/2010 regarding the National Mid-term Development Plan 2010–2014, it is indicated that the government has assigned BATAN to study new sites for nuclear power plants, and to carry out socialisation campaigns, both supported by a considerable state budget.

There has not been a clear statement made by the national leaders on whether Indonesia will develop nuclear power, with only scattered media reports on statements made by government officials in seminars, NGOs or ministers.

Indonesia's nuclear industry has come a long way since the 1950s, and many infrastructure issues in nuclear power have been addressed along the years. According to the results of an INIR mission to evaluate the status of nuclear infrastructure issues, Indonesia has shown considerable efforts in preparing the nuclear infrastructure for Phase 1 (pre-project phase).

CHAPTER 10

KOREAN NUCLEAR POWER TECHNOLOGY

Hae Ryong Hwang and Shin Whan Kim

ABSTRACT

Three decades after the first introduction of commercial nuclear power, Korea has emerged as the most competitive nation in the commercial nuclear power market. Over the past 20-plus years, Korea has successfully achieved technology self-reliance in the commercial nuclear power plant area and has developed indigenous technologies such as the Optimised Power Reactor (OPR) 1000 and the Advanced Power Reactor (APR) 1400. In December 2009, a Korean consortium led by Korea Electric Power Corporation (KEPCO) won a contract to build four nuclear plants in the United Arab Emirates (UAE), which is the single largest nuclear power plant construction contract. This paper presents the status of nuclear power in Korea, its importance to the Korean economy and the experience of technology self-reliance and the development of technologies. In addition, the competitiveness of the Korean nuclear technology and industry in terms of technology, commercial aspect, vendor capability for a long-term partnership and human resource development is presented. This explains how the KEPCO team won the UAE contract. Finally, the paper discusses how the KEPCO team can support other countries planning to introduce commercial nuclear power plant by sharing its experience.

10.1 INTRODUCTION

Three decades after the introduction of commercial nuclear power, Korea became the world's sixth-largest nuclear power–producing nation. It now operates 23 nuclear reactors for electricity generation, which combine to provide about 30% of its total electricity demand.

Over the past 20 years, Korea has successfully achieved technology self-reliance in the commercial nuclear power plant area and has become a success model in introducing nuclear technology to a developing country. During this period, Korea developed its own brand model of the OPR1000 based on the technologies transferred by foreign vendors, and after that it even made a great stride to develop an advanced light water reactor (ALWR) model, the APR1400. Currently, four units of the improved OPR1000 type are in operation and one OPR1000 unit and four APR1400 units are under construction.

On 27 December 2009, a Korean consortium headed by KEPCO won a contract to build four nuclear plants in the UAE. The selection of the contractor was made following a comprehensive review of three internationally recognised bidders, focused on safety, deliverability, human resource development and commercial competitiveness. By winning the contract, the competitiveness of Korean nuclear technology has been demonstrated, and Korea, 30 years after it first introduced commercial nuclear power, transformed itself from a nuclear technology–importing country to a technology-exporting country.

This paper presents the importance of nuclear power in the Korean economy and the history of commercial nuclear power plant developments in Korea, including localisation, technology transfer and technology self-reliance. Also presented are brief introductions of Korean reactor models, OPR1000 and APR1400, and the competitiveness of the Korean nuclear industry. Finally, the paper discusses how, based on its experience in continued construction, operation and technology development, the Korean industry can support other countries planning to introduce commercial nuclear power plants by sharing its experience.

10.2 IMPORTANCE OF NUCLEAR POWER IN KOREA

Since the first commercial operation of Kori Unit 1 in 1978, nuclear power has been one of the most important sources of energy in Korea. The role of nuclear power has been to minimise dependence on energy resource imports, to secure the country's rapid economic development by supplying low-cost electricity and to reduce greenhouse gas emissions from energy production.

As one of the poorest countries in the world in terms of natural resources, especially for energy, the selection of nuclear power as a major energy source in the 1970s in Korea was not an option but an inevitable choice to secure a stable and economic energy supply in pursuing national economic growth. Over the past three decades, Korea's annual gross domestic product (GDP) growth has averaged 8.6%, with a corresponding growth in electricity consumption — 33 billion kilowatt hours (kWh) in 1980 to 439 billion kWh in 2007. At present, 23 nuclear power plants accounting for 28.5% of the installed capacity provide 36% of the country's electricity generation. A further five plants are under construction and four plants are in the planning phase. The generation share of nuclear power is projected to reach 59% of electricity supply by 2030. In 2007, nuclear power reduced the amount of total energy imports by 15%.

Nuclear power has contributed to the country's economic development by maintaining low costs of electricity generation. Since 1982 and for 26 years from 1982, consumer prices have increased by 178% while electricity rates only increased by 5.4%. Nuclear power costs are the lowest in Korea: the rate of electricity produced by nuclear power in 2009 was 39 Korean won (KRW), compared with coal at 51 KRW, oil at 192 KRW, liquefied natural gas (LNG) at 164 KRW and hydro at 134 KRW, as published by the Ministry of Knowledge Economy (MKE) in 2009.

Nuclear energy is clean, cost-effective, reliable and safe. In particular, it is recognised as a practical solution to the dilemma of reducing greenhouse gas emissions while supplying the world's increasing demand for energy. As of 2008, 439 nuclear power plants operating worldwide prevented more than 2 billion tonnes of the annual carbon dioxide (CO_2) emissions — equivalent to 10% of the total CO_2 emissions in the world. In Korea, CO_2 emissions due to electricity generation account for 24% of the total annual CO_2 emissions and are expected to gradually increase as the electricity demand increases. In 2008, nuclear power prevented 140 million tonnes of CO_2 emissions in Korea (MKE, 2009).

10.3 HISTORY OF COMMERCIAL NUCLEAR POWER PLANTS IN KOREA

The genesis of the Korean nuclear industry can be traced to 1957 when it became a member of the International Atomic Energy Agency (IAEA) and immediately implemented a nuclear research programme. The country's first nuclear reactor, a small research unit, achieved criticality in 1962. Thereafter, its first commercial power plants were developed by foreign contractors, with Kori 1 being the first to supply electricity from April 1978. Korea's almost 40-year history of commercial nuclear power plants can be divided into four phases: introduction of nuclear power, promotion of localisation, technology self-reliance and advanced reactor development.

In the first phase, marked as the introduction of the nuclear power period, from the early 1970s to the late 1970s, the construction of nuclear power plants was fully dependent on foreign technology. Starting with Kori Unit 1 in 1978, two more units, Kori Unit 2 and Wolsong Unit 1, were constructed based on a turnkey contract with foreign suppliers. Kori Units 1 and 2 are pressurised water reactors (PWRs), and Wolsong Unit 1 is a CANDU-type reactor. The foreign suppliers had overall responsibility for the design, procurement, construction and commissioning operation. Involvement of local industries was limited to civil and architectural work in service facilities. Major goals for technology self-reliance in this period were to identify available items to be localised and to imitate the construction technology of the suppliers.

The second phase took place from the late 1970s to the mid-1980s when six more PWRs were constructed based on the component contract with foreign prime contractors for the nuclear steam supply system (NSSS) and balance of plant (BOP). In this phase Korean utility KEPCO, with the assistance of a foreign architectural and engineering (A/E) company, managed the construction projects. Local suppliers were subcontracted for detailed design especially in the BOP design, site design and BOP equipment procurement. During this phase local participation was gradually increased and basic foundations for technology self-reliance were prepared as well.

The period from the late 1980s to the mid-1990s is marked as the technology self-reliance phase. In the mid-1980s the Korean nuclear industry embarked upon a plan to standardise the design of nuclear plants and to achieve much greater self-sufficiency in building them. In 1987 the industry entered a 10-year technology transfer programme with foreign suppliers, to achieve technical self-reliance. As the first project in the plan, construction of Yonggwang Nuclear Units (YGN) 3 & 4, the reference model for the OPR1000, was started. In the project KEPCO assumed overall responsibility by making prime contracts with local suppliers, with foreign suppliers serving as subcontractors to local firms. The base of Korean nuclear power technology self-reliance was established and was promoted early in this phase through technology transfer and joint design contracts made between local and foreign suppliers. After the successful construction of YGN 3 & 4, construction of Ulchin Nuclear Units (UCN) 3 & 4, which are the first OPR1000-type units, was started. Unlike in the previous project, the local suppliers took overall responsibility in all aspects of project implementation, and the role of foreign suppliers was reduced to limited consulting due to successful implementation of the technology self-reliance programme.

A sidetrack from the development of the OPR1000 was the ordering of three more CANDU-6 pressurised heavy water reactor units to complete the Wolsong power plant. These units were built with substantial local input and were commissioned between 1997 and 1999.

In the late 1990s, to meet evolving requirements, a programme to produce an improved OPR1000 was started. This programme involved design improvements of many components, improved safety and economic competitiveness, and optimising plant layout with streamlining of the construction programme to reduce capital cost. Shin-Kori 1 & 2, which are in operation at present, will represent the first units of the improved OPR1000 programme. Beyond this, development of an advanced light water reactor, APR1400, was started in 1992. The basic design was completed in 1999. It offers enhanced safety and a 60-year design life. Shin-Kori 3 & 4 will be the first APR1400-type plants and their construction will be completed by 2014. The period from the late 1990s to now is designated as the advanced reactor development phase.

Self-reliance in nuclear technology for Korea was successfully achieved. A series of OPR1000 plants now operating are among the world's best plants in performance. The technology made great strides to develop an advanced light water reactor model. There were many factors which made the current success in Korea possible. Among others, strong support by the Korean government, preparation of infrastructure, and teamwork during the implementation of the self-reliance programme were the key elements for the success.

Introducing commercial nuclear power plants requires vast amounts of initial investment. Therefore, it was very difficult for the industry to lead the initial stage, and strong support from the government with a strong commitment to technology self-reliance was a key factor to the success. The primary roles of the government were to establish the national nuclear energy programme, policy making, funding of the programme, teaming for the programme and regulation. The programme included plans to establish infrastructure necessary to adopt the new technology. These involved, among others, preparing human resources and letting local firms gradually participate in construction projects to acquire the necessary technical basis. Implementation of such a big programme required the involvement of many domestic organisations. Therefore, it was very important to clearly define the responsibilities of each of the participating entities and manage them in an integrated and coordinated manner. Teamwork based on a smooth inter-organisational relationship toward a common target was another key factor to the success.

10.4 DESCRIPTIONS OF THE OPR1000 AND APR1400 DESIGNS

10.4.1 OPR1000 Design Features

The design of YGN 3 & 4, the reference design for the OPR1000, was mainly based on the Combustion Engineering System 80 NSSS design. The first OPR1000-type nuclear units, UCN 3 & 4, were designed with the aim of improved performance and safety by adopting various design improvements as well as complying with the new, elevated safety requirements. The next OPR1000 plants, YGN 5 & 6 and UCN 5 & 6, continued to improve plant performance and safety by incorporating the construction and operating experience gained from the previous plants and by adopting advanced design features. Major design objectives of the OPR1000 are

Table 1 Major Design Features for OPR1000 and APR1400

Items	OPR1000	APR1400
Capacity	2825 MWt	4000 MWt
Plant design lifetime	40 years	60 years
Seismic design	SSE 0.2 g/OBE 0.1 g	SSE 0.3 g/OBE 0.1 g
Safety requirements		
— Core damage frequency	$<10^{-4}$/RY	$<10^{-5}$/RY
— Containment failure frequency	$<10^{-5}$/RY	$<10^{-6}$/RY
— Occupational radiation exposure	<1.2 man·Sv/RY	<1 man·Sv/RY
— Operator action time	Min. 10 minutes	Min. 30 minutes
— SBO coping time	Min. 4 hours	Min. 8 hours
— Thermal margin	8%	More than 10%

presented in Table 1 as compared to those of the APR1400 (Lee *et al.*, 1992; Lee *et al.*, 1998).

The primary loop configuration of the OPR1000 has two reactor coolant loops. The NSSS is designed to operate at a maximum core thermal output of 2,815 megawatts thermal (MW_t) to produce an electric power output of 1,050 megawatts electric (MW_e) in the turbine/generator system. The major components of the primary circuit are the reactor vessel; two reactor coolant loops, each containing one hot leg and two cold legs; one steam generator and two reactor coolant pumps; and a pressuriser connected to one of the hot legs. All components are located inside the containment vessel. The two steam generators and four reactor coolant pumps are arranged symmetrically. The steam generators are located at a higher elevation than the reactor vessel for natural circulation purposes.

The plant power control system is capable of daily load-following operations with a load variation profile typical in Korea: 16 hours at 100% and 4 hours at 50%, with 2-hour ramps for power decreases and increases. The reactor core control should be capable of a step power change of 10% and ramp changes of 5% per minute without detrimental effects on the fuel rod integrity. The load rejection capability at rated power is also incorporated. Thus the reactor will not be automatically tripped in the event of a turbine trip if the transient causing the turbine trip is limited to the secondary system.

The reactor protection system and other safety-related systems are designed to meet the strict regulatory codes and standards that have been issued for digital safety systems. A high degree of reliability is required in safety-related systems, and therefore design methodologies such as redundancy, diversity and self-diagnostics have been incorporated in order to achieve both the desired reliability and availability of the systems.

The safety concept of the OPR1000 is based on the multiple-level defence-in-depth approach: prevention of accidents or deviations from normal operation, detection of accidents through monitoring, control of accidents to prevent their propagation into severe accidents, and mitigation of severe accidents. This safety objective is pursued by compliance with deterministic requirements, supplemented by probabilistic methods. Later, various design changes were made to the OPR1000 for improved safety and economic competitiveness. Moreover, the plant layout was optimised with streamlining of the construction programmes to reduce capital cost.

10.4.2 APR1400 Design Features

The APR1400, a standard advanced light water reactor, had been developed for 10 years starting from 1992, as one of the G-7 long-term government projects. The design was based on the experience that had been accumulated through the construction and operation of the OPR1000. Moreover, the APR1400 incorporates a number of design modifications and improvements to meet utility requirements (KEPCO, 1999) for enhanced safety and economic goals and to address the new licensing issues such as the mitigation of severe accidents.

Since the APR1400 is an evolution from its predecessor, the OPR1000, the basic configuration of the NSSS is the same, i.e. it has two steam generators with four reactor coolant pumps in an arrangement with two hot legs and four cold legs. However, the APR1400 has many advanced features such as the direct vessel injection (DVI) of the safety injection system, in-containment refuelling water supply system, advanced safety depressurisation system and systems for severe accident mitigation. The NSSS configuration is

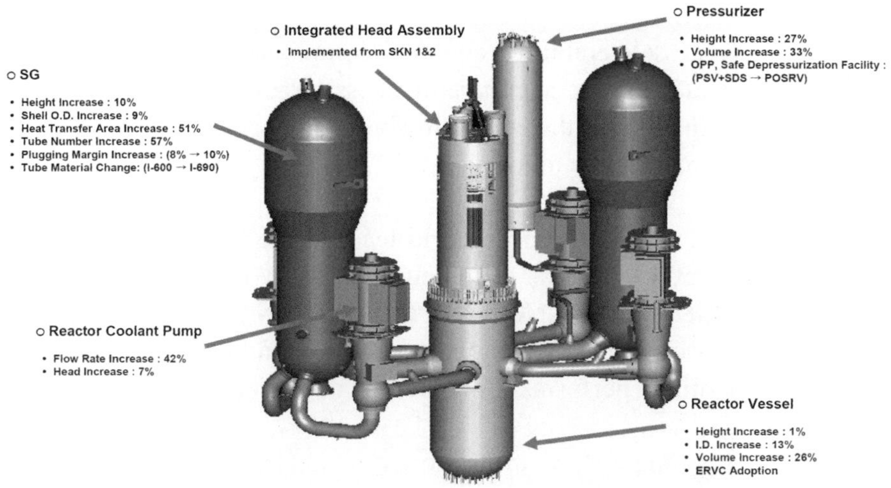

Figure 1 Design Improvements for APR1400 Reactor Coolant System

schematically presented in Figure 1, and design improvements compared with the OPR1000 can be seen in Table 1 (Kim and Kim, 2002).

The power level of the APR1400 is around 1,450 MWe with a thermal power of 4,000 Mw_t, which is 40% higher than that of the OPR1000. The main control room, designed with the human factors and digital instrumentation and controls in mind, is another example of the design improvement. Specifically, the general arrangement has been improved by reflecting on the operation and construction experiences of the OPR1000. Currently, a construction project to build the first APR1400 in Korea is in progress with the goal of commercial operation of the first unit in 2013.

10.5 COMPETITIVENESS OF KOREAN NUCLEAR TECHNOLOGY

On 27 December 2009, the Emirates Nuclear Energy Corporation (ENEC) of the UAE announced that it had selected a Korean consortium led by KEPCO to design, build and help operate civil nuclear power plants for the UAE peaceful nuclear energy programme. The decision was made following a comprehensive and detailed review of three bids from EPR of Areva, ABWR of the GE-Hitachi consortium and APR1400 of the KEPCO team.

In the selection, ENEC focused on five core criteria in reaching its final decision: safety, deliverability, contract compliance, human resource development and commercial competitiveness (WAM, 2009).

As stated in the media, the competitiveness of Korean nuclear technology can be summarised as follows:

- Recognition of KEPCO as a world leader in safety and plant reliability and efficiency, as assessed by the World Association of Nuclear Operators (WANO); KEPCO currently receives among the highest scores in the WANO Performance Indicator Programme, which quantifies performance standards of nuclear operators around the world.
- KEPCO's strong record in constructing nuclear power plants that meet stringent industry quality standards and are delivered on time and on budget.
- KEPCO's capability to supply the full scope of works and services for the UAE civil nuclear power programme, including engineering, procurement, construction, nuclear fuel and operations and maintenance support with the assistance of other Korean members of the KEPCO team.
- Design of the APR1400 as a Generation III, 1400 MW_e nuclear power plant with evolutionary improvements in safety, performance and environmental impact that meet the highest international standards for safety and performance.
- Design to meet heightened safety goals developed in accordance with the latest international safety standards, which aim to secure an additional margin of safety to protect the public health.
- Incorporation of more than 30 years of operational learning and the resulting enhancements of safety, reliability and efficiency into the design.
- Design features to prevent or mitigate severe accidents by ensuring reactor shutdown, removing decay heat, maintaining the integrity of the containment facility and preventing radioactive releases.
- Dedication of a highly experienced team to the project and a commitment to transferring the knowledge gained from Korea's 30 years of successful nuclear industry operation to the UAE programme.

10.6 SHARING THE EXPERIENCE OF THE KOREAN NUCLEAR INDUSTRY

In a nuclear power programme, basic policy mistakes can be exceedingly costly due to the capital intensiveness of the technology. Therefore, it is very important to refer to best practices of and also problems faced by others in formulating the nuclear power programme.

As presented in the previous sections, the achievement of the Korean nuclear industry is exceptional, considering the rather short period of time since its first steps into the commercial nuclear power. Given its success, the Korean nuclear industry can be a role model for countries contemplating the introduction of commercial nuclear power plants. Based on its experience, the Korean nuclear industry can assist other countries preparing to introduce commercial nuclear power plants. Potential areas of assistance include the establishment of a nuclear power programme, feasibility studies, preparation of infrastructure, development of human resources and training, planning localisation and site selection.

10.7 CONCLUSION

Nuclear power has been and will continue to be an important energy source in Korea. With few natural resources, nuclear energy provides a means to secure Korea's economic development.

Three decades after the introduction of commercial nuclear power, Korea has emerged as the most competitive nation in the commercial nuclear power market. Over the past 20-plus years, Korea has successfully achieved technology self-reliance in the commercial nuclear power plant area and has developed indigenous technologies such as the OPR1000 and the APR1400. As a Generation III reactor model, the APR1400 provides a high level of safety and economic advantages over other reactor models as demonstrated by its winning a contract in December 2009 to build four nuclear plants in the UAE.

Given the success of the Korean nuclear industry in the introduction and development of nuclear power technology, it can be a role model for countries contemplating the introduction of commercial nuclear power plants, and it is ready to share its experience with them.

REFERENCES

KEPCO. *Korean Utility Requirement Document*, 1999.

Kim, D. S. and Kim, I. S. "Key Design Features of APR1400 for Safety Enhancement", *Proceedings of the 17th KAIF/KNS Annual Conference Embedded Special Meeting*, 2002, pp. 37–45.

Lee, B. R. *et al.* "Korean Standard Nuclear Power Plant: Safer, Simpler, Easier to Build", *Nuclear Engineering International*, 37 (1992), pp. 29–35.

Lee, J. H. *et al.* "Ulchin 3 and 4: The First Korean Standard Nuclear Power Plants", *Nuclear Engineering International*, 43 (1998), pp. 12–16.

Ministry of Knowledge Economy. *White Book on Nuclear Power 2009*. Seoul: Ministry of Knowledge Economy, 2009.

"UAE Selects Korea Electric Power Corp. Team as Prime Contractor for Peaceful Nuclear Power Program", WAM (Emirates News Agency), 27 December 2009.

CHAPTER 11

MALAYSIAN PERSPECTIVES, PLANNING AND PROBLEMS WITH REGARD TO NUCLEAR ENERGY

Shahidan Radiman

ABSTRACT

Malaysia plans to have its first nuclear power plant by 2021. With the establishment of a Nuclear Steering Committee and three working committees by the Cabinet in 2009, the original plan from the early 1970s for nuclear power has been revived. This paper briefly describes the country's plan, roadmap and possible problems in human capacity building in achieving nuclear power status post 2020.

11.1 INTRODUCTION

The generation of electricity from fossil fuels is a major and growing contribution to carbon dioxide (CO_2) emissions, which contributes significantly to global warming. There are only a few realistic options to reduce CO_2 emissions produced by electricity generation, namely:

- Increased efficiency in electricity generation and end-use;
- Introduction of carbon capture and sequestration at fossil fuel plants on a massive scale;

- Expanding the use of renewable energy resources, such as wind, solar, biomass and geothermal;
- Increased use of nuclear power.

It is likely that we shall need all of these options and, accordingly, it would be a mistake at this time to exclude any of these four options from an overall carbon emissions management strategy.

11.2 THE EVOLUTION OF NUCLEAR POWER

Nuclear power plants have evolved from Generation 1 in the 1950s, which consisted of prototype reactors; to Generation 2 in the 1970s and 1980s, which comprised of commercial reactors, such as CANDU and light water reactors (LWRs); to Generation 3 in the post-2000 period to 2010, including advanced LWRs; to Generation 4 in the post-2010 period. Generation 5 in the post-2030 period is expected to consist of nuclear energy systems which are highly economical, have enhanced safety features, minimise waste and are proliferation-resistant.

11.3 THE GLOBAL ENERGY CHALLENGE

Energy and global economic growth are clearly linked. As the United States and other countries advance economically, there is bound to be greater competition for energy resources. China's relentless quest for energy resources is a good example of this competition. The question is: how will the US and other great powers be able to satisfy growing energy demand in a tightening global energy marketplace? It is now time to step up again to the next great challenge facing the world: energy security.

11.4 CURRENT MALAYSIAN ENERGY SITUATION

Figure 1 shows the projected Malaysian energy load from 2008 to 2030.

Figure 2 shows the Malaysian power generation mix forecast (until 2030). It illustrates the "unhealthy" energy mix, which depends very much on coal and natural gas. It is hoped that nuclear energy will alleviate this problem together with energy stability and security.

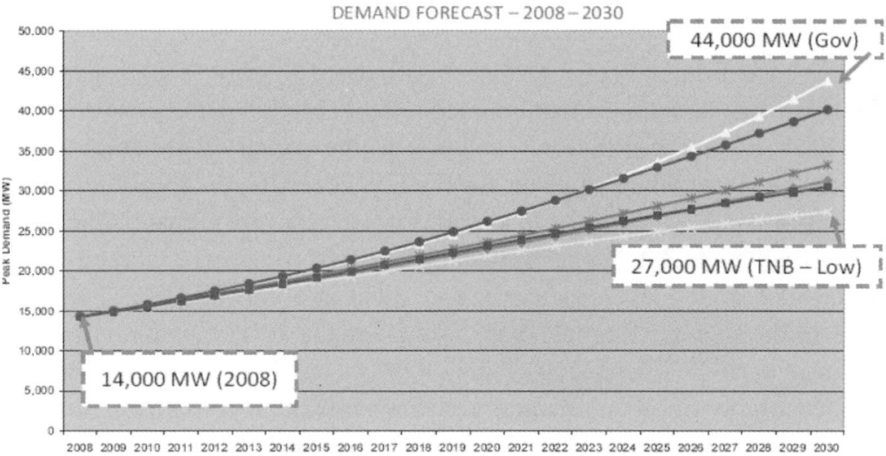

Figure 1 Malaysia Load Projection (2008–2030)

Source: Tenaga Nasional Berhad

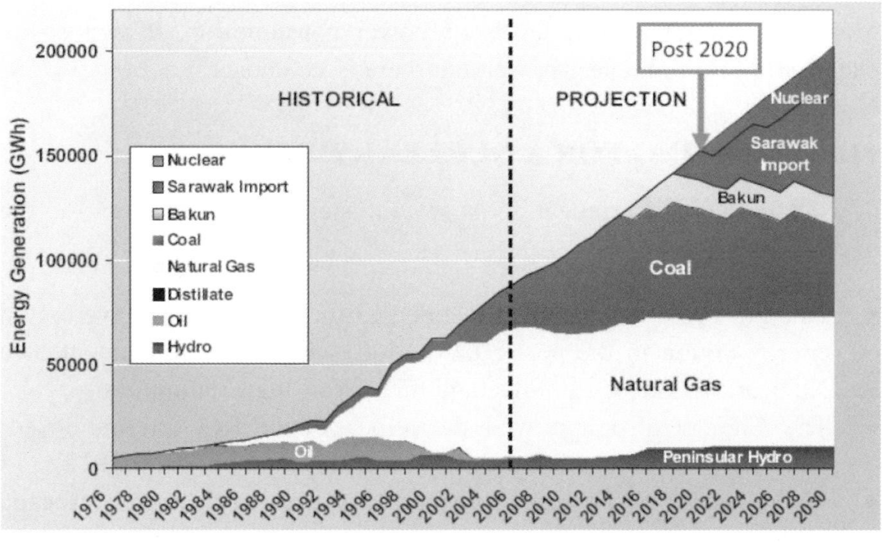

Figure 2 Malaysia Generation Mix Forecast (until 2030)

Source: Tenaga Nasional Berhad

11.5 MALAYSIA PLANS FOR NUCLEAR POWER BY 2021

An Agence France-Presse (AFP) report dated 4 May 2010 stated that Malaysia had announced that it aimed to build its first nuclear power plant by 2021, as this was the only solution to the country's growing energy needs. Mr. Peter Chin, Minister for Energy, Green Technology and Water, said that there would be a lead time of 10 years to prepare. The state energy company Tenaga has stated that it could construct Malaysia's first 1,000-megawatt (MW) nuclear power plant at a cost of US$3.1 billion. The Malaysian government had asked Tenaga to review the situation during a period of increasing global oil prices and in view of the country's limited supply of oil and natural gas. Currently, half of Malaysia's power plants run on gas, and the rest run on coal and hydropower. Nuclear power is the only viable energy option for Malaysia, said Minister Peter Chin. Malaysia has looked at South Korea, France, Japan and China as possible sources of nuclear technology. Newspaper reports indicate that the Port Dickson area is a possible site for a nuclear plant. Electricity usage is currently 14,000 MW, whilst total capacity is 23,000 MW. By 2017, Malaysia will hit critical levels of power consumption. It is a costly exercise to turn to nuclear power, but there is no choice.

11.6 PLANNING FOR A NUCLEAR OPTION

The Malaysian government took several steps as preparation for the nuclear option:

- 26 June 2009: The Cabinet decided to include nuclear power as an energy option in the post-2020 period, with the establishment of a Nuclear Steering Committee and three Working Committees.
- The Cabinet also approved the allocation of RM 25 million for planning and preparation purposes over three years (2010–2012).
- 29 August 2008: The Board of the national energy company, Tenaga Nasional Berhad (TNB), agreed to form a Nuclear Energy Unit and a Nuclear Pre-project Team; the TNB Board also approved a budget of RM 2 million for planning and preparation.
- June 2009: TNB and Korea Electric Power Corporation (KEPCO) signed an agreement for KEPCO to carry out over 12 months a Nuclear

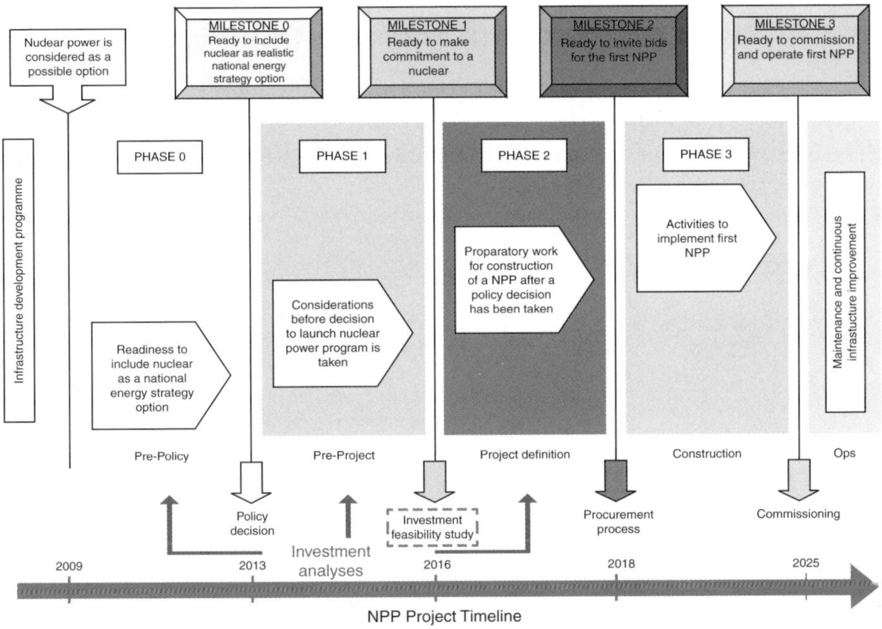

Figure 3 Proposed Malaysia Nuclear Roadmap

Source: Tenaga Nasional Berhad, Nuclear Roadmap for Malaysia, 2009

Preliminary Feasibility Study, including training of TNB staff in nuclear technology. See Figures 3 and 4 for the proposed Malaysia nuclear roadmap, and the five-step plan for the development of nuclear power.

11.7 NUCLEAR ENERGY HUMAN RESOURCES DEVELOPMENT

Several Malaysian agencies are involved in developing human resources for nuclear energy, some of which are as follows:

- The Atomic Energy Licensing Board, which trains staff in safety, safeguards and security, and also in regulation, multilateral agreements and protocols.
- The Ministry of Energy, Green Technology and Water, responsible for implementation of the energy protocol and which acts as the service regulator.

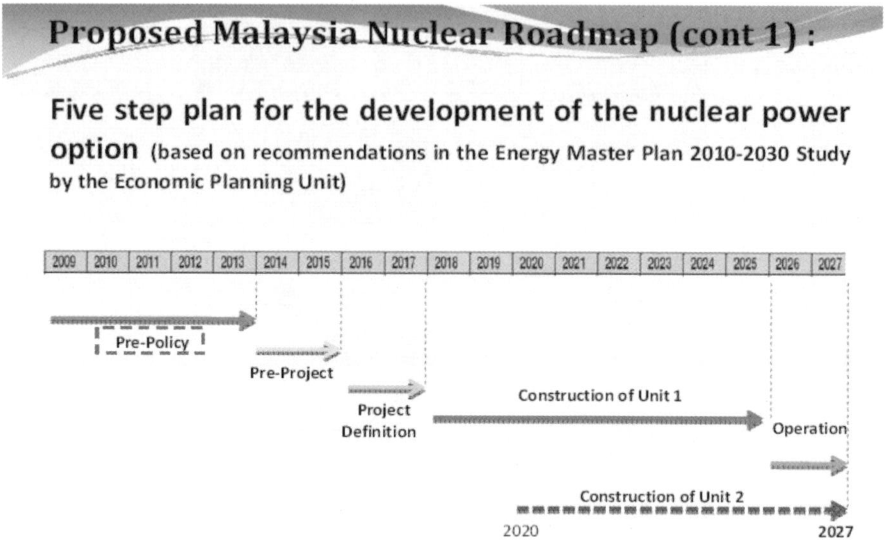

Figure 4 Five-Step Plan for Development of Nuclear Power Option

Source: Tenaga Nasional Berhad, Nuclear Roadmap for Malaysia, 2009

- The Energy Commission and the Energy Planning Unit, working in the Prime Minister's Office; the latter will assist in the implementation of the nuclear programme, especially in the introduction of nuclear power and the transfer of nuclear technology.
- The Ministry of Higher Education; this ministry approved Universiti Teknologi Malaysia (UTM) to start its undergraduate nuclear engineering programme, whilst Universiti Sains Malaysia concentrates on health physics and nuclear medicine; meanwhile, Universiti Kebangsaan Malaysia (UKM) deals with nuclear science, and Universiti Tenaga Nasional (UNITEN) handles nuclear engineering.
- The Malaysian Nuclear Agency is responsible for educating the public on nuclear energy, with plans to upgrade its Triga Mark II Reactor for research and training.

Figure 5 shows Malaysia's nuclear human resources currently available at the Malaysian Nuclear Agency, where it is estimated that three to four times this number of people is required. Universities and the Atomic Energy Licensing Board should also pursue a reasonable competency for research, licensing and regulating a nuclear power plant facility by 2020.

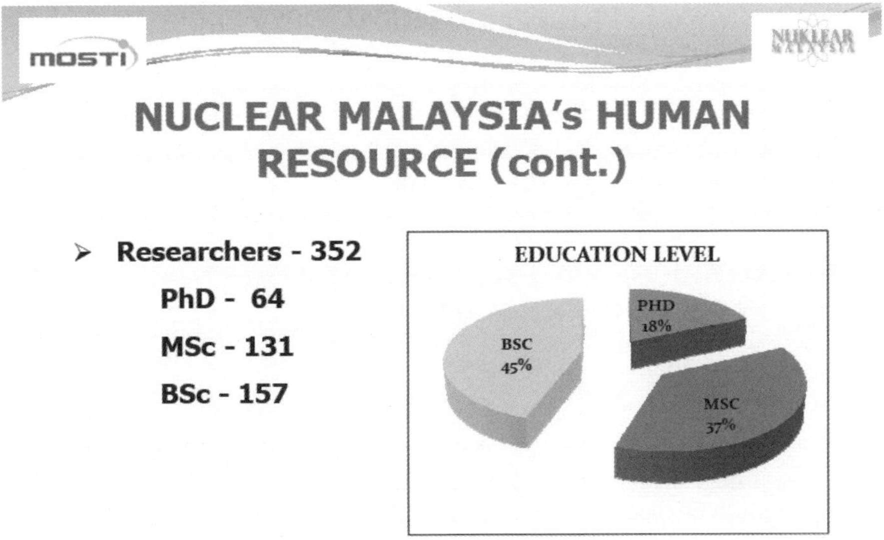

Figure 5 Malaysia's Nuclear Human Resources

Source: Malaysian Nuclear Agency

The Faculty of Science and Technology at Universiti Kebangsaan Malaysia, which has been offering degrees in nuclear sciences since the 1970s, has an undergraduate enrolment of 40 to 50 students per year, and a postgraduate enrolment of 10 to 15 students per year. Since 1980, 1,057 Bachelors of Science in Nuclear Science have been awarded, and 87 students with Masters and PhDs in nuclear sciences have graduated. The UKM Faculty of Engineering and Built Environment is currently aiming to offer nuclear engineering degree programmes within one to two years.

11.8 EDUCATING AND ENGAGING THE MALAYSIAN PUBLIC ON NUCLEAR ISSUES

There have been several efforts and measures to engage the public. One was setting up the Malaysian Nuclear Society in 1989, with the aim of promoting the peaceful use of nuclear science and technology. Another step was to organise the Malaysian Nuclear Conference 2010 on the UNITEN campus in Kajang, Selangor. Winter and summer schools have also been organised at UKM in various nuclear sciences, with foreign professors teaching at these winter schools and delivering public lectures.

11.9 NON-PROLIFERATION TREATY (NPT) AND MALAYSIA

Malaysia is member to the NPT, which has 189 members. Malaysia has also adopted a Strategic Trade Bill in 2010, which aims to curb the illicit trafficking of weapons of mass destruction.

11.10 PROBLEMS FACING THE MALAYSIAN NUCLEAR PROGRAMME

Some of the problems include the following:

- Stakeholders — less than 50% can be made up by the government, but since integrity is of the utmost importance, the Cabinet has to be hands-on;
- Competence of regulatory body — it is very important to have competent manpower to issue licensing and regulate controls on the safety of the nuclear power plant;
- Research and development in nuclear power technology — issues of waste management, integrity of reactor core materials, test rigs, etc., need to be developed in-house by local bodies;
- Competence in nuclear laws and technology transfers, involving relevant government agencies and universities;
- Back-up support for facility installations;
- Commitments from stakeholders and investors;
- Public awareness and acceptance;
- Consistent government policies and political will;
- Safety work culture which must be emphasised at all levels;
- Long-term target and development of nuclear power plants, involving education bodies, training agencies and public funding;
- Continuous manpower training and development since a typical nuclear power plant can operate for up to 60 years.

11.11 CONCLUSIONS

The Malaysian government is now engaged with many nuclear power plant developers, such as Areva and KEPCO, in order to implement its plan to build its first nuclear plant by 2021. Several universities, such as UKM, UNITEN and UTM, are involved in developing human resource capabilities, for example nuclear engineers. Also, several mass media channels are involved in educating the public about nuclear energy. Finally, it appears that nuclear energy is the only clean or carbon-free, renewable and reliable energy option to increase the supply of energy for the country to achieve the status of a developed nation by 2020.

CHAPTER 12

THE ASIAN DEVELOPMENT BANK'S REGIONAL PERSPECTIVES, POLICIES AND ISSUES REGARDING NUCLEAR ENERGY AND SUSTAINABLE DEVELOPMENT IN SOUTHEAST ASIA

Anthony J. Jude[1]

ABSTRACT

Providing a background to the concept of "sustainable development", this chapter explores the interlinked concepts of energy demand and financing needs with specific focus on regional electricity demand and the energy supply situation.Energy resource options including hydropower, natural gas, coal, and geothermal are discussed and the specific question of nuclear energy versus regional cooperation is addressed. Finally, the chapter explores the long-term planning that is needed for nuclear energy development and the role of the Asian Development Bank in this process.

---

[1]The author of this paper is Director, Energy and Water Division, Southeast Asia Department of the Asian Development Bank. The views expressed in this paper are his views based on his experience and working knowledge of the region and do not reflect the views of the Asian Development Bank.

12.1 SUSTAINABLE DEVELOPMENT

Sustainable development was defined in 1987 by the Brundtland Commission, known formally as the World Commission on Environment and Development, as "...development that meets the needs of the present without compromising the ability of future generations to meet their own needs". This definition emphasises the importance of economic development to satisfy needs, and the importance of the natural environment as both a resource provider and waste absorber.

Five years after the Brundtland Commission's report, the United Nations Conference on Environment and Development (UNCED) was held in Rio de Janeiro. Among other things, UNCED produced the UN Framework Convention on Climate Change (UNFCCC) and Agenda 21. The latter is a comprehensive action plan for sustainable development. It is effectively UNCED's translation of the Brundtland Commission's definition into more specific policy directions. It has 40 chapters on all aspects of sustainable development and covers energy issues, but has no separate chapter dedicated to energy.

The UN established the Commission on Sustainable Development (CSD) that meets annually to address selected topics covered by Agenda 21. Energy was addressed for the first time at the ninth session of the CSD (CSD-9) in 2001. The CSD-9 decision on energy was thus the first dedicated effort by the CSD to further translate the Brundtland Commission's definition of sustainable development into specific policy directions with respect to energy.

Nuclear power was a particularly controversial topic during the preparatory process of the CSD-9. There was a long debate on nuclear energy between countries that considered nuclear an essential component of their sustainable development strategies and countries that considered nuclear power incompatible with sustainable development. The 2002 World Summit on Sustainable Development (WSDD) in Johannesburg called all relevant regional and international organisations, governments, and other relevant stakeholders to implement the recommendations of the CSD-9. The Johannesburg Plan of Implementation (JPOI) called for actions to promote widespread availability of clean and affordable energy, specifically the promotion of renewable energy resources, efficiency improvements, and advanced energy technologies, including cleaner fossil fuel technologies (clean coal technologies). Nuclear energy was included in the category of advanced energy technologies.

12.2 ENERGY DEMAND AND FINANCING NEEDS

Projections of global energy demand show large increases to 2030 and scenarios have been modelled to slow this growth in demand. The principal drivers are global population and economic growth, especially in developing countries. The world population currently at 6.5 billion is projected to grow to more than 9 billion by 2050. Energy is central to achieving the goals of sustainable development but is also the primary engine for economic development. Over time energy systems have grown more complex, particularly urbanisation and industrialisation. Modern manufacturing, service industries, agriculture, and today's urban environments all rely on electricity. All demographic projections show continued urbanisation which coupled with economic development will cause increases in electricity demand.

Access to good infrastructure is an important enabler of growth in all types of economies. This is particularly relevant in the current global financial climate where infrastructure-based economic stimuli are being pursued by governments all over the world. The Asian Development Bank's (ADB) long-term strategic framework[2] identifies infrastructure as one of the nine leading challenges facing the region's future. The framework identifies several causes for the infrastructure deficit, including (a) low levels of public sector revenue mobilisation; (b) comparatively weak institutions; (c) regulatory failures; and (d) under-developed financial systems, resulting in barriers to the flow of long-term private capital.[3]

The bottlenecks in the energy sector infrastructure are an issue within the Asia-Pacific region as this constrains growth. The energy demand growth within the Asia-Pacific region is projected to grow 2.4% per annum.[4] This translates into investments of US$7–10 trillion in the energy

---

[2] ADB, *Strategy 2020: The Long-Term Strategy of the Asian Development Bank, 2008–2020* (Manila: ADB, 2008).

[3] Ibid.

[4] ADB, "Energy Investment Outlook" (draft), 2010.

sector up to 2030. Electricity generation will account for the lion's share of this investment (64%) followed by the oil and gas sector (18%), coal development (12%), and domestic oil and gas trade infrastructure (6%). Within the Asia-Pacific region, the largest share (49.6%) of the investments will be in East Asia (People's Republic of China); followed by South Asia (15.8%), the Developed Group (Australia, Japan, Korea, and New Zealand, accounting for 15.1%), Southeast Asia (12.8%), Central Asia (6.2%), and the Pacific region (0.5%).[5]

12.3 REGIONAL ELECTRICITY DEMAND AND ENERGY SUPPLY SITUATION

The International Energy Agency (IEA) base case scenario shows that electricity demand is growing at 2.4% per annum within the Asia-Pacific region. To meet this demand growth, the world electricity generation capacity needs to increase from 4,000 gigawatts (GW) to 7,800 GW by 2030. This means almost doubling the installed generation capacity between now and 2030. Therefore, the equivalent of today's capacity must be newly constructed over the next 20 years, and additional capacity must also be built to replace many of today's power plants that will be retired during the same period. The IEA projects that the Association of Southeast Asian Nations (ASEAN) will see an average annual increase of 2.5% in its primary energy demand until 2030. The IEA estimates ASEAN electricity demand to increase 76% between 2007 and 2030. Meeting the ASEAN countries' electricity demand will require investing more than $1.1 trillion in the next 25 years.

In meeting the region's growing demand for energy, it is important to recognise that each country uses a different mix of energy, and that all countries are different. Each country uses a different mix of energy sources for a number of reasons and there is no right mix for each country. It depends on how fast the country's economy is growing and one has to look first into the available resources within the country as well as the alternative sources of supply to meet the projected demand growth. The available financing options may determine the level of investment in a deregulated market that would provide a higher investment to a private

[5]Ibid.

investor or to the utility. There are tradeoffs among issues such as environment versus cheap electricity, job creation, import dependence, energy security, and climate change that are all personal and national preferences that need to be resolved by the countries themselves.

In the case of Thailand, no new coal power plants can be built as the general public and the non-governmental organisations are against such projects. For this reason, 75% of Thailand's power generation is based on natural gas, partly from domestic resources and partly from imported natural gas (from Myanmar). Thailand has taken a decision that it will import low-cost electricity generated by hydropower plants located in Lao PDR and Myanmar. Hydropower is clean but the construction of the plants themselves will need to take into consideration sustainable development of the affected people living in the project area and ensure that livelihood components built around the project are sustainable in the long term. It has also taken measures to promote the use of renewable energy such as solar-, wind-, and biomass-based generation for grid application and has promulgated the Renewable Energy Law with appropriate feed-in tariffs to get private sector participation.

The fastest growing economy within Southeast Asia has been Viet Nam, averaging 9% growth per annum over the past 10 years.[6] This has resulted in a power demand growth of 15% per annum over the past decade. Power demand growth in the first seven months of 2010 was 17%. This demand growth is emerging as a result of economic reforms (Doi Moi policy) initiated in 1986. Increased foreign direct investments, coupled with industries moving from countries where the cost of doing business was getting expensive to Viet Nam, where labour and electricity costs were low, has contributed to this demand growth. Also, the service sector has improved over the past 10 years, resulting in an increase in tourists.

12.4 ENERGY RESOURCE OPTIONS IN SOUTHEAST ASIA

12.4.1 Hydropower

The Southeast Asian region is rich in energy resources but the level of resources varies among the 10 ASEAN countries. Hydropower potential

---

[6]ADB, "Viet Nam Country Operations Business Plan (2010–2012)", 2009.

within the region is the largest in Myanmar, which has a potential of 110,000 megawatts (MW), followed by Laos (55,000 MW), Malaysia (25,000 MW), Cambodia (8,000 MW), and Viet Nam (3,000 MW). Only 10% of this potential has been developed by these countries, with the exception of Viet Nam.

Cambodia's power demand is growing as the economy develops. The hydropower potential identified by the Mekong River Commission is mostly along the main Mekong River, with some on the tributaries. Developing a hydropower plant on the main Mekong within Cambodia will have serious consequences for the water flow regimes downstream, fisheries and also Tonle Sap, the largest freshwater lake in the region. The Cambodian government is cognisant of this fact and has only agreed to develop hydropower on the tributaries of the Mekong and other river systems not part of the Mekong.

Viet Nam has developed most of its large hydropower resources and only small and medium-sized sites are left. Hydropower is capital intensive but has low operating costs and no fuel costs. The gestation period is long (six to seven years) for a hydropower plant compared to a conventional thermal power plant (four years). Viet Nam used to have more than 60% of its electricity generation from hydropower, which had lower generation costs (3.0–4.5 US cents/kilowatt hour (kWh)) than thermal plants, but these hydropower plants could not meet the demand during the dry season, resulting in power outages. The government has taken measures to increase the proportion of thermal plants (coal and gas-fired) in the generation mix. Hydropower in the generation mix is around 37% and projects with a capacity of about 3,300 MW are under construction. One of the largest hydropower plants in Viet Nam is the 2,400 MW So La Hydropower Plant that will be commissioned in 2012.[7]

Myanmar has the largest hydropower resources within Southeast Asia with less than 5% of the country's potential developed. The largest plant under construction by a consortium of Chinese and Thai investors is the 7,000 MW Tasang Hydropower Project.[8] About 10% of the electricity generated will be consumed within the country, while the remaining power will be exported to Yunnan Province and Thailand.

---

[7] Viet Nam, "Sixth Power Development Master Plan", 2007.

[8] ADB, "Regional Power Development Master Plan for GMS", 2008.

Lao PDR began developing its hydropower potential in the 1950s with the planning of Nam Ngum 1 Hydropower Plant which was built in phases, initially with a 30 MW capacity in 1971 to a final installed capacity of 150 MW. In 1987, Laos began developing the Xeset Hydropower Plant (45 MW),[9] which was commissioned in 1992. The surplus electricity from these two power plants is sold to Thailand. This put in place policies and a legal framework within which private sector developers could participate in developing Laos's hydropower potential for export to Thailand and Viet Nam. As such the Theun Hinboun Expansion Project, Nam Ngum 2, Nam Ngum 3, Nam Ngiep 5, and Xe Kaman 1 are all in different phases of development. Nam Theun 2 (1,058 MW) was recently commissioned with 95% of the electricity being exported to Thailand and 5% being consumed locally. Laos has signed agreements with both Thailand and Viet Nam to export about 6,000 MW and 5,000 MW, respectively.

Most of Malaysia's hydropower resources are located in Sarawak, Borneo. The largest hydropower plant here is the 2,400 MW Bakun Hydropower Project which is scheduled for commissioning in phases from 2011. The Sarawak state government's plan is to develop renewable energy sources to meet the demand growth from its planned industrial zones. There are several other hydropower plants where feasibility studies are being prepared. Eventually most of the power generated will be exported via high-voltage direct current (HVDC) undersea cables to Peninsular Malaysia. This is a strategic decision of the government to use more of its renewable energy resources, while still earning foreign exchange revenues from export of its natural gas resources.

12.4.2 Natural Gas

Natural gas resources are mostly located in Indonesia (112 trillion cubic feet (Tcf)) and Malaysia (84 Tcf). Most of the gas from these two countries is exported as liquefied natural gas (LNG), while some is used for power generation. Myanmar and Viet Nam both have about 18 Tcf, while the Philippines has about 4 Tcf. Myanmar has more gas than it can currently utilise for its own use and hence is exporting natural gas to Thailand

[9]The ADB, Xeset Hydropower Project, 1987, is the name of the project.

and more recently to Yunnan Province, People's Republic of China. This brings in much-needed foreign exchange earnings for the country. Explorations ongoing in Cambodia have shown some promise of natural gas deposits but further drilling and analysis is needed. The development of a natural gas field is expensive and there needs to be an anchor such as a power project to justify the investment costs.

In Viet Nam most of the natural gas produced from the offshore Nam Con Son Basin and PM3 is used for power generation. The natural gas from Block PM3 is a joint production sharing agreement with Malaysia that is used both for power generation and fertiliser production. The Block B/52 offshore gas field, currently being developed by PetroVietnam and Chevron, is for power generation. About 3,600 MW of new gas-based generation will be put into operation in southern Viet Nam from 2014–2016.

Lao PDR does not have any proven gas reserves but there are two sites that could have gas. The government plans to begin drilling on the site. If there is natural gas, this can be used for baseload generation which Laos will use to fill the generation gap during the dry season. Indonesia on the other hand has sufficient natural gas but most of the gas is contracted in long-term LNG contracts to Japan, Korea, and Taipei. Historically, Indonesian natural gas production has been geared toward export markets, but the country has made an effort to shift natural gas toward domestic uses in recent years as a substitute for the country's declining oil output. However, Indonesia's limited natural gas transmission and distribution network remains an obstacle to further domestic consumption. Indonesia's two major LNG production plants, Arun and Bontang, have experienced declining production in recent years. To help make up for this shortfall, Indonesia has vigorously engaged in natural gas exploration activities, as it strives to meet its long-term LNG contract obligations and also to satisfy increasing domestic demand. Several new projects are under development, the most high profile of which is the Tangguh LNG project in West Papua.

After several delays, the first shipment from Indonesia's $5 billion Tangguh LNG project finally set sail for South Korea in July 2009. But the future of other proposed LNG projects is uncertain, as debate continues over whether the country's natural gas reserves should be retained for domestic consumption rather than exported. The BP-operated Tangguh project will help Indonesia maintain its position among the world's largest LNG exporters — the country sits in second place, behind Qatar, in terms of capacity, but has slipped to third after Malaysia in terms of traded volume. But the project has suffered a series of delays, caused by issues ranging from technical problems at the export plant, to the failure of China National Offshore Oil Corporation's (CNOOC) re-gasification facility in Fujian, China, to be ready on time.

12.4.3 Coal

Indonesia has the largest coal resources (1.7 billion tonnes) within the region, followed by Viet Nam (150 million tonnes). Most of Indonesian coal is bituminous and sub-bituminous coal which is good for power generation. However, given climate change issues and sustainable development, there is a need for Indonesia to consider using cleaner coal technologies for power generation. Some options are to stop building coal power plants using conventional pulverised coal technology and to use supercritical or ultra-supercritical boiler technologies that have higher thermal efficiencies and use less coal to generate 1 kW of electricity, resulting in lower carbon dioxide (CO_2) emissions.

Asia cannot do away with coal in its generation mix as it is a cheap energy source and produces electricity at an affordable cost to many poor people within the region. It is estimated that about 1.6 billion in the world are without electricity connections and 80% of these people are in Asia. Given this scenario, coal will continue to be in Asia's energy mix.

Viet Nam's coal is mainly anthracite, which is good quality coking coal (6,000–8,000 kcal/kg) used for steel manufacture. Only the waste coal (lower quality), mixed with a little higher quality coal, is being used for power generation. Anthracite coal is hard and difficult to burn in supercritical and ultra-supercritical power plants. Hence, local coal is used mainly in pulverised coal power plants. Viet Nam, cognisant of the climate change impacts on its delta area in southern Viet Nam, is taking measures now to build new supercritical power plants to reduce CO_2 emissions from the power sector. Given a power demand growth averaging

15% per annum over the past decade, renewable energy based on biomass, wind, and solar cannot meet this demand growth.

Malaysia and Laos do have some coal resources. Malaysia's coal resources, located in Sarawak, are a mix of peat and sub-bituminous coal which is sufficient for generation within Sarawak. Coal-based power plants in Peninsular Malaysia use imported coal from Indonesia. Laos has lignite resources (80 million tonnes) in northern Laos. As such a 1,670 MW lignite power plant is being constructed, of which about 100 MW will be consumed locally in northern Laos.

12.4.4 Geothermal

The Philippines and Indonesia are the two countries within the region with significant amounts of geothermal resources. Indonesia's geothermal energy potential, estimated to be about 27,000 MW,[10] is the world's largest. Currently, the installed generating capacity is 1,050 MW, accounting for just over 4% of the total potential. Presently, there is about 1,000 MW of unexploited geothermal power potential under private control and over 3,000 MW with state-owned enterprises. About half of these resources are in fields that are currently producing electricity or with confirmed reserves ready for further expansion. The government has intensified its efforts to revive and scale up geothermal development in the past few years. In 2003 the Geothermal Law (ref. 23/2003) was promulgated, making this form of renewable energy the only one to be governed by its own law. The Law, among other things, mandated that future geothermal fields must be transparently and competitively tendered for development. In 2004, the Ministry of Energy and Mineral Resources issued a Blueprint for Geothermal Development in Indonesia which was intended as a roadmap for the development of another 6,000 MW by 2020. It should be noted, however, that government regulations complementing the Law were only issued in 2007 (ref. PP-59/2007), and other related regulations were developed later in 2009.

---

[10] Indonesian Ministry of Finance, "Ministry of Finance Green Paper: Economic and Fiscal Policy Strategies for Climate Change Mitigation in Indonesia", Ministry of Finance, and Australia Indonesia Partnership, Jakarta, 2009.

The government has intensified its efforts to revive and scale up geothermal development in the past few years. In terms of development relevant to the private sector, the Ministry of Energy and Mineral Resources issued a Ministerial Decree (No. 30, issued in 2009) recognising the high costs associated with geothermal power development in Indonesia relative to coal-based power, and guided Perusahaan Listrik Negara (PLN), the state electric company of Indonesia, to consider paying a power purchase price of as much as $0.097/kWh.[11] The government of Indonesia is also considering arrangements for sharing the upstream risks[12] and field development costs to further stimulate investment. For example, the Ministry of Finance has developed a proposal for the establishment of a revolving fund[13] that will help lower exploration risks on greenfield sites. Once an adequate pricing and incentive programme is implemented, an increasing number of independent power producers will be able to develop their geothermal concessions since they will be able to secure a return on their investments commensurate with the risks they face in the sector.

The estimated potential in the Philippines is 7,000 MW and about 1,935 MW[14] is currently in operation. The first area to be explored was the Tiwi geothermal area in southern Luzon. The government's strategy of offering prospective geothermal sites wherein earlier studies have been

[11] However, the government is still in the process of developing a set of sources for funding these higher costs. This has led to an initial reluctance on PLN's part to enter into power purchase agreements (PPAs) with the independent power producers.

[12] Steam resource assessments involve several steps, including aerial surveys, seismic surveys, detailed site-level geological characterisation and, finally, drilling of exploration wells. These assessments are expensive. For example, each test well could cost up to $5 million. At each step, there is considerable risk that the investments may not yield an economically viable steam resource.

[13] The fund would pay for initial geological assessments and exploration drilling across a range of greenfield sites. For sites where an economically viable resource has been established, the government of Indonesia would provide the resource data to all potential IPP bidders, and the winning bidder would be required to reimburse the fund for exploration expenses. Thus the "revolving" nature of the fund allows for exploration to occur on additional greenfield sites.

[14] F. M. Dolor, "Phases of Geothermal Energy Development in the Philippines", paper presented at the Workshop for Decision Makers on Geothermal Projects and Management, organised by UNU-GTP and KenGen in Naivasha, Kenya, 14–18 November 2005.

conducted through open and competitive bidding under the Philippine Energy Contracting Round has provided opportunities to secure additional geothermal investments.[15] The passage of the Renewable Energy Law also provided further opportunities for existing service contractors to undertake expansion and optimisation projects. The Renewable Energy Law envisions a feed-in tariff for geothermal power; however, the specific rates are being negotiated and are expected to be announced by the end of 2010. About 1,200 MW of new power plant capacity will be offered to private investors by 2013.

12.5 WHY NUCLEAR ENERGY? WHY NOT STRENGTHEN REGIONAL COOPERATION?

Given the energy resource potential within the Southeast Asian region, the question that needs to be asked is why nuclear energy? Are there no other alternatives or have all other alternatives been examined and exhausted? A number of ASEAN countries have recently been indicating through press releases their plan of having nuclear power by 2020–2025. Why are these countries planning to build nuclear power plants and what is driving this thinking? Is it energy security and self-reliance or is it because of climate change concerns and the need to reduce CO_2 emissions as part of country commitments/pledges made at the Copenhagen meeting?

Clearly, Cambodia and Laos will not need nuclear power to meet their electricity needs. Cambodia can easily meet its power needs by importing low-cost electricity in the short to medium term from Laos, Thailand, and Viet Nam. In the longer term, it should be looking at developing both hydropower- and coal-based generation to provide a mix of peaking and baseload generation in its power system as grid expansion occurs. Laos has adequate hydropower resources to meet its demand growth. But in the longer term, as Laos extends its transmission and distribution grids to achieve 90% electrification by 2020, it will need coal-based generation as

[15] C. Tiangco, "Geothermal Energy Development in the Philippines", presentation made to the Mapua Institute of Technology, School of Mechanical Engineering, and the Philippine Institute of Mechanical Engineering Educators, Inc. (PIMEE).

baseload generation to even out the low hydro output during the dry season.

Malaysia and Thailand could be thinking about nuclear energy in the longer term to ensure security of supply as gas and oil resources decline. In recent years, we have seen fluctuations in energy markets (price swings) and these countries may be trying to be more prepared. Also, given the energy resources available in Peninsular Malaysia and in Sarawak, nuclear should be a long-term option. However, if Malaysia's oil and gas resources are declining and the government wants to maximise revenues from the sale of LNG, then it does make sense to be forward looking. In that case, the government should be looking at a series of nuclear plants and not just a single nuclear power plant.

Thailand on the other hand may find it difficult to convince its people that nuclear energy is good for the country, since 71%[16] of generation in Thailand is already based on natural gas, which is cleaner than coal. The government aims to achieve 10% of power generation from renewable energy (solar, biomass, and wind). Besides, Thailand is already importing electricity from Lao PDR and will be importing electricity from Myanmar from 2017 onwards.

Indonesia has also given some thought to having a nuclear power plant built by 2021 and has started building institutions to help support this development. However, again given the potential indigenous energy resources available, efforts would be better placed to develop those. For this to happen, resource mobilisation will be required and incentives for renewable energy development, such as geothermal (pricing and upfront drilling risks), solar and wind, need to be addressed. Lastly, given the vast geographical spread of Indonesia, it is also important to address the expansion and upgrading of transmission and distribution systems within the country.

The countries should also explore implementation of energy efficiency and demand-side management, which could help forego investments in new generation. The author would strongly support regional cooperation within Southeast Asia or ASEAN. There are commitments and planned

[16] Electricity Generating Authority of Thailand, "Thailand Power Development Masterplan", 2010.

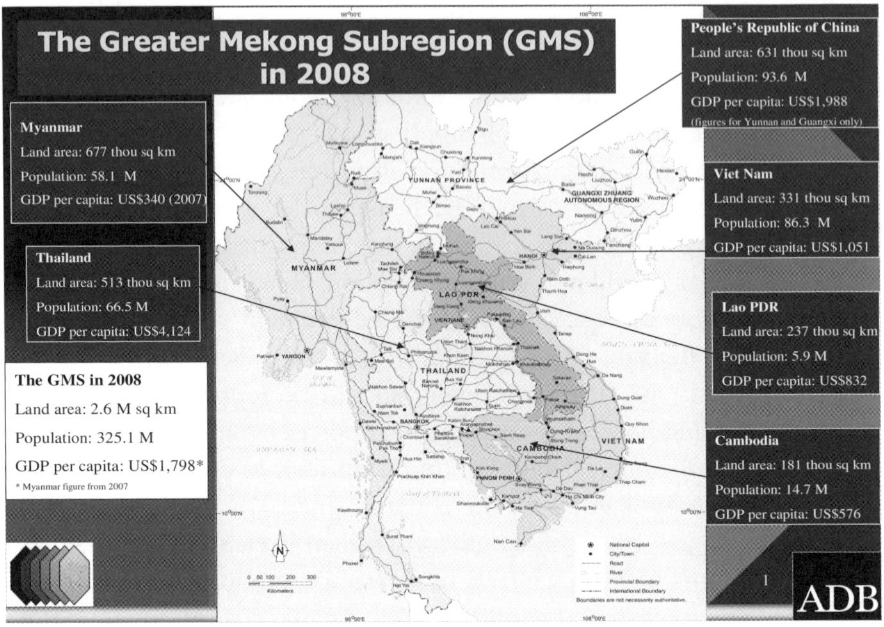

Figure 1 Greater Mekong Subregion Map

Source: ADB.

projects for sharing energy resources within ASEAN and the Greater Mekong Subregion[17] (Figure 1).

A number of power interconnections have taken place within GMS states (Cambodia, Lao PDR, provinces of Yunnan and Guangxi in the People's Republic of China, Myanmar, Thailand, and Viet Nam; see Figure 1) but only a few have emerged between Malaysia and Thailand, Malaysia and Singapore, Malaysia and Indonesia, Indonesia and Singapore, and Malaysia and Brunei.

See Figure 2 for planned interconnections by 2015. These countries have the potential to share energy resources among themselves as there is not only a one-hour time difference between Malaysia and Indonesia but also differences in peak power demand. If surplus energy is available that could be shared or traded between the countries, it could also help save these countries' investments in new generation capacity. However,

[17] ADB, *Greater Mekong Subregion*, www.adb.org/gms/.

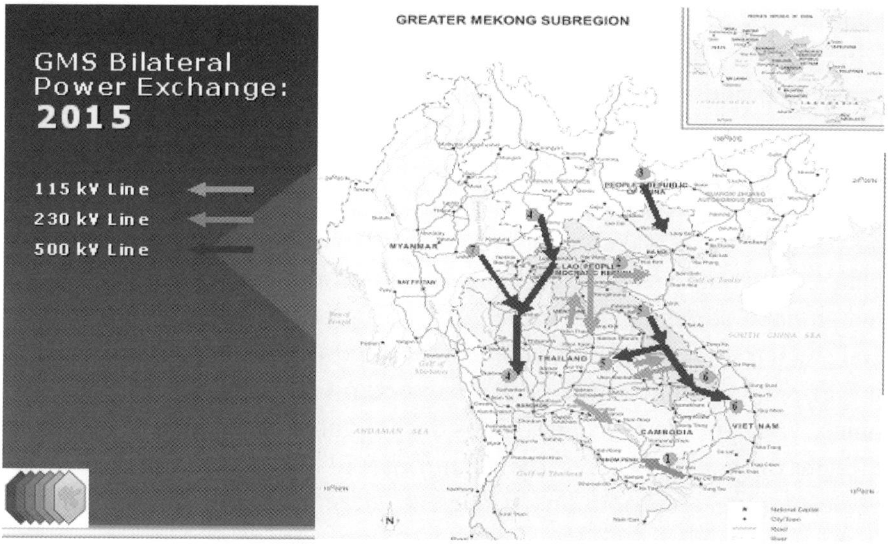

Figure 2 Power Trading within the GMS

Source: ADB.

investments in power interconnections will need to be made which will help pay for these investments within three years. The 275-kilovolt (kV) interconnection between Sarawak and West Kalimantan[18] is a good example of a cross-border energy exchange which benefits both countries.

12.6 LONG-TERM PLANNING NEEDED FOR NUCLEAR ENERGY DEVELOPMENT

The only country within ASEAN or Southeast Asia that has really thought through the need for nuclear energy is Viet Nam. Viet Nam is way ahead of all the ASEAN countries in terms of planning as it had been thinking about the option 15 years ago. Development of nuclear energy requires long lead times and countries need to put in place policies, regulations, and a legal framework that will support nuclear energy development. If countries are thinking about nuclear energy, they will need to

[18] Trans Borneo Power Grid: Sarawak to West Kalimantan Link (Malaysia Section) –275 kV Transmission Line project, July 2011.

plan for a series of nuclear plants as fuel processing plants and storage will cost more or less the same for one or two plants. Countries will need to develop and strengthen the high-voltage power transmission lines to evacuate the power to load centres. Given that nuclear power plants cannot be shut down like a coal- or gas-fired power plant, it is essential to ensure that the energy generated at night is used efficiently. In some large power systems, it makes economic sense to build pumped-storage power plants that could use this surplus electricity for pumping at night and for the pumped-storage plants to be used during peak power periods to generate electricity. This will enable the shutdown of expensive peaking power plants within a system that is based on fuel oil, diesel, or gas turbines. The skills required and skills development of a country need to be thought through very carefully. Countries will also need to think in terms of developing a curriculum on nuclear energy within local universities that will support the nuclear industry. Countries need to address some of the following critical questions before embarking upon a nuclear programme:

- **Policy-related barriers:** How can ASEAN governments formulate a clear and stable policy commitment to nuclear energy as part of the overall energy strategy?
- **Industrial capacities and skilled human resource barriers:** In order to build, operate, and maintain nuclear plants, are the country's industrial capacity and human resources adequate? If not, how can this be improved over the next few years to support nuclear energy development?
- **Financial barriers:** Should governments support nuclear investment through measures such as loan guarantees or invite investments on a government-to-government basis from countries that have the technology?
- **Public acceptance barriers:** What measures can ASEAN governments take to gain greater public acceptance for nuclear programmes? Will it be through the media, schools, and/or public disclosures?
- **Advanced disposal of high-level radioactive waste:** What management and disposal strategies should be adopted for spent nuclear fuel?

- **International system of safeguards to prevent proliferation of nuclear fuels and technology:** These need to be maintained and strengthened where necessary. If the capacity is not there within the country, how will this shortcoming be addressed?

12.7 NATIONS PLANNING PEACEFUL NUCLEAR POWER DEVELOPMENT

Almost one quarter of global electricity could be generated from nuclear power by 2050,[19] the International Energy Agency said in a report published on 16 June 2010. According to the IEA forecast, nuclear capacity could grow to 1,200 gigawatts electric (GW_e) by 2050, providing 24% of global electricity, if fully supported and well developed. The foreseeable expansion of nuclear generation capacity will contribute to a 50% cut in energy-related CO_2 emissions by 2050, as stated by the IEA. In the same report the IEA claims the expansion of nuclear generators presents no technological challenges; however, these challenges need to be addressed.

A number of Middle East and North African countries have taken steps to make nuclear power part of the generation system. The reason for this shift is to diversify their energy resource dependence but also to continue exporting oil and gas resources to earn foreign exchange. Some of the plans are as follows:

- **Saudi Arabia:** Has established a New Energy Centre for nuclear and alternative energy technologies.
- **UAE:** Planning for 14 nuclear power plants. Three plants to be operational by 2020. In 2009, the UAE awarded a $20 billion contract to a South Korean consortium (KEPCO) to construct four plants (5,600 MW).
- **Jordan:** Prepared a nuclear programme that will provide 30% of electricity by 2040. It plans to issue the tender in 2010. Jordan currently imports over 95% of its energy needs, and with increasing and fluctuating oil prices, its dependence on energy imports is becoming

[19] "World Energy Outlook 2010." International Energy Agency.

a huge burden on the economy and is hindering its development and economic growth.

- **Kuwait:** Established a nuclear committee in 2009 and signed a nuclear cooperation agreement with France in early 2010.
- **Algeria:** Recently announced a new centre for nuclear and alternative energy technologies.
- **Tunisia:** Feasibility study to be completed by 2012.
- **Egypt:** Identified El-Dadaa, a coastal town, as the site for its first nuclear power plant. It aims to have four plants in operation by 2025, with the first plant in 2019.
- **Syria:** Announced in March 2010 its intention to develop nuclear energy for power generation.
- **Turkey:** Plans to build 3,000–10,000 MW of nuclear capacity. South Korea and Russia have expressed a keen interest in working with Turkey on its civilian nuclear power programme. In May 2010, Russia signed an agreement to build and operate Turkey's first nuclear power plant, a project estimated to cost up to $20 billion.
- **Morocco:** Plans to begin construction of its first nuclear plant in 2016–2017 and has begun drafting legislation.

Nuclear power project financing and understanding the risks involved and how to mitigate them are perhaps the most important aspects of which countries planning to embark on a new nuclear build should have a clear and comprehensive understanding. Financing also plays an important role in deciding which technology to adopt. For many of the countries, financing will be a deciding factor in selecting technology for their first commercial nuclear reactor. A sustainable funding scheme will be a major consideration in selecting an international company to build the country's first nuclear power plant.

12.8 SALIENT POINTS ABOUT NUCLEAR ENERGY AND PLANS IN DEVELOPED COUNTRIES

- The US enacted a law in 2005 to encourage new nuclear power plants. Twenty-four applications have been submitted but even after five years, no project has obtained statutory clearance (indicative of the strict scrutiny that all nuclear projects come under).

- Germany's policy is to phase out nuclear power reactors (17 reactors with an aggregate power generation capacity of 20 GW). It has added 20 GW of wind power capacity but these plants only produce 170 terawatt hours (TWh), whereas the nuclear power plants produce 355 TWh annually.
- Sweden also has a policy to phase out nuclear power plants (10 reactors, 9 GW) but has not taken any action to close them.
- The gas fields in the United Kingdom have declining yields and the government is talking about nuclear energy. The UK Sustainable Development Commission recommended against nuclear energy given that the waste disposal and decommissioning of these plants is expensive. Still, the UK government has decided to build new nuclear plants but identifying the sites has been difficult.
- Of the 49 reactors under construction, two are in OECD Europe (one each in France and Finland), two in Canada, one in the US, nine in Russia, 31 in Asia (regional developing member countries (DMCs)), one in South America, one in the Middle East, and two in Eastern Europe.
- The time available to adequately address greenhouse gas (GHG) emissions is running out. The recent economic downturn may have provided a small window of opportunity to put in place significant policy initiatives that could result in stabilising the atmospheric GHG at 450 parts per million (PPM). The Pacific countries are concerned about this target and want it to be lowered. If global GHG emissions rise to 550 PPM, this will have a devastating impact because of sea-level rises.
- Nuclear energy is one of several options to optimally reduce GHG emissions. If any of the options were to be discarded, the overall cost of mitigation would increase.
- There has been a resurgence and about 60 countries (30 countries already use nuclear energy) have approached the International Atomic Energy Agency (IAEA) to better understand the nuclear energy option.
- Nuclear power is not universally economical and depends on the situation (e.g. renewable resources, rate of growth of demand). It meets baseload demand (unlike wind and solar which are weather

dependent), it is expensive to build but cheap to run (like renewables). The "cost charts" are deceptive because they do not compare all costs and benefits, e.g. the cost of the price volatility of oil and other fuels, the protection a nuclear power plant offers against fuel price increases over 40–50 years.

- GHG emission reduction options include carbon capture and storage (CCS). While most of the linked technologies are already in use, the largest commercial-scale CCS project in operation is only 10 MW. There are significant uncertainties and if found to be unfeasible, the pressure on developing nuclear energy will increase. Similarly, improving energy efficiency involves low costs but politicians are generally biased towards visible, greenfield project investments and favour cost reductions less. The implementation of wind power has been successful in Germany but has required annual subsidies of €4–6 billion and even now supplies only 7% of the country's demand.
- Adding large wind capacity has technical issues, as was observed in Denmark. It has 3,180 MW of wind capacity that supplies about 7 TWh out of the total annual demand of about 43 TWh. However, when the wind resource is good, it meets nearly all of Denmark's demand and some wind power is even exported. In early 2009, a wind farm with a large capacity was in operation when a wind shear suddenly occurred, the wind speed over the country increased within minutes, and the wind turbines cut out (the blades stalled on high wind speed to protect the equipment). The sudden loss of wind power supply to the grid led to significant changes in power flow in the transition period, which could have resulted in large blackouts in Denmark; however, as it happened over the weekend when demand was not high, the protection and control systems acted properly and an incident was avoided.
- Project financing has not been used for nuclear power plants. It is implemented by utilities with large financial resources as they also want low-cost power over very long periods.
- Generally markets want short-term results; this tends to support investments that have low capital costs even when operating costs are high — typically for gas-based and other fossil fuel–based power

plants. Therefore, the government support for nuclear power is seen as addressing a "market failure".

- While multilateral development banks (MDBs, such as the ADB, World Bank, European Investment Bank, European Bank for Reconstruction and Development, and African Development Bank) directly contribute, if any policies change towards supporting nuclear energy, their financial support will remain relative to the share of total capital investment required. However, their participation could reduce risk perception and help mobilise commercial financing at an affordable cost.
- Developing nuclear energy project proposals are increasingly facing not-in-my-backyard (NIMBY) resistance. The location of nuclear power plants requires extra effort in consultations and obtaining support from the local population.
- The IAEA provides advice, technical support, and capacity building to member countries, but it is not a global "regulator". Its advice is not binding, but it encourages countries to publish its advice.
- The IAEA cannot judge the performance of member countries (e.g. if safety standards are being implemented properly). The PRC held a conference on nuclear energy in April 2009 and around the same time there was a media report quoting the PRC regulator that more assistance was needed to support the country's aggressive nuclear capacity addition. The PRC planned to add about 20,000 MW of new nuclear generation capacity by 2025. Subsequently, the IAEA was formally approached to provide peer review and capacity building assistance.
- Decisions to support or not support nuclear energy need not be taken by the government on economic and technical bases alone; it is usually a matter of preference and taste of the government concerned (e.g. how much does the electorate value safety?).

12.9 ROLE OF THE ADB

The ADB's Board approved a new ADB energy policy[20] in 2009 to guide ADB operations in the energy sector. The 2009 Energy Policy aligns the

[20] ADB, "Energy Policy", 2009.

ADB's energy operations to meet energy security needs, facilitate a transition to a low-carbon economy, and achieve the ADB's vision of a region free of poverty. The new energy policy is congruent with the draft energy strategy developed in consultation with internal and external stakeholders, and is aligned with the ADB's long-term strategic framework for 2008–2020, Strategy 2020. It represents a coherent translation of important elements of Strategy 2020 that prioritise energy-related objectives and identify the institutional capabilities needed for the future within a changing regional, global, and technological context. The ADB's new energy policy aims to help DMCs to provide reliable, adequate, and affordable energy for inclusive growth in a socially, economically, and environmentally sustainable way. However, this policy does not support nuclear energy projects. The ADB does not have the relative advantage in nuclear energy where the investment needs are huge and it does not have the technical capacity that the IAEA has in dealing with the technical issues as well as the non-proliferation issues.

The ADB's sustainable development goal is to support the development of energy sources to ensure that its member countries do have an adequate supply of electricity to meet the economic development needs but also to ensure that the unconnected rural population is connected to the grid. The ADB will also continue supporting its DMCs in formulating energy policies that would help limit GHG emissions. Some of these policies will be in the areas of (a) energy efficiency; (b) fuel diversification, from coal to gas or other cleaner fuels such as renewable energy (wind, solar, and biomass), and natural gas; and (c) clean coal technologies such as supercritical and ultra-supercritical boiler technologies, and carbon capture and storage.

CHAPTER 13

BIRTHING AN ASEAN NUCLEAR ENERGY COOPERATION REGIME: DRIVERS, STATUS AND WAY FORWARD

Francisco G. Delfin Jr.

ABSTRACT

The creation of an ASEAN regional nuclear energy cooperation regime is driven by inter-related concerns on energy, the environment, and supra-national governance. How this regime will be crafted and operated will present major challenges to ASEAN given the varying levels of commitment to nuclear power by individual governments, challenges posed by NGOs and religious groups, and regional nuclear technological capability. Several meetings held on the proposed ASEAN nuclear energy cooperation network since 2007 have not finalised the terms of reference and work plan. Some member states have been sensitive to proposed regime elements that are seen to diminish internal nuclear policies and programmes. This highlights the need for a gradual approach that anticipates a civilian nuclear industry emerging in ASEAN by 2020 rather than for the immediate formation of a full-blown legal regime.

13.1 INTRODUCTION

Anticipating the inevitability of a civilian nuclear power industry in the region, ASEAN heads of states during the 12th ASEAN Summit in Cebu, the Philippines, called for the formation of a regional nuclear energy regime that will govern the safe use of nuclear energy within ASEAN. The establishment of a Nuclear Energy Cooperation Sub-Sector Network (NEC-SSN) became the responsibility of the ASEAN Senior Officials on Energy (SOE) through the ASEAN Ministers on Energy Meeting (AMEM) framework. The administrative support for this undertaking comes from the Jakarta-based ASEAN Centre for Energy (ACE).

This chapter starts with an examination of the energy, environmental, and governance factors driving nuclear power use and regulation in the region. It then summarises the status of national nuclear energy programmes and describes ASEAN's effort to craft a NEC regime and the challenges facing this effort. Building on such constraints, the chapter ends by exploring how this regime can be developed.

13.2 ENERGY, ENVIRONMENTAL, AND GOVERNANCE DRIVERS

The creation of an NEC (originally called nuclear energy safety or NES) regime is driven by several factors related to energy supply and demand, environmental concerns, and supra-national governance.

13.2.1 Energy Drivers

Energy supply uncertainty, highlighted by volatile world oil prices, is arguably one of the strongest factors prodding ASEAN nations to undertake or revive nuclear power programmes. Although Indonesia, the Philippines, and Thailand had established nuclear power programmes dating back to the 1960s (Alexandra, 2009; Delfin, 2008; Takabut, 2007), and the Philippines actually completed the 620 MW Bataan Nuclear Power Plant (NPP) in 1985 (Figure 1), these programmes were terminated or deferred in the mid-1980s for several reasons, including abundant and cheap oil supply. In 2007 when crude prices topped \$60/barrel, the pace of ASEAN policy pronouncements and activities on nuclear energy quickened, especially with the 12th ASEAN Summit Cebu Declaration expressing openness to nuclear energy use.

Exploring the nuclear option is just one mode of fuel diversification to enhance national energy security. Meeting this objective often includes

Figure 1 The 620 MW Bataan NPP Completed in 1985 But Mothballed by the Aquino Government

Source: NPC

some of the following measures: 1) a cutback in fossil fuel consumer subsidy, 2) reserving fossil fuel production for exports rather than for power generation, 3) promoting biofuels in the transportation sector, 4) more aggressive development of renewable energy for power generation, and 5) going nuclear.

Growing electricity demand, fuelled by continuing economic growth and prosperity in the region, is another major driver for nuclear power. Recent electricity outages in the urban centres of Indonesia, the Philippines, and Vietnam (Alexandra, 2009; Quiros, 2009; Tuan, 2009) show that current power capacities in these countries are unable to meet rising needs. Electricity demand is forecasted to grow 4.8% annually, tripling from 37.9 million tonnes of oil equivalent (Mtoe) in 2005 to 123.1 Mtoe by 2030, necessitating major investments in new generation facilities (ADB, 2009).

Another factor that promotes the region's long-term nuclear energy use and regulation is the ASEAN power grid project (APGP) (Figure 2). Aimed for initial operation by 2015 (Chonglertvanichkul, 2007),

Result of ASEAN Interconnection Master Plan Study

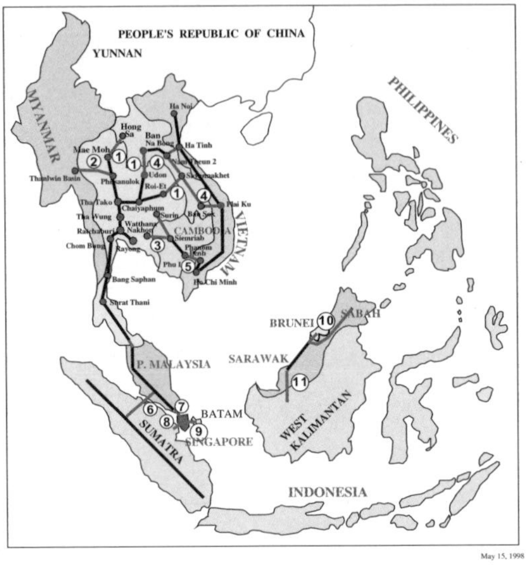

	Year
1) Thailand-Lao PDR	2008/2010
2) Thailand-Myanmar	2013
3) Thailand-Cambodia	2004/2016
4) Vietnam-Lao PDR	2007-2016
5) Cambodia-Vietnam	2003/2006
6) P.Malaysia-Sumatra	2008
7) Singapore-P.Malaysia	2012
8) Singapore- Sumatra	2014
9) Singapore- Batam	2014
10) Sabah/Sarawak-Brunei	2019
11) Sabah/Sarawak-West Kalimantan	2007

Figure 2 ASEAN Power Grid Components and Estimated Linkage Dates
Source: P. Chonglertvanichkul, 2007

interconnecting national power grids involves both physical linkage of facilities and harmonisation of grid operations and policies. Excess power supply in one national grid system can thus be transmitted to those with power deficit. The wider electricity market to be provided by the APGP enhances the economic viability of large-capacity nuclear plants. The 2015 scheduled operation of the APGP will be very timely for the first nuclear power stations of the region coming on stream around 2020 (Figure 2).

13.2.2 Environmental Drivers

The use of nuclear power, with its low greenhouse gas (GHG) emissions, has been revived by global warming concerns. Nuclear power plants have the least direct and total life cycle CO_2 emissions (9–21 grams of CO_2 equivalent per kWh) compared with plants using coal (966–1,306), natural gas (439–688), solar (100–280), hydro (4–236), and wind (10–48)

(Spadaro *et al*., 2000). Nuclear power plants currently in operation effectively reduce global CO_2 emissions by 1,600 million tonnes per year (IAEA, 2008). And despite ASEAN's modest contribution to global GHG emissions, it is a strong supporter of the Kyoto Protocol; ASEAN's 2007 Declaration on Environmental Sustainability called for increased cooperation in climate change–mitigating strategies and implicitly acknowledged nuclear power's role in this strategy.

On the other hand, regional regulation of nuclear power is driven by lingering doubts about the hazards of nuclear power. Member states which may not necessarily use nuclear energy are understandably concerned about the effects of nuclear accidents in one state spilling over to their territories. Such cross-border externalities were vividly illustrated by the 1997 Indonesian forest fires. In that disaster, haze drifted to neighbouring Brunei, Malaysia, and Singapore and even to parts of Thailand, Vietnam, and the Philippines (Figure 3) and had varying environmental and health impacts (Frankenberger *et al*., 2005). It is thus understandable why Singapore and Malaysia which previously opposed nuclear power have become advocates of regional nuclear cooperation.

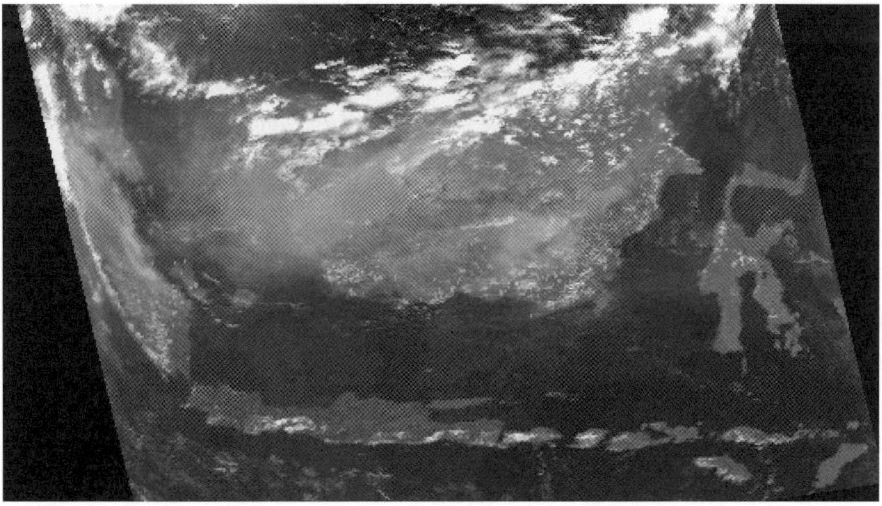

Figure 3 Satellite Image of Haze Spreading from the 1997 Indonesian Forest Fires
Source: http://www.fao.org/ag/againfo/programmes/en/lead/toolbox/Indust/BioBurEA.htm

13.2.3 Governance Drivers

Several regional and global regimes also favour the use and regulation of civilian nuclear power in ASEAN. First, the Southeast Asian Nuclear-Weapon-Free Zone (SEANWFZ) Treaty signed in 1995 obligated members to refrain from producing and possessing nuclear weapons and from discharging radioactive material into the sea or atmosphere. This addresses both security fears that civilian nuclear technology may be diverted for weapons purposes and the environmental worry about potential nuclear waste dumping into the region's commons. Second, all ASEAN members have ratified the Nuclear Non-Proliferation Treaty (NPT) and many members have also ratified or signed other conventions of the International Atomic Energy Agency (IAEA) pertaining to nuclear materials, accidents, and liability (Table 1).

Third, the ASEAN Regional Forum (ARF) July 2004 Statement on Non-Proliferation further encourages ASEAN members to comply with

Table 1 Status of Signing and Ratification by ASEAN States of Key International Nuclear Treaties

Treaty/Convention	BRU	CAM	IND	LAO	MAL	MYN	PHI	SIN	THA	VIE
Non-Proliferation Treaty[1]	RA	RA	RA	RA	RA	RA	RA	RA	RA	RA
Nuclear Safety[2]			RA				SG	RA		
Nuclear Material Protection[3]		RA	RA				RA			
Notification of Accident[4]			RA		RA	RA	RA	RA	RA	RA
Assistance in Accidents[5]			RA		RA		RA	RA	RA	RA
Spent Fuel Management[6]			SG				SG			
Civil Liability[7]							RA			

RA: Ratified or acceded; SG: Signed.

[1]Nuclear Non-Proliferation Treaty;

[2]Convention on Nuclear Safety;

[3]Convention on the Physical Protection of Nuclear Material;

[4]Convention on Early Notification of a Nuclear Accident;

[5]Convention on Assistance in the Case of a Nuclear Accident or Radiological Emergency;

[6]Joint Convention on the Safety of Spent Fuel Management and on the Safety of Radioactive Waste Management;

[7]Vienna Convention on Civil Liability for Nuclear Damage.

international non-proliferation obligations to enhance the region's security. Finally, the signing of the ASEAN Charter in 2005 and the aim of establishing an ASEAN Economic Community by 2015 will speed up economic integration that favours regional cooperation and standard setting on a host of issues, including presumably nuclear energy use.

13.3 THE ASEAN NEC-SSN: STATUS AND CHALLENGES

The pace and direction of regional nuclear cooperation depend also on the state of individual national nuclear energy programmes. Vietnam is widely regarded to be on track to commission its first 4,000 MW NPP by 2020 (see Table 1). Vietnamese officials are so confident about their legal, technical, safety, human resource, and financial preparations that they recently upgraded their nuclear goal to 16,000 MW by 2030 (AFP, 2010). Malaysia may be the second ASEAN country to tap nuclear power after its Cabinet in 2010 approved the operation of its first NPP by 2021 (AP, 2010), although it is likely to face more internal debate than Vietnam. And, though Singapore has declared nuclear power is unlikely to be used even within 10 years, its decision to start a careful economic and technical feasibility study of nuclear power (Iswaran, 2010) raises the possibility that Singapore may go nuclear earlier than expected.

In contrast, nuclear power programmes in Indonesia and the Philippines have suffered political and legislative setbacks as shown in Table 1 that may complicate their NEC-SSN involvement. Recent media reports about Myanmar's alleged secret nuclear weapons deal with North Korea (Macdonald, 2009) will surely bring added scrutiny, if not urgency, to NEC-SSN formation.

13.3.1 Status of the NEC-SSN

The NEC-SSN's terms of reference (TOR) and work plan were drafted by host Singapore during the November 2007 SOE meeting. In that draft, the proposed regime included five key elements: 1) a legal framework for implementation of standards, 2) a mechanism for peer review and inspection of facilities, 3) joint research, 4) a regional radiation monitoring network, and 5) a system for early notification and provision of assistance during accidents. The work plan, on the other hand, called for information sharing, personnel exchanges and site visits, and joint research and conferences among the region's scientists and policy makers.

Despite the mandate from the ASEAN heads of states and the broad consensus among the energy ministers to form the NEC-SSN, the Senior Officials on Energy have not been able to finalise the documents after almost three years of work and meetings (see Table 2). The last AMEM in July 2009 in Mandalay encouraged them to finalise the documents for approval during the next AMEM in 2010.

Table 2 Chronology of Major Milestones in ASEAN Nuclear Energy Development (1986–2010)

Date	Event
April 1986	Philippine President Aquino mothballs newly completed 620 MW Bataan NPP.
September 1989	Indonesia's National Energy Coordination Board decides new NPP feasibility study is needed.
December 1995	Southeast Asian Nuclear-Weapon-Free Zone Treaty (Treaty of Bangkok) is signed.
May 1996	Final feasibility report confirms Muria peninsula as best site for Indonesia's first NPP.
March 2002	Vietnam forms Nuclear Energy Programme Implementing Organization (NEPIO).
January 2006	Vietnam approves long-term strategy for nuclear development to 2020 and beyond.
January 2007	12th ASEAN Summit in Cebu calls for creation of a regional nuclear energy safety regime.
April 2007	Thailand approves 2007–2022 Power Development Plan which includes the first 2,000 MW of nuclear power by 2021.
May 2007	Myanmar signs deal with Russian atomic agency Rosatom to build 10 MW nuclear research reactor.
June 2007	Vietnam's Prime Minister approves nuclear energy master plan to 2020.
September 2007	Indonesian Muslim clerics and scholars declare *fatwa* on planned Muria NPP.

(*Continued*)

Table 2 (*Continued*)

November 2007	Special ASEAN Senior Officials Meeting on Energy (SOME) in Singapore endorsed in principle the draft terms of reference (TOR) for the Nuclear Energy Safety Sub-Sector Network (NES-SSN).
January 2008	First meeting of the NES-SSN in Singapore fails to finalise TOR and work plan. IAEA mission reviews the Philippines' plan to rehabilitate the Bataan NPP.
June 2008	Vietnam's National Assembly passes Atomic Energy Law.
August 2008	26th ASEAN Ministers of Energy Meeting (AMEM) in Bangkok tasked the SOME to complete the TOR of the NES-SSN in time for the 14th ASEAN Summit.
September 2008	Cambodian government announces plan to build first NPP by 2020.
October 2008	The Philippines' National Power Corp. (NPC) signs cooperation agreement with South Korea Electric Power Company (KEPCO) for a feasibility study on BNPP rehabilitation.
March 2009	14th ASEAN Summit Chairman's Statement does not mention the proposed NES-SSN.
May 2009	Special SOME in Chiang Mai endorses name change to Nuclear Energy Cooperation Sub-Sector Network (NEC-SSN) to denote larger sphere of cooperation.
June 2009	KEPCO submits feasibility report to the Philippine Congress, NPC, and DOE stating that the BNPP may be successfully rehabilitated.
July 2009	27th AMEM in Mandalay endorses name change to NEC-SSN and encourages the SOE to finalise TOR and report to the next AMEM.
November 2009	Vietnam's National Assembly endorses operation of first 4,000 MW NPP by 2020.
February 2010	14th Congress of the Philippines fails to pass bill for Bataan NPP rehabilitation and commissioning.
April 2010	Singapore Prime Minister declares government will begin careful study of nuclear energy.
May 2010	Malaysia's Cabinet approves operation of the 1st NPP by 2021.
June 2010	Myanmar denies secret nuclear weapon cooperation programme with North Korea. Vietnam increases nuclear power target to 16,000 MW installed capacity by 2030.

13.3.2 Challenges to the NEC-SSN

Concerns about potential diminution of national nuclear policies appear to be the biggest barrier to NEC-SSN formation. Specifically, the proposed promulgation of regional legal standards to govern national nuclear power industries are seen by Indonesia and Vietnam as problematic. This is understandable given the need to protect decades-long investments and emplaced standards on national programmes made by these countries. A related but less valid concern is that peer review and inspection of facilities impinge on members' national security. Given that all ASEAN countries have ratified the NPT which mandates IAEA inspection of nuclear facilities, the objection to ASEAN-level inspection is somewhat illogical. But this concern raises a third and broader issue among members — that the NEC-SSN will be duplicating functions and mandates already exercised by the IAEA. In addition, the IAEA-supported Asian Nuclear Safety Network (ANSN), which counts six ASEAN countries as members (Indonesia, Malaysia, the Philippines, Thailand, Singapore, and Vietnam), already exists to promote nuclear safety through capacity building on a voluntary basis.

ASEAN officialdom will also need to respond in a transparent, credible, and sustained manner to civil society opposition to nuclear power if a regional nuclear regime is to be successful. Although Western environmentalists are now split on nuclear energy, with Greenpeace founder Patrick Moore and the US-based Environmental Defense Fund among the prominent endorsers of nuclear energy, most ASEAN environmental organisations are likely to continue the 1970s and 1980s ethos of opposing anything nuclear.

Some religious elements will add their voice against nuclear energy even if environmentalists begin to acknowledge the climate benefits of nuclear power. The political clout of religious groups is demonstrated by the deferment of the Muria power station due to a *fatwa* issued by Indonesia's Islamic clergy and scholars (Tanter, 2007) and by the defeat of the congressional bill reviving the Bataan nuclear plant, supported by a network of Philippine civil society groups, including elements of the Catholic Church (M. Cojuangco, personal communication, 2010; Punzalan, 2010).

Another challenge to NEC-SSN formation and implementation also comes from ASEAN's still modest nuclear science and technology capacity. Much of the work envisioned in the NEC-SSN TOR and work plan will require advanced theoretical and experiential understanding of the entire nuclear fuel cycle. In the short term, this can be addressed by engaging experts from the IAEA, business vendors, and foreign governments marketing their nuclear technology such as France, Japan, or South Korea. Over the long term, the region's universities should ultimately produce the necessary human resources for the emerging ASEAN nuclear energy industry. Academic departments that may benefit from the use of nuclear power such as engineering, physics, mathematics, and some natural sciences may seize the opportunities provided by the NEC-SSN to build up their curricula, faculty, and facilities.

13.4 SKETCHING A WAY FORWARD

Rather than aiming for a comprehensive and full-blown legal regime now, ASEAN can proceed along a more gradualist approach. A three-stage process can be envisioned whereby most of the NEC-SSN goals may be achieved by 2020, or in time for the anticipated operations of the region's first nuclear power stations. It can start by framing the NEC-SSN to focus initially on a more restricted sphere of cooperation such as building a regional radiation monitoring network and a system for nuclear accident notification and emergency assistance. By focusing on the limited scientific and safety aspects of cooperation, ASEAN members can nurture trust, communication, and reciprocity on a highly charged subject. Regional cooperation can then move in the medium term to a higher and more technical sphere such as creating a platform for national regulatory agencies and implementing organisations to share policies, practices, and personnel. This should help strengthen the institutional independence and technical competence of ASEAN nuclear regulators which are central to a safe and secure nuclear industry in the region (Fitzpatrick, 2009). Discussions on common standards, joint research, and facilities inspection can also begin at this time. The last stage is envisioned to be where agreements can be started, if not reached, on more politically contentious but critical areas such as a possible common regional repository for nuclear wastes, joint contracts with vendors on nuclear fuel supply, and sanctions on non-compliant or erring member states.

The energy, environmental, and governance imperatives sweeping the region and the globe that increasingly favour using low-carbon nuclear energy can only be ignored at the peril of ASEAN's continued prosperity, harmony, and security. Creating a regional nuclear cooperation regime that meets ASEAN's unique needs will not be easy, popular, or inexpensive but it is needed if only to prevent the nuclear self-interest of nations from fracturing and endangering ASEAN.

REFERENCES

ADB. *Energy Outlook for Asia and the Pacific*. Manila: Asian Development Bank, 2009.

Agence France Press (AFP). "Vietnam to Build Eight Nuclear Plants to Ease Infrastructure", *Business World*, 24 June 2010, p. 7.

Alexandra, L. A. "Indonesia's Nuclear Energy Initiative", *ESI Bulletin*, 2, no. 3, (2009), pp. 7–8.

Associated Press (AP). "Plan to Go Nuclear Under Fire", *The Straits Times*, 5 May 2010, http://www.straitstimes.com/BreakingNews/SEAsia/Story/STIStory_522857.html.

Chonglertvanichkul, P. "The ASEAN Power Grid: Progress and Direction", paper presented at the ASEAN Energy Business Forum, Singapore, 22–24 August 2007.

Delfin, F. G. Jr. "Revive Nuclear Power", *Philippine Daily Inquirer*, 27 April 2008, p. A16.

Fitzpatrick, M. "Nuclear Renaissance Arrival in Southeast Asia Will Pose Challenges", *ESI Bulletin*, 2, no. 3, (2009), pp. 3–5.

Frankenberger, E., McKee, D. and Thomas, D. "Health Consequences of Forest Fires in Indonesia", *Demography*, 42, no. 1, (2005), pp. 109–129.

International Atomic Energy Agency (IAEA). Electricity, Nuclear Power, and the Global Environment. Fact Sheets & FAQs", 2008,

http://www.iaea.org/Publications/Factsheets/English/electric.html.

Iswaran, S. Speech by Mr. Iswaran, Senior Minister of State for Trade and Industry, during the Committee of Supply Debate under Head V (Ministry of Trade and Industry) on 8 March 2010.

Macdonald, H. "Revealed: Burma's Nuclear Bombshell", *The Sydney Morning Herald*, 1 August 2009, http://www.smh.com.au/world/revealed-burmax2019s-nuclear-bomshell-20090731-e4fw.html.

Punzalan, K. "Civil Society Organizations and the Nuclear Energy Debate in the Philippines", paper co-presented at the RSIS-NTS Workshop on Nuclear Energy and Human Security, Trader's Hotel, Singapore, 23 April 2010.

Quiros, J. "Mindanao Hit by Power Outages", *Philippine Daily Inquirer*, 11 October 2009, http://newsinfo.inquirer.net/topstories/topstories/view/20090-911-224726/Mindanao-hit-by-power-outages.

Spadaro, J., Langlois, L. and Hamilton, B. "Greenhouse Gas Emissions of Electricity Generation Chains — Assessing the Difference", *IAEA Bulletin*, 422 (2000), http://www.iaea.org/Publications/Magazines/Bulletin/Bull422/article4.pdf.

Takabut, K. "Nuclear Power Plant Option for Thailand", paper presented at the ASEAN Energy Business Forum, Singapore, 22–24 August 2007.

Tanter, R. "Nuclear Fatwa: Islamic Jurisprudence and the Muria Nuclear Power Station Proposal", Australia Policy Forum, 13 December 2007, 07-25A.

Tuan, T. M. "Implications of Vietnam's Planned Nuclear Power Station", *ESI Bulletin*, 2, no. 3 (2009), pp. 5–6.

CHAPTER 14

SHOULD ASEAN GO NUCLEAR?

Lee Yoong Yoong

ABSTRACT

Over the years, energy security has become a key economic and strategic issue in ASEAN. Though rich in energy resources — nine ASEAN Member States have proven oil and/or gas resources or other natural resources — ASEAN is not totally immune from the impact of rising oil prices or other external shocks to energy supply. Such a threat is further magnified by the pace of progress and growth of Asia in the global economy. Amid such circumstances, one way forward for the grouping is to address its own energy security. One outcome is to make diversification of energy supply resources a principal policy agenda, such as investing in renewable energy. A number of ASEAN Member States have in reality gone a step further and contemplate the option of civilian nuclear power. While such nuclear power ambitions are not actually new, there remains the concern of safety and security. This paper examines the pros and cons as well as the costs and benefits for ASEAN to go nuclear. In conclusion, the paper would highlight that, though it is a controversial issue, ASEAN, as a region, seems to gradually embrace the notion and the use of nuclear power to address the energy security dilemma. This is evident through the incorporation of the use of civilian nuclear energy in its latest plan of action for energy cooperation. It will be fascinating, after all, to see how the ambition of nuclear energy would eventually evolve into the reality of ASEAN.

14.1 INTRODUCTION

Energy security has, in recent years, become a key economic and strategic issue. Defined as the securing of reliable, adequate and affordable sources of energy, energy security is a critical issue for almost every state and government because it plays an essential role in accomplishing strong and sustainable socio-economic growth.

Global energy supply is a direct corollary of the worldwide energy demand and consumption, which increase with population growth. It is reported that over 1.6 billion people, equivalent to about 36% of the developing world's population,[1] are living without access to electricity, power and energy. Predictions of energy demand for the next 50 years vary, though experts anticipate that providing an acceptable quality of life for the majority of the world requires thrice the energy consumed in the early years of this millennium,[2] highlighting the close linkage between poverty eradication and energy demand.

14.2 ENERGY SECURITY IS CRITICAL TO ASEAN

After the Asian financial crisis in 1997–1998, Southeast Asian countries promoted new investments and consumer confidence, resulting in a decade of strong growth since. As a result, the energy sector is racing to keep up with the speed of growth, creating varying opportunities from country to country in the region. The 10 member states of the Association of

---

[1] Global Network on Energy for Sustainable Development, "Reaching the Millennium Development Goals and Beyond: Access to Modern Forms of Energy as a Prerequisite", 2007, p. 5.

[2] Ryoichi Yamamoto and Masayasu Kitagawa, "Science on Sustainability", Research on the Scientific Basis for Sustainability, 2006.

Southeast Asian Nations (ASEAN)[3] represent one of the world's rapidly growing regions, and one that has a rapidly rising energy demand driven by economic and demographic development.

ASEAN's primary energy requirement was projected to triple between 2005 and 2030 (reference scenario).[4] Meeting such energy needs — with unprecedented increases in coal use, oil and gas imports, as well as greenhouse gas (GHG) emissions — will be the acid test. The challenge to ensure a secure regional energy supply is an overriding concern.

The ASEAN region is rich in energy resources. Nine member states have proven oil and/or gas resources or other natural resources, such as coal, hydro and biomass (see Figure 1), with two of the states, Brunei Darussalam and Indonesia, ranked among the world's top liquefied natural gas (LNG) producers.[5] ASEAN also produces nearly 40% of the oil and gas resources in the Asia-Pacific rim. Oil and gas contribute an approximate value of US$48 billion to ASEAN economies annually.[6]

---

[3]The Association of Southeast Asian Nations, commonly abbreviated ASEAN, is a geopolitical and economic organisation of 10 countries in Southeast Asia. It was founded on 8 August 1967 by Indonesia, Malaysia, the Philippines, Singapore and Thailand. Since then, membership has expanded to include Brunei Darussalam (entered in 1984), Cambodia (1999), Laos (1997), Myanmar (1997) and Viet Nam (1995). Its aims include the acceleration of economic growth, social progress, cultural development among its members, protection of the peace and stability of the region, and provision of opportunities for member countries to discuss differences peacefully.

[4]The ASEAN Secretariat, "ASEAN Plan of Action for Energy Cooperation (APAEC) 2010–2015: Bringing Policies to Actions — Towards a Cleaner, More Efficient and Sustainable ASEAN Energy Community", p. 5. ASEAN's energy demand is expected to hit 1,252 Mtoe (million tonnes of oil equivalent) in 2030 from 474 Mtoe in 2005, an increase with an average annual growth rate of 4%. This is higher than the world's average growth rate of 1.8% for primary energy consumption through 2030.

[5]Weerawat Chantanakome and Akhmad Nidlom, "The Role of Energy Cooperation in ASEAN Region: Challenges and Opportunities towards Enhanced Energy Security", presented at the 2007 Annual Conference, "Energy Security: Visions from ASIA and Europe", Centre for Strategic and International Studies (CSIS) and Research Unit on International Security and Cooperation (UNISCI), Complutense University of Madrid, Jakarta, 8–10 November 2007.

[6]26th ASEAN Ministers on Energy Meeting (AMEM), Bangkok, Thailand, 7–8 August 2008, http://www.information.gov.bn/VER2/index.php?option=com_content&task=view&id=213&Itemid=93.

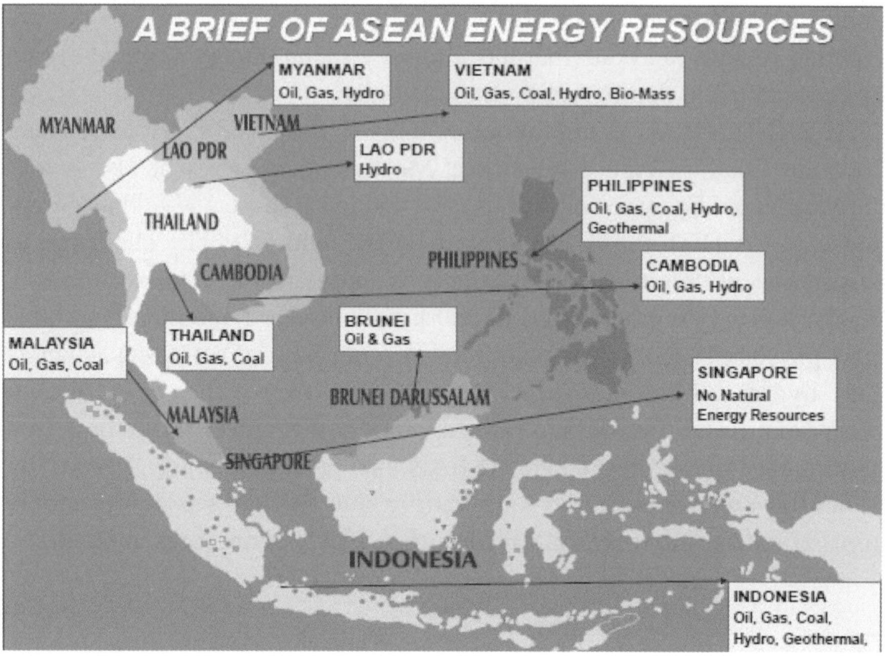

Figure 1 Overview of ASEAN Energy Resources

Source: ASEAN Council on Petroleum (ASCOPE)

Undoubtedly, energy plays an imperative role in the integration and prosperity of ASEAN. It is a constituent that binds the ASEAN member states to one another, and is an equally crucial component in ensuring the transformation of the region into an economically competitive, resilient and secure community by 2015.

With a vast reserve of 22 billion barrels of oil, 227 trillion cubic feet (Tcf) of natural gas, 46 billion tonnes of coal, 234 gigawatts (GW) of hydropower and 20 GW of geothermal capacity,[7] member states are relentlessly forging cooperation for the utilisation of the region's energy potential (Figure 1).

Still, despite boasting such impressive energy reserves, ASEAN was not totally immune from the impact of rising oil prices. Member states, such as the Philippines, Singapore and Thailand, remain particularly

[7]The ASEAN Secretariat, "ASEAN Plan of Action for Energy Cooperation (APAEC) 2004–2009", p. 2.

vulnerable to disturbances in energy supply given that their economies are intensely dependent on oil imports. Such a threat was further magnified by the breakneck pace of progress and growth of Asia compared to other continents in the world.

For one, the rising energy demand has led to ASEAN member states scouting and contending for every available energy resource — either for consumption or, more significantly, for sale-export to fellow Asian neighbours such as China, India and Japan, all of which are economic powerhouses also looking to strengthen their own energy security. To complicate the situation, ASEAN's projected reliance on fossil fuels means that the region has incidentally become a large contributor to global warming. ASEAN member states are at risk from the impact of climate change as several of them have limited technical ability and capacity to cope with its effects. Some of them, faced with financial constraints, are also likely to be confronted with additional costs associated with climate change mitigation and adaptation in the future.

Amid such circumstances, a way forward for ASEAN is to address the growing challenge of energy security while preventing irreversible damage to the environment. A number of initiatives have been developed to raise awareness and to prepare for mitigation and adaptation. One example is the Singapore Declaration on Climate Change, Energy and the Environment, signed and adopted at the Third East Asia Summit (EAS) by the leaders of the 16 countries — the 10 ASEAN member states, Australia, China, India, Japan, Korea and New Zealand — which expressly underscored that East Asia "will urgently act to address the growth of global greenhouse gas emissions".[8]

The upward trend in demand makes it critical for ASEAN to have its arms open to all accessible and possible sources of energy to sustain its growth trajectory. One outcome is to make diversification of energy supply resources a principal policy agenda. Apart from conventional natural gas and fossil fuel, it would be a strategic realignment by ASEAN to invest in renewable energy. This should provide the region with an adequate foothold in the international energy arena. It was with this in mind that a number of ASEAN member states have, in recent years, adopted proactive policies towards renewable energy utilisation, and energy efficiency and conservation. A handful of them went a step further, by opening doors anew to civilian nuclear power.

[8] Singapore Declaration on Climate Change, Energy and the Environment, Singapore, 21 November 2007, http://www.aseansec.org/21116.htm.

14.3 OUTLOOK FOR NUCLEAR ENERGY

Within ASEAN, Indonesia, Malaysia, Myanmar, the Philippines, Thailand and Vietnam have all, at different times, announced their sombre intention to execute/reignite their national nuclear programmes, although more often than not, funding challenges and changing priorities have resulted in holdups and project deferrals. It was reported that these ASEAN member states had notified the International Atomic Energy Agency (IAEA) of their proposals to operate nuclear power plants as an alternative to non-renewable energy resources.[9]

Regional nuclear power ambitions are actually not new. Undersized nuclear research reactors were constructed in the early 1960s in several Southeast Asian countries, namely, Indonesia, the Philippines, Thailand and the then South Vietnam (backed by the Atoms for Peace programme launched by the United States). One perspective was that investment in nuclear energy would enable newly independent states to achieve advanced industrial status quickly.[10]

While the rest of ASEAN — Brunei Darussalam, Cambodia, Lao People's Democratic Republic and Singapore — may not be in the vanguard in pushing for a national nuclear energy policy, the reality is that these four smaller member states are receptive to working together with the rest of the region to fortify energy security. This was evident at the convening of the 25th ASEAN Ministers on Energy Meeting (AMEM) in Singapore, in August 2007, where the ministers

> in-principle agreed to the establishment of an ASEAN Nuclear Energy Safety Sub-Sector Network to explore nuclear safety issues.[11] The Ministers also tasked the senior energy officials to determine the Terms of Reference and composition of the network.[12]

---

[9]Phir, "ASEAN's Path to Energy Security: Not without the Hidden Cost", Singapore Institute of International Affairs, 2009.

[10]Andrew Symon, "Nuclear Power in Southeast Asia: Implications for Australia and Non-Proliferation", Lowy Institute for International Policy, April 2008.

[11]The ASEAN Nuclear Energy Safety Sub-Sector Network (NES-SSN) is now renamed the ASEAN Nuclear Energy Cooperation Sub-Sector Network (NEC-SSN).

[12]Joint Ministerial Statement of the 25th ASEAN Ministers on Energy Meeting (AMEM), Singapore, 23 August 2007.

On the whole, it is expected that up to as many as eight ASEAN member states may well possess some form of nuclear power generation capabilities by 2025 (Table 1).

The burning question remains: Should ASEAN go nuclear? A useful way to answer this is to look at two perspectives: pros versus cons, benefits versus risks (Table 2).[13–17]

Based on this analysis, there are two primary apprehensions as the temptation to use nuclear energy spreads in ASEAN, namely:

(a) The dilemma of "safety and security issues". A nuclear power plant in ASEAN could be easy prey for terrorists. The risk is potentially greater for a small country with limited territorial expanse or where the urban population is very close to the nuclear facility.
(b) The concern over nuclear waste disposal. Are the ASEAN member states willing and prepared to pump in vast amounts of investments to manage the waste from nuclear plants? Given the geographic proximity of neighbouring states, the challenge is to have waste management which appeases the next-door countries.

The other debatable point is whether nuclear energy can really achieve energy independence from fossil oil and natural gas, and combat rising energy costs. Most countries are not able to reduce their dependence on oil by building nuclear power plants. Nuclear energy — because it currently only produces electricity — is intrinsically imperfect in its ability to reduce this dependence. Oil and natural gas are consumed in much

[13] Sharon Squassoni, "Nuclear Energy: Rebirth or Resuscitation?", Carnegie Endowment for International Peace, 2009.
[14] Sueo Machi, Forum for Nuclear Cooperation in Asia (FNCA) Coordinator of Japan and former commissioner of the Japan Atomic Energy Commission. He spoke at the Public Seminar on Nuclear Energy organised by FNCA at the Philippine Nuclear Research Institute (PNRI) headquarters in Quezon City, January 2010.
[15] Ralph Kinney Bennett, "Nuclear Power in Perspective", *Reader's Digest*, June 1981, pp. 131–137.
[16] Time for Change, *Pros and Cons of Nuclear Power*, 11 January 2007, http://timeforchange.org/pros-and-cons-of-nuclear-power-and-sustainability.
[17] Michael Richardson, "Nuclear Energy: The Options for Singapore", *The Straits Times*, 1 March 2010, p. 22

Table 1 ASEAN Member States' Nuclear Status

ASEAN Member State	Nuclear Status
Brunei Darussalam (Not IAEA member)	Has no nuclear energy plans but neither has it ruled them out. May not see real need for nuclear energy in the short term as it has considerable oil and natural gas resources.
Cambodia [Joined IAEA in November 2009)	Has no nuclear infrastructure; no nuclear facilities; no organisational structure or the skilled manpower trained to operate, manage or regulate nuclear programmes. However, Prime Minister Hun Sen announced in September 2008 that his administration would build nuclear power plant to tackle future energy needs and reduce the dependency on oil. Expected to focus on developing the infrastructure and investing in forms of renewable energy in the short term. *Hopeful of acquiring bask nuclear capacity by 2020.*
Indonesia (IAEA member since 1957)	Arguably the most -determined ASEAN member state to possess civilian nuclear facilities. In the mid-1990s, it conducted a feasibility study on constructing 12 nuclear power plants. However, the project was postponed due to condemnations from environmentalists cum the occurrence of the Asian Financial Crisis. A decade on, Jakarta has once more expressed the intention to build its first major nuclear power plant — on Muria Peninsula, Central Java, by 2015. However, no decision has been finalised. Once again, the plan was severely censured by environmental organisations. There are also plans to construct a 70MW floating nuclear plant in Gorontalo, North Sulawesi. Three trial nuclear reactors have already been built in Yogyakarta, Central Java, and in Serpong and Bandung, both in West Java. Several motivations for desiring nuclear reactors: • Domestic energy consumption is growing rapidly, • Indonesia has become a net importer of oil. Nuclear energy will reduce dependence on oil. • Producing renewable energy from other sources, such as wind power and solar power, is far more costly. • If domestic energy consumption can be met through nuclear energy, it would be possible to export more oil. • States such as Japan, where earthquakes frequently occur, have already several nuclear reactors.

(*Continued*)

Table 1 *(Continued)*

ASEAN Member State	Nuclear Status
	Indonesia has at least two uranium mines, the Remaja-Hitam and Rirang-Tanah Merah mines, both in West Kalimantan. Also has option of importing uranium from friendly nations. Australia, one of its nearest neighbours, has indicated willingness to supply uranium for peacefu l purposes. Jakarta also signed several treaties on nuclear cooperation with Australia, Korea, Russia, and the JSA in 2006. *Estimated date of acquiring nuclear capacity is 2016.*
Lao PDR (mot IAEA member)	Has no nuclear programme, facilities or bureaucracy of any kind. Has never expressed any concrete interest in nuclear power. Main energy opportunity remains hydropower, which already provides for about 97% of its electricity. A large share of the economic revenue derives from export of hydropower to nearby Thailand and Viet Nam, and possibly to Guangxi, China. May see no gripping need for nuclear energy in the short run, given its hefty proven hydropower capabilities.
Malaysia (IAEA member since 1969)	Has shown signs of considering the nuclear option by establishing a nuclear agency, Nuclear Malaysia, in 1972, and the Atomic Energy Licensing Board, under the Ministry of Science, Technology and Innovation (MOSTI), in 1985. Acknowledged that its gas resources are diminishing — probably depleted by 2017. Currently it is a net exporter of oil, although by 2012, it would likely become a net oil importer if no new oil and gas fields are discovered and developed. With this in mind, PETRONAS, its state-owned oil and gas company, has entered into several agreements with regional countries to buy gas for electricity generation. 60% of its power needs are met by burning gas. In 2009, Tenaga Nasional Berhad, its largest electric utility company and also the largest power company in Southeast Asia with MYR69.8billion worth of assets, expressed its intention to hire Korea Electric Power Corporation to

(Continued)

Table 1 (*Continued*)

ASEAN Member State	Nuclear Status
	help it prepare a preliminary feasibility study for the first nuclear plant. Tenaga wants the government to approve the study, as. it would take a lengthy timeframe and process to get a reactor up and running by 2020. *Estimated date of acquiring nuclear capacity: Around 2020.*
Myanmar (IAEA member since 1957)	While it is resource-rich and does not actually require nuclear energy for power-generation purposes, it is embarking on a small research reactor, built with technical assistance and guidance from Rosatom Nuclear Energy State Corporation of Russia. In 2007, both countries signed an agreement for Russia to design and build a nuclear studies centre to manage a 10 MW light water reactor and facilities for processing and storing nuclear waste. Has assured its ASEAN neighbours that it is not producing nuclear weapons. At the national level, a Department of Atomic Energy was created in the Ministry of Science and Technology in 1997 to do R&D, and training in the field of atomic energy, to ensure the safety of the radiation sources and protection from nuclear radiation hazards. *Estimated date of acquiring nuclear capacity: Uncertain.*
The Philippines (IAEA member since 1958)	Probably the first Southeast Asian state to initiate a nuclear programme with the formation of an atomic Energy Commission in 1958. President Marcos, in July 1973, announced plans to build a nuclear power plant, in response to the 1973 oil crisis. Construction on the Bataan Nuclear Power Plant (BNPP) began in 1976, and it was designed to produce 621 MW of electricity. Following the 1979 Three Mile Island accident, BNPP construction halted. Among the issues raised was that BNPP was built too near to a major earthquake fault-line. By 1984, when BNPP was nearly completed, building costs hit US$2.3 billion. With the departure of President Marcos from power and the Chernobyl disaster — both in 1986 – the succeeding administration of President Aquino decided not to operate the BNPP. Debt repayment on BNPP became the biggest sole national obligation. The compensation was eventually

(*Continued*)

Table 1 (*Continued*)

ASEAN Member State	Nuclear Status
	completed in 2007. While successive administrations evaluated proposals to modify BNPP for other energy productions, all have been deemed not commercially viable. In 2004, President Arroyo, in outlining the energy policy, highlighted plans to convert BNPP to a gas-powered facility. Worthy to note is that the BNPP, despite never been commissioned, has remained intact and is in well-maintained condition. Merely a question of seeking funding to re-launch it. *Estimated date of acquiring nuclear capacity: Uncertain.*
Singapore (IAEA member since 1967)	Handicapped by resource constraints and technical complications in pursuing nuclear energy. Choosing a safe site for a nuclear power reactor in a compactly inhabited islet-nation is a big challenge. Prime Minister Lee Hsien Loong, in December 2008, stated that he "does not rule out the possibility of Singapore having a nuclear power plant in the long term, (although) there would be difficulties...due to scale of such a project". He acknowledged that "there would be safety issues...but technology may evolve so that such challenges can be resolved." The Economic Strategies Committee (ESC), in February 2010, also proposed that Singapore should examine the feasibility of nuclear energy in the long term as a way to meet its energy needs. In the short to medium term, Singapore could look into generating energy from coal and importing electricity from neighbouring countries. As an energy-disadvantaged country, it cannot rule out the nuclear energy option. Recognising that investments in energy R&D can lead to new energy solutions, it has been focusing on developing energy technologies. Perceived as the only ASEAN member state that is publicly advocating nuclear safety and adherence to IAEA safeguards. It lobbied ASEAN to establish a nuclear energy safety network at the 25th AMEM in 2007.

(*Continued*)

Table 1 *(Continued)*

ASEAN Member State	Nuclear Status
Thailand (IAEA member since 1957)	Declared its intention to pursue nuclear energy only recently. The state-owned Electricity Generating Authority intends to build its first two nuclear power plants — 1 GW in 2020 and 1GW in 2021 — subject to the Cabinet's approval in the first half of 2011. Such a decision was condemned by Greenpeace, which suggested that the country should focus on alternative power supplies from hydropower {from Lao PDR) and smaller bio-fuel plants. Plans to establish safety and regulatory infrastructure by 2014 and has commissioned a three-year feasibility study early in 2008. Current political instability seems to stall the process of going nuclear. *Estimated date of acquiring nuclear capacity: Between 2020 and 2021.*
VietNam (IAEA member since 1957)	Undertook two preliminary nuclear power studies in the 1980s, stressing the need to introduce nuclear energy for satisfying the growth in electricity demand. Approved a national energy plan which envisages a 2000 MW nuclear power plant, the work on which would start by 2010. South Korea signed a deal in 2006 for long-term nuclear energy cooperation, including developing power plants First nuclear power plant likely to be commissioned by 2017. Also plans to build four nuclear power plants at 1GW each in 2020 and 2021. Will determine the design of the power plants based on the preliminary feasibility study. To ease public and international concerns, national power utility, Electricity Vietnam, the Ministry of Industry and Trade and Vietnam Atomic Energy Commission (Vinatom) hold public exhibitions on nuclear energy and power generation in the major cities. Regulatory frameworks are being created. A law on nuclear energy is before the national legislature. *Estimated date of acquiring nuclear capacity: 2017.*

Source: Contents and projected nuclear timelines are based on a compilation of governments' assessments, media reports and evaluations by experts.

Table 2 Pros and Cons of ASEAN Going Nuclear

Pros/Benefits	Cons/Risks
Carbon emission:	**Contamination of the environment**:
As demand for electricity soars, the pollution produced from fossil fuel-burning plants is heading towards dangerous levels. Coal-, gas- and oil-burning power plants are responsible for half the air pollution of economic giants like the USA and China. Burning coal produces carbon dioxide (CO_2), which depletes the protection of the ozone. The soft coal, which many power plants burn, contains sulfur. When gaseous byproducts are absorbed into clouds, precipitation becomes sulfuric acid. Coal also contains radioactive material. Coal-fired power plants emit more radiation into the air than nuclear power plants, although the entire life cycle of producing electricity from nuclear power does emit CO_2. This is comparable to the emissions of other zero-carbon sources, such as wind, hydro and photovoltaics.[14] To give a better illustration, for the operation of a 1,000 MW power plant for one year, a nuclear-powered plant emits 0.15 million tonnes of CO_2, while one powered by coal emits 6.51 million tonnes of CO_2. Replacing a 1GW coal-power plant with nuclear power saves 6.4 million tonnes of CO_2 a year. In Japan, the operation of 55 nuclear power plants has reduced CO_2 emission by about 20%.[15]	ASEAN is a region prone to acute natural catastrophes. ASEAN member states that have pronounced their nuclear ambitions must deal with the challenge of seismic perils and danger of radiation seepage. Although most nuclear plants would be designed to endure the natural disasters, much would still ride on the sufficient safety standards placed in areas such as radiation defence, crisis vigilance, and disposal management. The Chernobyl disaster will always be a blemish in the chronicle of nuclear energy development. There is a risk of such a disaster re-occurring and destroying everything in its wake at all times. The designing and maintenance of nuclear reactors is critical in preventing such mishaps. No nuclear energy plant in the world could hold out against an attack similar to the 9/11 terrorist destruction of the World Trade Center in New York. Such an act would have catastrophic consequences for the world. It is also true that the results of a compromised reactor core can be disastrous, but the precautions that check this from happening prevent it well. Each year, 10,000 to 50,000 US nationals die from respiratory diseases due to the burning of coal, and 300 are killed in mining accidents. In contrast, no Americans have died or been badly hurt because of a reactor accident or radiation exposure from nuclear power plants.[16]

(*Continued*)

Table 2 (*Continued*)

Pros/Benefits	Cons/Risks
Reliability: Nuclear power is possibly one the safest methods of producing energy. Nuclear power plants need little fuel, so they are less vulnerable to shortages due to workers' strikes or natural disasters. International politics may bear little effect on the fuel supply to the reactors because uranium — the feedstock of nuclear energy — is found in various places around the world. However, the supply of uranium is reportedly to last for the next 30 to 60 years, pending actual demand.[17]	**Lengthy process**: The timeframe needed for formalities, planning and building of a new nuclear power generation plant is in the range of 25 to 30 years.[18] In other words, nuclear power plants cannot be constructed quickly. Very often, when a nuclear plant is commissioned, the relevant technology has become dated and this has a cost impact on the operation of the nuclear facility. Public reaction may turn sour and it would undermine the value of this alternative source of energy.
Energy security and energy efficiency: Nuclear energy is essentially seen to be (a) sustainable by combating rising energy cost; (b) a means of strengthening energy security; and (c) a diversification of reliance on fossil fuels. When it comes to efficiency output, nuclear power has more "pluses" than other alternative power sources, such as wind, solar, hydro etc. Compared to energy output by a nuclear reactor, output from these alternative sources is relatively small. With the rise in energy demand by an increasing population, renewable sources beyond nuclear energy may not yield the desired quantity in the coming years.	**Nuclear meltdowns**: A nuclear meltdown happens when there is an acute shortage of coolant water in the nuclear reactor. This can lead to disastrous consequences, exposing the world to high dosages of radioactivity. Although accidents are rare, human errors and technical faults cannot be eliminated.
Low operating cost: One of the attractions of nuclear power is that although the capital cost is high, the running cost is low.	**High capital cost**: Studies have shown that the construction of a nuclear power plant is much more expensive, i.e. higher capital cost, compared to the construction of solar panels and wind turbines.

(*Continued*)

Table 2 (*Continued*)

Pros/Benefits	Cons/Risks
Stability of nuclear energy prices: A country (or a utilities company) can buy years of supply of uranium when the price is low; it doesn't take up much space-area and can be easily stockpiled until needed. Most uranium is purchased using long-term contracts, making it less susceptible to price fluctuations. In contrast, most countries (or utilities companies) do not have storage capacity for more than 3 months' supply of fossil fuels.	**Radioactive concerns**: The hazards of radioactive exposure during mining and extraction of uranium-like ores have emerged in developing countries. The radioactive shards and fragments left after mining, if not properly handled, can lead to ailments such as cancer. Safe disposal of radioactive waste is thus a tricky issue. According to the US Environmental Protection Agency standards, nuclear waste has to be warily looked after for "thousands of years". During the operation of nuclear power plants, radioactive waste is produced, which in turn can be used for the production of nuclear weapons. In addition, the same know-how used to design nuclear power plants can to a certain extent be used to build nuclear weapons.
Not much land needed: Investment in solar energy is very costly as it requires a relatively big space and layout area for the photovoltaic panels. Similarly, in the case of wind power, the space required is three times more due to construction of windmill generators. Nuclear plants, in comparison, do not require a large area of land to generate power.	**Nuclear weapon proliferation**: More often than not, nuclear reactor programmes are disguises for the development of nuclear weapons. There is no guarantee that nuclear fuel supplied to a country would not be used to produce weapons of mass destruction. This could lead to nuclear weapon proliferation and the associated dangers to international peace and stability.

Source: Multiple sources of reports, technical studies and publications.

larger proportions in industry and transportation, and for residential and commercial heating worldwide.[18] Countries that have turned to nuclear power to reduce their dependence on fossil fuel have largely been unsuccessful.[19] In fact, it is said that "energy independence" is a myth because even oil-producing giants such as Saudi Arabia and Iran import gasoline.

Similarly, while nuclear power could provide a greater diversity of energy resources, it will not solve ASEAN's dilemma of dependence on foreign oil. In other words, until electricity can fully replace fossil fuels or produce hydrogen, nuclear energy will not be able to substitute oil, and dependence on foreign energy sources will continue. In fact, ASEAN should expect more interdependence when it comes to nuclear energy because of the existing supply structure and location of uranium (in Australia, Africa, etc.).

14.4 CONCLUSION

The sharp rise of global oil prices in the past four decades has pushed governments worldwide to scramble for alternative sources of fuel. With the impact of climate change, confirming that carbon dioxide emissions from fossil fuels cause global warming, the search for alternative and renewable energy sources has been preoccupied with clean fuels. This has prompted the use of renewable energy sources such as biofuels and hydropower. Nuclear power, practically ignored for two decades after the Three Mile Island and Chernobyl accidents, has re-emerged as an attractive option. The IAEA reported that nuclear energy produces only 2–6 grams of carbon per kilowatt hour, about the same as wind or solar power, and less than 1% of the amount of carbon produced by coal, oil or natural gas.[20]

Nuclear power is a controversial issue. Having said that, whatever the ultimate choice is for ASEAN and its member states, there is no doubt that

---

[18] Squassoni, op. cit. In the United States, 40% of the energy consumed comes from oil, yet oil produces only 1.6% of electricity. Natural gas usage in the US is split almost evenly among industrial uses, residential and commercial heating, and electricity generation.

[19] Squassoni, op. cit.

[20] The International Atomic Energy Agency, "Sustainable Development & Nuclear Power", 1997.

the region, on the whole, is gradually moving towards embracing civilian nuclear power. ASEAN member states are no longer shying away from the mention of "nuclear". The best evidence came at the 27th AMEM convened in Myanmar in July 2009 when the ASEAN Energy Ministers adopted the ASEAN Plan of Action for Energy Cooperation (APAEC) 2010–2015, which would serve as guiding principles for regional energy cooperation to support the realisation of the ASEAN Economic Community (AEC).

The APAEC 2010–2015 consists of seven programme areas, of which one is civilian nuclear energy. This is where member states agreed to cooperate, on a voluntary and non-binding basis, and share and exchange information and knowledge, technical assistance, networking and training on nuclear energy for power generation. The cooperation will be achieved progressively:

> in accordance with the laws and regulations of the respective member states and the relevant international agreements, co-operation and standards within the framework of existing international and regional organisations and cooperation on nuclear energy, i.e. IAEA, Asian Nuclear Safety Network, Forum for Nuclear Cooperation in Asia, among others.

Perhaps this is the most apt way to go forward at the moment — confidence and capacity building; sharing and exchanging information; and networking among officials, experts and the private contractors involved. It is not wrong to highlight that almost every ASEAN member state lacks the technical expertise and knowledge for nuclear power generation and its aftermath, such as waste management. It is also not incorrect to stress that nuclear energy could bring positive advantages to ASEAN member states. The quandary is that a need for clean renewable energy does not imply an unreserved compromise for nuclear energy. Therefore, it would be fascinating to see how the nuclear energy ambitions evolve into reality in ASEAN.

CHAPTER 15

MYANMAR AND THE NUCLEAR OPTION

Thaung Tun

ABSTRACT

Nuclear energy is a possible option for all countries in ASEAN and at one time or another; all countries within ASEAN have explored the possibility of nuclear power, except Brunei, Cambodia and Laos. When this paper was written in 2010, Myanmar was under suspicion of developing a nuclear weapons programme with the government that was in power then denying the allegations. Since the time of writing, Myanmar has undergone a political transformation and this paper serves as a commentary on the period before the changes took place.

There is currently no nuclear power plant operating in any ASEAN country. But considering that the demand for clean energy in ASEAN is growing by leaps and bounds, the situation is likely to change in the near future. There is already a palpable move forward. At the 28th ASEAN Ministers on Energy Meeting held in Viet Nam on 23 July 2010, Prime Minister Nguyen Tan Dung of Viet Nam, the current Chairman of ASEAN, urged member countries to consider nuclear energy as an alternative source to sustain the region's rising economic growth.

Nuclear energy presents an important option for ASEAN. In the past, the discussions on nuclear energy were tentative but with the rising cost of fossil fuels and the debate on global warming, the situation has changed and the discussions have become more serious.

All ASEAN member countries, save Brunei, Cambodia and Laos, have at one time or another expressed interest in harnessing nuclear power for peaceful purposes, particularly to meet the growing energy demand. Only one among them, Myanmar, is alleged to be harbouring plans to develop a nuclear weapons programme. Allegations first surfaced in 2001, when Myanmar sought the assistance of the International Atomic Energy Agency (IAEA) in acquiring a research reactor. In May 2002, *The Moscow Times* confirmed that Myanmar had been negotiating with Russia for the supply of a nuclear research reactor. Subsequently, the Myanmar Ministry of Science and Technology and Russia's Atomstroyexport, a joint stock company under the Russian Federation Ministry of Atomic Energy, were reported to have signed a contract for a reactor complex that includes a 10-megawatt thermal-research reactor, two laboratories and facilities for disposal of nuclear waste. Russia has since been training Myanmar scientists in fields related to the construction and operation of the nuclear reactor.

Various dissident groups and foreign researchers allege that covert nuclear facilities already exist in Myanmar and that they include nuclear reactors, uranium mines and enrichment facilities. Some speculate that Myanmar may be using its North Korean connection to acquire sensitive nuclear material and dual-use state-of-the-art industrial equipment. They point to the growing ties between the two countries, particularly following the visit of General Thura Shwe Mann, Chief of Staff of the Myanmar Army, Navy and Air Force, to North Korea in November 2008, at the invitation of his North Korean counterpart, Staff General Kim Gyok Sik. They also cite as evidence the reported presence in Myanmar of officials from Namchongang Trading, a North Korean trading company that is included in the United Nations sanctions list. A 2004 *Asian Times* article also claims that a nuclear reactor deal was signed by Myanmar and North Korea that year. But such claims remain unsubstantiated.

The allegations that Myanmar is secretly acquiring key components for a nuclear weapons programme are largely based on interviews with a

Myanmar Army major who defected last year and analysis of the information and photographs he provided. However, the sheer number of alleged secret sites posited by the defector boggles the mind and casts doubts on the claim that Myanmar is actively pursuing a nuclear weapons programme. It is unlikely that such attempts would go unnoticed by non-partisan organisations, such as the Washington-based Institute for Science and International Security (ISIS), which is dedicated to stopping the spread of nuclear weapons and bringing about greater transparency of nuclear activities worldwide. According to ISIS, Myanmar has little known indigenous nuclear infrastructure and expertise to support the construction of nuclear facilities. The institute employed satellite imagery to assess the veracity of the reports and confirmed that specific sites claimed to be nuclear were not. It also looked into the news article that was carried by the *Sydney Morning Herald* about a covert uranium mine and mill near Mandalay. It considers the mill to be too large to be a clandestine uranium operation and found that the photographs matched those of an established commercial cement plant rather than a nuclear facility. According to some European sources, Russia is reported to be assisting Myanmar in exploring and extracting uranium. However, the project is said to be small and has not extended to the construction of mills to process uranium ore. The Myanmar Ministry of Energy itself lists five areas, mainly near the town of Mogok, as having potential for uranium mining.

Myanmar will likely remain under the microscope as the world attempts to fathom the motives behind Myanmar's decision to procure a research reactor together with sophisticated, high-precision, dual-use industrial equipments that include computer numerically controlled (CNC) machine tools. The CNC equipment is considered to be too large for the declared purpose of use in the manufacture of diesel locomotive engines. In this circumstance, suspicions will linger. But it is evident that the charges made by various dissident groups and the methods used so far to identify nuclear facilities in Myanmar are too simplistic and do not inspire confidence. A more professional approach than is currently employed would be required.

The Myanmar government has firmly denied that it has any ambitions to develop a nuclear weapons programme. In January 2002, U Khin Maung Win, Deputy Minister for Foreign Affairs, confirmed reports of negotiations between Myanmar and Russia on the purchase of a research reactor but stressed that the reactor was intended for research and training purposes and for the production of radioisotopes to be used in the fields of medicine and agriculture. He said the Myanmar government had informed the International Atomic Energy Agency (IAEA) of its decision and that it would carry out its nuclear programme systematically He denied that Myanmar had provided sanctuary to two Pakistani nuclear scientists, Suleiman Asad and Muhammed Ali Mukhtar, who left Pakistan in late 2001 and are wanted by the United States authorities for questioning. He stressed that Myanmar's interest in nuclear power was neither new nor fleeting. He recalled that Myanmar became a member of the IAEA when it was founded in 1957 and that Myanmar trainees had profited from the Agency's training programmes. He also drew attention to the fact that Myanmar, in addition to being a party to the Nuclear Non-Proliferation Treaty, was also a signatory of the Southeast Asian Nuclear-Weapon-Free Zone (SEANWFZ), which obliges members not to develop, manufacture or otherwise acquire, possess or have control of nuclear weapons. More recently, the leader of the Myanmar delegation to the 54th Annual Regular Session of the General Assembly of the IAEA held in Vienna reiterated on 23 September 2010 that the application of nuclear science and technology in Myanmar was solely for peaceful purposes and that Myanmar would never engage in activities related to the production and proliferation of nuclear weapons.

The present-day Myanmar nuclear programme has its genesis in the modernisation drive initiated in the 1950s by then Deputy Prime Minister, U Kyaw Nyein. As part of the industrialisation plan, the Union of Burma Applied Research Institute (UBARI) was established in 1953 in collaboration with the Armour Research Foundation of the United States. Two years later the Atomic Energy Centre and the Atomic Minerals Department followed and dozens of promising Myanmar scholars and engineers were dispatched to the United States and a few other countries for postgraduate studies in nuclear physics, mining, metallurgy, engineering and technical training in nuclear instrumentation. Upon their return to their homeland, they joined the elite group that ran the Atomic Energy Centre. However, the nascent nuclear programme soon floundered as Deputy Premier U Kyaw Nyein fell from grace and the country's priorities shifted under the government led by General Ne Win. The head of the Atomic Energy Centre, U Hla Nyunt, himself left the country to take up a senior position at the IAEA headquarters in Vienna, as the interest of the government in atomic energy waned. Notwithstanding the setbacks, the scholars maintained their interest in nuclear science. They continued their applied research work and taught nuclear physics at the undergraduate and postgraduate levels at universities. They were instrumental in the setting up of a nuclear laboratory at the Rangoon Arts and Science University in the early 1960s with technical support from the IAEA and assistance from friendly countries. Subsequently, in the 1970s, the idea of acquiring an American-built mini research nuclear reactor suitable for training and the production of radioisotopes was mooted but died a natural death due to lack of funding. The idea has now been revived by the Ministry of Science and Technology as the country is buoyed by significant income from the export of natural gas and the prospect of increased revenue from the Myanmar-China oil and gas pipeline.

Energy plays a vital role in the development of countries. It should therefore cause no surprise that ASEAN sees merit in adding nuclear power to its electricity generation mix. Viet Nam has announced plans to build eight nuclear plants by 2030 and Thailand is reported to have plans to build two by 2022. Indonesia, Malaysia, the Philippines and Myanmar will all likely follow suit. Even Singapore, with its small size and densely populated urban centres, is keeping its options open. In his speech at the third Singapore International Energy Week on 1 November 2010, Prime Minister Lee Hsien Loong reminded the nation that Singapore could not afford to dismiss the option of nuclear power altogether.

The Nuclear Non-Proliferation Treaty recognises the inalienable right of sovereign states to use nuclear energy for peaceful purposes, as long as they can demonstrate that their nuclear programmes are not being used for the development of nuclear weapons. In these circumstances it is inevitable that the inexorable march of ASEAN countries, including Myanmar, towards acquiring and operating nuclear power stations will continue. However, as the commercially popular light water reactor nuclear power station uses enriched uranium fuel, it is understandable that some countries are concerned about the possibility of the spread of enrichment and reprocessing capabilities. To allay the fears of those countries, ASEAN states opting to add nuclear power plants to their existing energy generation mix must be prepared to demonstrate their readiness to abide by the regulations to maintain international standards of nuclear safety and non-proliferation.

Given the fact that it is in the interest of all countries to forge consensus on nuclear non-proliferation and climate change, the nuclear energy field is one area that is ripe for cooperation.

INDEX